ROADSIDE GEOLOGY

OF MISSOURI

CHARLES G. SPENCER

2011
Mountain Press Publishing Company
Missoula, Montana

Cover image constructed by Chelsea Feeney of Mountain Press Publishing Company from maps in this book, using the standard U.S. Geological Survey color scheme with a few exceptions, most notably earthy tones for rocks of Pennsylvanian age. For igneous rocks, red is used for granite and bright orange for volcanic rocks. Cambrian sedimentary rocks are shades of light orange, Ordovician are pink, Devonian and Silurian are purple, Mississippian are blue, Cretaceous are green, and Cenozoic are yellow. Faults are red lines, and anticlines are dashed green.

Photos © 2011 by Charles G. Spencer unless otherwise credited
Maps © 2011 by Charles G. Spencer unless otherwise credited

ROADSIDE GEOLOGY

Roadside Geology is a registered trademark of
Mountain Press Publishing Company

Library of Congress Cataloging-in-Publication Data

Spencer, Charles G., 1954–
  Roadside geology of Missouri / Charles G. Spencer
    p. cm.
  Includes bibliographical references and index.
  ISBN 978-0-87842-573-0 (pbk. : alk. paper)
  1. Geology—Missouri—Guidebooks. 2. Missouri—Guidebooks. I. Title
  QE131.S64 2011
  557.78—dc22

                    2010049465

PRINTED IN HONG KONG

MP Mountain Press
PUBLISHING COMPANY
P.O. Box 2399 · Missoula, MT 59806 · 406-728-1900
800-234-5308 · info@mtnpress.com
www.mountain-press.com

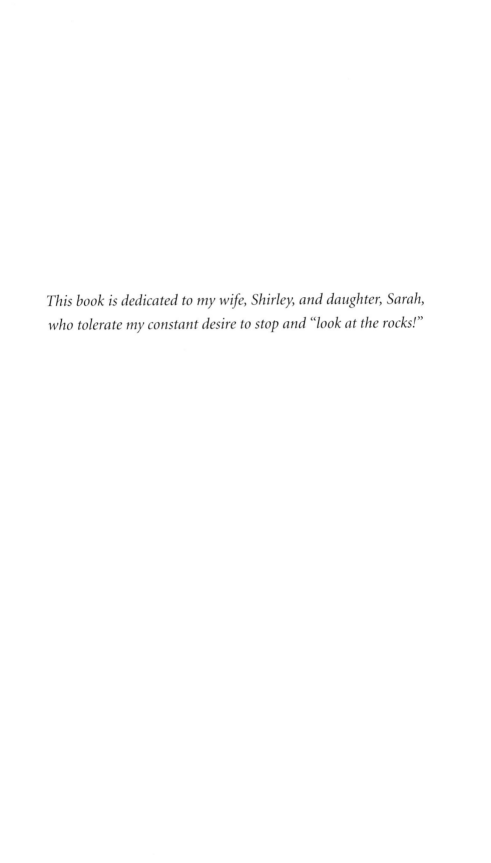

This book is dedicated to my wife, Shirley, and daughter, Sarah, who tolerate my constant desire to stop and "look at the rocks!"

ACKNOWLEDGMENTS

First and foremost I want to thank my editor at Mountain Press, Jennifer Carey, who made this book much, much better through her helpful suggestions and careful scrutiny. Also at Mountain Press, Chelsea Feeney did extraordinary work in editing and improving the maps and figures, and Jeannie Painter provided a superb layout.

Richard Gentile and Tom Thompson, both icons and oracles of Missouri stratigraphy, peer-reviewed the first draft and provided indispensable suggestions. Patrick Mulvaney, Neil Elfrink, Art Hebrank, Cheryl Seeger, and Hylan Beydler at the Missouri Department of Natural Resources provided technical information or helped obtain photographs. Gary Lowell at the University of Texas–Arlington was very generous with information about his research on caldera eruptions in the St. Francois Mountains and the Missouri Gravity Low. Shawn Snow of the U.S. Army Corps of Engineers provided information about Table Rock Dam. Tim Smith (Roaring River) and Larry Webb (Ha Ha Tonka) provided information about state parks.

Thanks also to contributing photographers Ken Stalder, Kevin Ginther, Kevin Conroy, Louis Odom, Mark Sherwood, and Ray Coveney. Bruce Steinmetz provided the Mozarkite samples for photographing.

Of course, any errors—and I hope there are few, if any—are mine.

PREFACE

I wrote this book for people who are not geologists but who are interested in Missouri's rocks, minerals, and landforms. Although technical terminology has been held to a minimum, the first chapter includes an introduction to geologic concepts and definitions that are important to understanding the geology discussed in subsequent chapters. The introduction also presents the state's geologic history in chronological order, from the origin of Missouri's oldest rocks to the recent meanderings of the Missouri and Mississippi Rivers. When reading the individual road guides, you may wish to refer back to the information in the first chapter to help put the geology in context. The remaining chapters are organized on the basis of the state's major physiographic regions: the Glaciated Plains of northern Missouri; the Osage Plains and Springfield Plateau of western Missouri; the Ozarks, including the Salem Plateau and St. Francois Mountains; and the Southeast Lowlands. Where a highway is located within a transitional boundary between regions, the route is placed in the chapter where the geology seemed to fit best.

With the exception of the Arcadia Valley loop in the St. Francois Mountains, the road guides cover only interstate and federal highways. However, not all of the state's geology is exposed along those routes. To include interesting geologic features and accommodate travelers with enough time, numerous side trips are described. If you are interested in a particular place, consult the index at the back of the book rather than try to figure out what road guide it is included in.

Most Missouri highways are posted with mile markers that serve to locate roadcuts. Where that is not the case, descriptions or photo captions include GIS coordinates to help you find the roadcuts along the highway.

Missouri's roadcuts are wonderful places to look for fossils or collect samples of the rocks described in this book. But please don't stop along the interstates (it is illegal, except for emergencies); be very careful along the shoulders of state or county roads (especially with kids); and stay off private property (don't cross fence lines). Also stay away from any roadcut in which the rock appears loose or unstable. Wear a hard hat, protective clothing, and safety goggles if you are pounding on rocks with a hammer. If all this sounds like common sense to you, you're right.

Highway construction often creates new roadcuts that expose interesting geologic features and fossils. Keep an eye out for them. Highway relocations sometimes result in new alignments, with the older road relegated to access road status. In most cases, the geology won't be terribly different along the new route. But you never know.

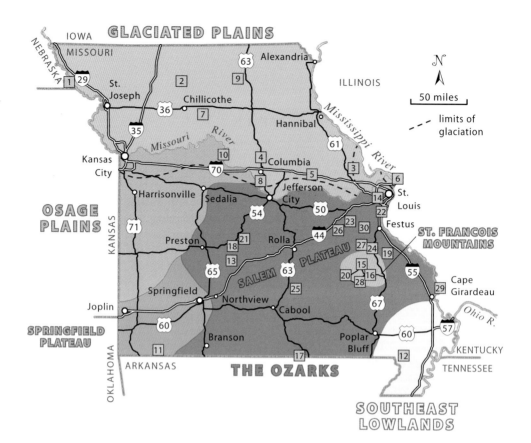

State Parks and State Historic Sites with geological features

GLACIATED PLAINS
1. Big Lake (oxbow)
2. Crowder (dissected till plain)
3. Cuivre River (sinkhole ponds)
4. Finger Lakes (reclaimed coal mine)
5. Graham Cave (sandstone bluff cave)
6. Jones–Confluence Point (sandbar)
7. Pershing (till plains)
8. Rock Bridge Memorial (karst)
9. Thousand Hills (petroglyphs)

OSAGE PLAINS AND SPRINGFIELD PLATEAU
10. Arrow Rock (source of chert)
11. Roaring River (bluffs, rock shelter, spring)

SOUTHEAST LOWLANDS
12. Morris (Crowley's Ridge)

OZARKS AND ST. FRANCOIS MOUNTAINS
13. Bennett Spring (springs)
14. Castlewood (limestone bluffs)
15. Elephant Rocks (granite boulders)
16. Fort Davidson (iron mining)
17. Grand Gulf (collapsed cave)
18. Ha Ha Tonka (karst)
19. Hawn (gneiss and eroding sandstone)
20. Johnson's Shut-Ins (volcanic rocks)
21. Lake of the Ozarks (caves, bluffs)
22. Mastodon (mammal fossils)
23. Meramec (cave, bluffs)
24. Missouri Mines (lead mining)
25. Montauk (springs)
26. Onondaga Cave (caves)
27. St. Joe (mine tailings)
28. Taum Sauk Mountain (igneous rocks)
29. Trail of Tears (Silurian and Devonian rock)
30. Washington (petroglyphs)

Roads and sections of Roadside Geology of Missouri. *State parks and state historic sites that are featured in the book because of their interesting geologic features are shown with gray boxes.*

CONTENTS

GEOLOGIC TIME SCALE

EON	ERA	PERIOD			AGE (million years)	MAJOR GEOLOGIC EVENTS
PHANEROZOIC	CENOZOIC	Quaternary	HOLOCENE			Ice sheets advance into northern Missouri. Mississippi and Missouri Rivers shift to their modern locations.
			PLEISTOCENE		2.6	
		Tertiary	NEOGENE		23	Entire state above sea level. Renewed uplift of the Ozark Dome in late Neogene.
			PALEOGENE		65	Last incursion of the ocean into the Southeast Lowlands. Remainder of the state above sea level.
	MESOZOIC	CRETACEOUS			145	Inundation in the Mississippi Embayment may have advanced into the southern Ozarks. Remainder of the state above sea level.
		JURASSIC			200	A shallow sea may have flooded the western part of the state, but any deposits have eroded.
		TRIASSIC			251	Most of Missouri above sea level. Only the Mississippi Embayment is submerged.
	PALEOZOIC	PERMIAN			299	Shallow sea drains away from Missouri in early Permian time. Weathering and erosion begin to remove previously deposited rocks.
		PENNSYLVANIAN			325	Coal swamps, deltas, and shallow warm ocean across state. Frequent sea level changes. Uplift of the Appalachian and Ouachita Mountains; major episode of Ozark Dome uplift; and folding and faulting. Lead and zinc ores are deposited.
		MISSISSIPPIAN			359	Shallow seas cover Missouri most of the period. Sea level fall in middle Mississippian time produces erosion and karst features that will later host southwest Missouri zinc and lead ores.
		DEVONIAN			416	Coastline may have bisected Missouri northeast to southwest. Tidal flats in the northeast, shallow oceans in isolated basins elsewhere.
		SILURIAN			444	Widespread inundation possible, but extended periods of erosion have removed rocks deposited.
		ORDOVICIAN			488	Initial uplift of the Ozark Dome. Shallow seas cover the state most of the time, except for a mid-Ordovician erosion episode.
		CAMBRIAN			542	Late: Sea level falls. Prolonged erosion episode. Middle: First sea level rise to inundate Missouri. Proterozoic-age rocks remain as islands for a short time. Sand is deposited on beaches.
PROTEROZOIC					1,400 1,500	Late: Prolonged period of weathering and erosion. Barren granite and rhyolite hills. Middle: Explosive volcanic eruptions (1.5 billion years ago). Intrusions of magma solidify to granite below former volcanoes. Early: Igneous and metamorphic rocks are added to the edges of the continent (1.8 billion years ago).
					1,800 2,500	Cores of early continents grow as plate tectonic collisions drive pieces of Earth's original crust together.

The geologic time scale and significant events that formed and shaped Missouri's rocks and landforms.

SHOW ME THE GEOLOGY

The Show-Me State has plenty of geology to show. Sure, there are no towering mountains, mile-deep canyons, or smoking volcanoes to divert your attention from the road, but 1.5 billion years of geologic history has left its mark on Missouri, from granite boulders the size of elephants to sinkholes filled with valuable ore. In that lengthy period of time, rifts split the continent, mountains formed and eroded, seas moved in and out, and ice sheets advanced and retreated. All of those events left geologic evidence behind. Topping it all off, the state's two majestic rivers, the Missouri and the Mississippi, established their modern channels in the last 50,000 years, a very short chapter at the end of a long and eventful story.

According to the Missouri Secretary of State's website, the origin of the nickname Show-Me State was an 1899 speech delivered by a Missouri Congressman. His oratory supposedly included the lines: "Frothy eloquence neither convinces nor satisfies me. I'm from Missouri. You've got to show me." However, as a geologist, I cannot pass up the opportunity to relate a geological origin for the nickname even though it may be apocryphal. During the mid-1890s, output from the silver mines around Leadville, Colorado, was crippled by a strike, and the mine owners brought in men from Missouri's lead mines to replace the striking miners. But because the Missourians were unfamiliar with the mining techniques employed at Leadville, these replacements constantly requested that their supervisors "show me." Frothy eloquence, indeed.

The work of rivers and glaciers accounts for most of Missouri's topographic relief, but the size, shape, and location of the hills, plains, and valleys depend on rock types and rates at which weathering and erosion have occurred. Areas with similar landscapes are called *physiographic regions*, and all or parts of five such regions are found in Missouri: the Glaciated Plains, the Osage Plains, the Springfield Plateau, the Ozarks (including the Salem Plateau and the St. Francois Mountains), and the Southeast Lowlands. Before I discuss what shaped these landscapes, however, I'll provide some basic information about Earth processes.

UNDERSTANDING THE EARTH

Plate Tectonics

The Earth formed about 4.5 billion years ago. At that time, it was just a spinning mass of molten material. The densest material, such as iron, gradually moved toward the center, and the lightest material, such as gases and water, moved toward the outside. Eventually the Earth had three distinct rock layers: a core of mostly iron, a large middle of hot plastic rock called the *mantle*, and a thin layer of brittle cool rock called the *crust*.

The original crust of the Earth solidified from magma prior to about 4.2 billion years ago. At some point not too long after that, currents within the hot, deformable rocks in the mantle broke the crust into pieces, called *plates*, that very slowly moved around the planet's surface and still do today. New rocks formed where magma welled up to fill the cracks between plates or breached the surface in volcanic eruptions. Most, if not all, of the original crust is gone, recycled back into the mantle and melted.

The oldest rock discovered thus far in North America is dated at just under 4 billion years old and is part of the core of the continent, called the *craton*. Surrounding the core of oldest rocks are younger rocks that were added to the continent over time as small plates and volcanic islands collided with and stuck to the craton. The hard rock that forms the foundation of continents is called *basement rock*, and in Missouri, it is exposed only in the St. Francois Mountains.

The movement of the plates is called *plate tectonics*. The plates can be made of continental crust (which has a chemical composition close to that of the igneous rock granite), oceanic crust (composed almost entirely of the igneous rock basalt), or both. Where two continental plates collide, large mountains form. Where an ocean plate collides with a continental plate or another ocean plate, one ocean plate is subducted, moving below the other plate. Volcanoes form above the edge of the subducting plate as it begins to melt. Where a plate splits, or rifts, apart, magma rises to the surface and new crust is formed. Where plates slide past one another, a fault forms along the boundary. Interactions

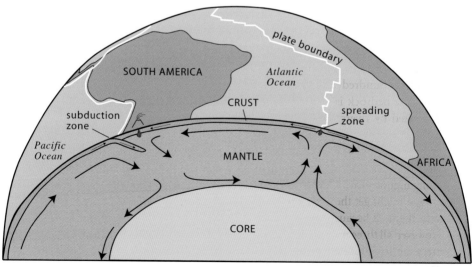

Slow-moving currents of hot, deformable rock in the mantle push and pull large pieces, or plates, of the Earth's crust. —Artwork by Mountain Press Publishing Company

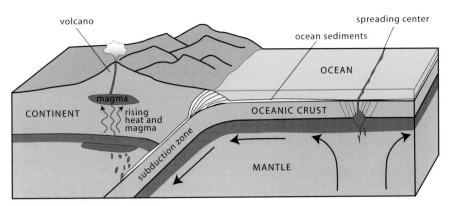

Oceanic crust is formed along mid-ocean ridges, where two oceanic plates are pulled apart. The magma that rises to fill the rift solidifies into basalt oceanic crust. At the other end of the plate conveyor system, old oceanic crust collides with another plate and is pushed beneath it in a process called plate subduction. At some depth the temperature is high enough to melt the rocks of the subducting plate, and the resulting magma moves up toward the surface. Volcanic mountain ranges, or island arcs, form above subduction zones, depending on whether the subduction zone is below a continent (as shown here) or on the sea floor, which happens if two oceanic plates collide. —Artwork by Mountain Press Publishing Company

between tectonic plates, including both collisions and rifts, are responsible for many of the geologic events that shaped Missouri. In fact, the largest earthquakes to hit the United States in historic times occurred along an ancient rift zone in the basement rocks of southeast Missouri.

Getting Down to Bedrock

It's time to discuss bedrock—not where the Flintstones lived but the rock beneath our feet. Bedrock is hard rock, not loose unconsolidated sediment. In northern Missouri, much of the bedrock is covered with glacial sediment, up to several hundred feet thick in some places. In the southeast corner of the state, the bedrock is buried beneath thousands of feet of clay, silt, and sand deposited by rivers. Elsewhere, sediment deposits are thinner or absent and bedrock is more widely exposed at the surface. Geologists call a natural surface exposure of rock an *outcrop*. The best places to see them are on hillsides, along stream valleys, or in the beds of rivers. The excavations that expose bedrock along highways are called *roadcuts*, and Missouri has a lot of them.

You might get the impression in Missouri that if you've seen one rock you've seen them all because the same types of rocks appear across most of the state. However, all three major rock types—sedimentary, igneous, and metamorphic—are represented in Missouri. Igneous rocks form when molten rock material cools and solidifies. Molten rock is called *magma* when it is belowground and *lava* when it erupts onto the surface. The solidification of molten rock is fundamentally a freezing process, although magma and lava "freeze" at much higher temperatures than water—at least 1,000 degrees Fahrenheit higher. Igneous rocks in Missouri include granite, rhyolite lava flows, and volcanic tuff, all of which outcrop in the St. Francois Mountains. The igneous rocks there are discussed in more detail in the Ozarks chapter.

Metamorphic rocks form when the composition or texture of an existing rock is changed by high temperature, pressure, or chemically reactive water or vapor. These conditions can develop when rocks are deeply buried, trapped in mountain building zones, or intruded by magma. Most rocks in Missouri have been spared these dramatic changes, so metamorphic rocks are rare. Metamorphic basement rocks are encountered in drill holes, but not in outcrops. The only outcropping rock that might be metamorphic—and there is some debate about it—is the Hawn Park Gneiss. It is poorly exposed east of the St. Francois Mountains in Hawn State Park. The rock looks like and has the mineral composition of granodiorite, an intrusive igneous rock that resembles granite but has more calcium-rich feldspar. The "gneiss" contains thin layers of biotite mica that resemble the layering produced during metamorphism but may have been produced during crystallization.

Several types of igneous and metamorphic rocks are found in glacial deposits in northern Missouri, perhaps the most famous of which is the Sioux Quartzite, a metamorphosed sandstone. This pink rock outcrops a couple hundred miles to the north in South Dakota, Minnesota, and Wisconsin, where it was eroded by a glacial ice sheet, with the ice transporting pieces to Missouri in Pleistocene time.

Sedimentary rocks, the third major rock category, are the most common in Missouri roadcuts. If you learn to identify sedimentary rocks at highway speed, you will know what's in 95 percent of the roadcuts you zoom past. Missouri's sedimentary rocks were deposited over a time span of 500 million years, so they provide information about a lot of the state's geologic history. Because of their importance throughout Missouri, I'll discuss them in more depth in this introductory chapter.

SEDIMENTARY ROCKS. All sedimentary rocks form from weathering and erosion, processes acting on the Earth's surface. Weathering breaks existing rocks into softer and smaller pieces, either by chemical reactions in water or by physical disintegration. Weathering is going on today, decomposing the rocks you see along the roads. Rocks that are more resistant to weathering tend to form ledges or cap hilltops, whereas softer rocks form slopes and are usually covered with vegetation.

Erosion is the process by which small weathered pieces of rock are picked up by streams, glaciers, wind, and waves and transported someplace else. Those bits and pieces of transported rock are collectively called *sediment*. The size of individual fragments, which are often referred to as *grains*, varies depending on many factors, including what type of rock was eroded, how extensively it was weathered, and how far it was transported and by what. The size of sediment grains and whether they are rounded or angular provide clues about which

Sedimentary Rocks of Missouri

Name	Description	Depositional Environments
Limestone	Composed of tiny grains of calcium carbonate produced by algae and other marine organisms. Typically gray when freshly exposed but turns dark gray, brown, or rusty brown when weathered. Occurs in beds that are separated by thin layers of shale. Almost always has fossils. Late Cambrian through Pennsylvanian.	Shallow, warm water on the continental platform, reefs, shoals, and tidal inlets.
Dolomite	**Primary:** Dolomite grains precipitated directly from seawater in an arid climate; one Missouri dolomite bed (in the Joachim Formation) may be of this type. Ordovician. **Secondary:** Originally deposited as calcite sediment, later altered by circulating groundwater that replaced calcium with magnesium; resembles limestone. Most Missouri dolomite originated this way. Cambrian through Devonian.	**Primary:** Briny tidal pools or shorelines of enclosed ocean basins. **Secondary:** Same as limestone.
Sandstone	Composed of sand grains glued together by quartz, calcite, or hematite mineral cement. Color varies from white to brown. Beds may contain ripple marks or crossbedding formed by currents or waves. May have tracks or trails on bed surfaces (trace fossils). Not as common as carbonate rocks. Cambrian through Neogene.	Beaches, nearshore shelf, deltas, floodplains, and river channels.
Shale	Composed of mud (silt and clay grains). Usually gray or tan, but can be white, red, green, or black. Marine shales may contain fossils; terrestrial shales sometimes contain burrows or trails of mud-dwelling organisms. Cambrian through Neogene.	Deep ocean basins, offshore of deltas, swamps, deltas, and floodplains.
Chert	Occurs in limestone and dolomite beds in thin, irregular layers or as nodules up to a foot across. Usually light gray or white but can be tan, black, or shades of pink. Composed of the remains of microscopic organisms that used silica for their shells or skeletal structures. Cambrian through Pennsylvanian.	Shallow, warm ocean.
Coal	Composed of plant material. Beds are typically only 1 to 2 feet thick. Pennsylvanian.	Coastal plain and delta swamps.

Igneous Rocks of Missouri

Granite	Coarse-grained rock that solidified in magma chambers belowground. Composed mostly of quartz and feldspar minerals. Several granite intrusions are exposed in the St. Francois Mountains. They differ in color (gray, pink, or dark red) due to slight differences in mineral content. All are Proterozoic age. Also found as cobbles and boulders in glacial till.
Rhyolite	Contains the same minerals as granite, but the grains are microscopic. Most of the volcanic rock formed from compaction of hot pyroclastics (volcanic ash) that collected during massive eruptions in Proterozoic time, and are also called *ash-flow tuff*, *ashfall tuff*, or *ignimbrites*. Colors vary from pink to almost black. Most contain two grain sizes of minerals, a texture called *porphyritic*.
Diabase	The least common of Missouri's igneous rocks. It contains no quartz and more iron-rich minerals than granite or rhyolite. It occurs as vertical, tabular shaped intrusions, called *dikes*, and as a intrusions between layers, called *sills*. Color is usually some shade of greenish brown. Proterozoic age.

Metamorphic Rocks of Missouri

Gneiss	A metamorphic rock composed of layers of different mineral composition. Only one outcrop is known to occur in Missouri. Proterozoic age.
Quartzite	Metamorphosed sandstone found only in glacial sediment.

Igneous, metamorphic, and sedimentary rocks found in Missouri.

agent of erosion transported it and how far. Transport by streams and wind, for example, knocks the edges off sediment and produces rounded grains like sand. The farther the sediment is transported, the rounder, and usually smaller, the grains become. Streams and wind typically can't transport sediment much larger than sand because the force of moving fluids is just not great enough to pick up or push large pieces. Streams will sometimes transport sediment as big as boulders during extreme flood stages, but not under normal circumstances. On the other hand, glaciers can move rocks the size of houses because solid ice is perfectly capable of carrying large chunks of rock. Glacier transport does not round off the sharp edges as efficiently as streams and wind, nor does it sort sediment by particle size. Rocks imbedded in the moving ice sometimes scratch the bedrock beneath the ice, and those same rocks are likewise scratched by the bedrock.

Sediment is deposited when the transporting agent is no longer capable of carrying it. In the case of streams or wind transport, this occurs when velocity decreases. Because streams and wind transport a limited range of particle sizes, the deposited sediment tends to be composed of similar grain size, all sand or all clay. Deposition by glaciers happens when the ice stops moving or melts. Because ice transport does not winnow out smaller pieces from the rest, glacier-deposited sediment can contain a wide range of grain sizes, from clay to boulders. If the sediment is transported away from the ice by a meltwater stream, sorting does occur, and those outwash sediments have the characteristics of stream deposits.

A place where sediment is deposited and collects over time is called a *depositional environment*. Examples are seafloors, lake bottoms, swamps, river deltas, glacial outwash plains, and beaches. Missouri has sediments and sedimentary rocks that were deposited in each of these environments. For example, Missouri's sandstones are made of sand grains eroded off the continent and deposited in such environments as ocean beaches and river deltas.

Weathering, erosion, transport, and deposition occurred in the geologic past just as they do today. However, the climate was usually different. Because of the movement of tectonic plates, Missouri's climate was more tropical than today over much of its geologic past. Limestone and dolomite, very common sedimentary rocks in Missouri, reflect those different conditions. They are composed of grains of the minerals calcite or dolomite (the name *dolomite* is used for both the rock and the mineral) that were produced by chemical reactions in seawater or are the skeletal remains of organisms that lived in shallow, warm oceans. This type of sediment is also known generally as *carbonate sediment* because of the carbon dioxide that is part of its chemical composition.

To form a solid rock from sediment, a process called *lithification*, requires thousands to millions of years of deposition, followed by a similar time span of compaction and cementation. As more and more sediment collects, its increasing weight compacts the lowest layers, expelling water and increasing density. At the same time, circulating groundwater deposits mineral cement that helps bind individual grains of sediment together. Chemical reactions that slightly alter the composition of the rock may accompany these physical changes.

LET'S PUT THESE ROCKS TO BED

Sediment is deposited in nearly horizontal layers. Because of that, sedimentary rocks that are not disturbed by mountain building or other tectonic forces have horizontal layers, too. A layer of sediment deposited over an uninterrupted interval of time is called a *bed*. The thickness of beds is controlled by the rate of sediment deposition, the length of time sediment was deposited, and how much compaction occurred while it solidified into rock.

The contact between any two beds is called a *bedding plane*, and it can represent either a pause in sediment deposition or a change in the type of sediment that was deposited. If a considerable amount of time passed between the deposition of a bed and the one that sits atop it, the contact is called an *unconformity*. During this time, sediment may have been eroded or weathered before deposition resumed. An unconformity represents a gap in the rock record, a period of time when sediment was not deposited or was deposited but wasn't preserved.

Dolomite, here in a roadcut of Jefferson City Dolomite along US 60 in southern Wright County, typically contains many beds that vary in thickness.

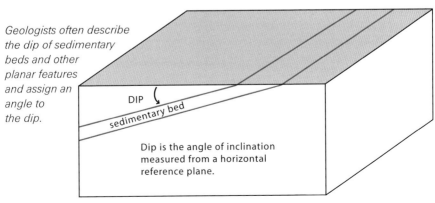

Geologists often describe the dip of sedimentary beds and other planar features and assign an angle to the dip.

DIP

sedimentary bed

Dip is the angle of inclination measured from a horizontal reference plane.

SEDIMENTARY ROCK NAMES

Geologists, being good scientists, like nothing better than to name things. The fundamental unit of rock naming is a formation, which consists of one or more rock layers that often outcrop together and can be identified over a large area. A formation contains sets of consecutively deposited beds, which represent more or less continuous deposition in a particular environment. The formation name is often that of the geographic location where the rock was first studied.

Some formations are made up of a single rock type. For example, there are many thick shale beds in Missouri that were deposited as deltas along the shore of an ancient sea. Each different type of shale comprises a formation and is assigned a unique name, such as the Liberty Memorial Shale. There are also a few formations in Missouri made up almost entirely of limestone formed during long periods of carbonate deposition, like the St. Louis and Kimmswick Limestones.

Some sedimentary rock formations include a combination of rocks (shale, sandstone, and limestone, for instance) formed from sediments deposited in a changing sequence of depositional environments. In these cases each distinct rock type in the sequence is given a name and is called a *member* of the formation. A few examples of rock members include the Gunter Sandstone Member of the Gasconade Dolomite, the Bethany Falls Limestone Member of the Swope Formation, and the Ardmore Limestone Member of the Verdigris Formation.

Although members of some formations outcrop over large areas, very often they change in composition, or disappear entirely, from place to place as a result of differences in depositional environments that existed at different locations at the same time. That means that rock layers with different names sometimes represent the same period of geologic time in different parts of the state. For example, the Bachelor Formation, Compton Limestone, and Northview Shale were deposited in earliest Mississippian time in southwest Missouri, while the Hannibal Shale was deposited in northeast Missouri during the same time span.

The use of member names for the rocks exposed in every roadcut would be overwhelming considering the sheer number of them in the thousands of feet of sedimentary rocks in Missouri. In the road guides, I have used member names when it helps to identify rocks that can be seen in different places, or for rocks that are significant for one reason or another. Sets of formations, called *groups*, represent much longer segments of geologic time. I use group names in this book primarily for discussions of Pennsylvanian sedimentary sequences that contain dozens of members in many formations.

Geologic Structures in Bedrock

A *geologic structure* is not a building made of rock: it is a term geologists use to describe breaks, bends, or tilting of rocks. Forces generated within the Earth, usually involving the shifting of tectonic plates, cause rocks to compress, stretch, or slide. When they move, they often break or bend. Missouri's geologic structures fall into three categories: folds, joints, and faults.

FOLDS. Folds are geologic structures that involve tilting or bending of rocks. They are easiest to see in sedimentary rock layers because those rocks were originally deposited as essentially horizontal beds. Sedimentary rocks also tend to be less brittle than other types and therefore have the capacity to deform to a certain extent before breaking. Most of the folds in Missouri's sedimentary rocks formed in Late Pennsylvanian time when several continents were colliding with the North American tectonic plate, forming the Appalachian and Ouachita Mountains. One way to identify a fold or tilted layer in a roadcut is to compare the tilt of the beds to the angle of the road.

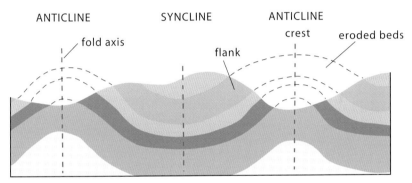

A series of folds in layered rock. Anticlines are folds in which layers are domed upward. Synclines are folds in which layers sag downward. The fold axis is a plane through the center of the fold and, in this book, is shown on the geologic maps with a dashed line where it intersects the surface.

JOINTS. Just like people, rocks sometimes reach their breaking point. Usually this happens in very dense, brittle rocks, or when forces are applied so quickly that rocks can't respond by folding. Every rock formation in Missouri is broken by sets of joints, planar fractures that formed when tectonic forces were transmitted through the rocks. At various times those forces were applied from different directions. This resulted in multiple sets of fractures. Paleozoic rocks in Missouri are broken by two major joint sets: one oriented northwest-southeast, and a second nearly north-south. There are other sets of joints aligned in different directions, but often they are less well formed and not as obvious. The basement rocks of the state contain the same joint sets found in younger rocks, as well as a third major set of joints oriented east-west.

You can see joints in nearly every roadcut in Missouri, although they can be difficult to recognize if they haven't been widened by weathering. Be aware that rocks are also fractured by explosives during road construction. Those breaks sometimes look like joints, but they don't typically occur as vertical breaks at regularly spaced intervals. Also, don't mistake the drill holes used to blast rock in roadcuts for joints.

The vertical fractures cutting through this roadcut in the Bethany Falls Limestone in eastern Jackson County are joints. They have become widened due to weathering and erosion and are filled with clay soil.

FAULTS. If tectonic forces are strong enough or are applied for long enough, the rocks on either side of a fracture will respond by sliding past each other. In that case, the fracture is a fault. Faults form when rocks are either stretched by tensional forces or squeezed by compressional forces from opposite directions. Sometimes the rocks nearest the fault surface are broken when movement occurs.

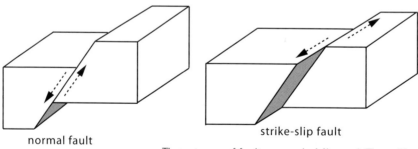

normal fault

strike-slip fault

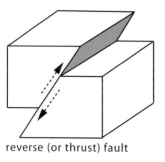

reverse (or thrust) fault

Three types of faults occur in Missouri. They differ with respect to how rocks moved on either side of the fault. Top left: A normal fault, where rocks above the fault appear to slide down the fault plane as a result of tensional forces. Most Missouri faults are of this type. Top right: A strike-slip, or transverse, fault, where rocks on either side of the fault slide sideways relative to one another. Bottom: A reverse, or thrust, fault which produces movement opposite that of a normal fault, as a result of compressional forces.

Geologic Time

One of the fundamental concepts in geology is that of deep time, the realization that our planet's history goes back a whopping 4.5 billion years. Most geologic processes work slowly, but given huge amounts of time, even things that happen at a snail's pace can return big results. It's important to remember the length of geologic time when looking at the rocks in Missouri. Nearly every roadcut exposes thousands of years of geologic history, yet tells only a small part of the story of Missouri's past.

Geologists have a tendency to throw ages such as Cambrian and Cretaceous around rather casually, and for many folks that begs the question: How do they know if rocks are 500 million years old or 50 million years old? In 1795 Scottish naturalist James Hutton published his ideas about how rock formations came to be. Included in that treatise was the first formal recognition that a considerable amount of time had to be involved. An important concept that came from the early study of sedimentary rocks was that because sediment was deposited in horizontal layers, the oldest sedimentary rocks had to be at the bottom of any set of rock layers. Using this method, geologists could establish the age of rocks in sequence relative to each other.

Eventually geologists had studied enough formations stacked one atop the other to realize that older sedimentary rocks had different types of fossils in them than younger ones. So they began to use fossils to identify rocks that were deposited during the same time interval, even when they were not located near each other. In the early nineteenth century, geologists labeled the time intervals after regions where rocks of that age were found. For example, the Cambrian Period is named after Cambria, a region in England.

The geologic time scale established using the sequence of rock layers was constructed entirely from *relative* age dates. Although early geologists knew that older sedimentary rock layers were lower in any sequence, they lacked a way to assign a numerical age to the rocks. They tried to calculate how long it might have taken to deposit the sediment in a rock, but those efforts were not very successful, mostly because geologists didn't yet understand the importance of pauses in deposition and compaction of sediment.

In 1862 physicist Lord Kelvin got into the action by trying to calculate the age of the Earth based on the temperature gradient that was measured from the surface downward in mines—it gets hotter the deeper you go. Starting with an approximately 7,000-degree-Fahrenheit temperature of the original molten planet, he figured that it must have taken 100 million years for the planet to cool to its present temperature. Not a bad idea, but what Kelvin didn't know was that heat is constantly being generated deep in the Earth by radioactivity.

And as it turned out, it was radioactivity that provided the answers to the age of our planet. Some elements—uranium is probably the best known—occur in varieties, called *isotopes*, that have unstable atomic nuclei. These atoms spontaneously release energy, called *radioactivity*, when they convert into other elements, a process known as *radioactive decay*. The rate at which decay happens is measurable, as are the new elements that form, which are usually referred to as *daughter elements*.

So, how does all this give us the age of rocks? Radioactive elements like uranium are locked into minerals in igneous rocks when the minerals crystallize from magma or lava. When the elements decay, their daughter elements are also often trapped in the minerals. By measuring the amounts of the original and daughter elements that remain inside a mineral and using their decay rates, the number of years that have passed since the decay began can be calculated. These radiometric age dates represent the number of years since an igneous rock solidified.

Here's a simple analogy to help understand the concept. Suppose you have two buckets, one above the other. The top bucket is filled with water but has a hole through which water drips at a measurable rate. At any time, you could measure how much water remains in the top bucket and how much has collected in the bottom bucket. If you also measure the volume of a droplet and the number of those drops per minute, you can figure out how long the top bucket has been leaking.

So far, so good. But radiometric age dates cannot be directly calculated for sedimentary rocks, even if they contain mineral grains with radioactive

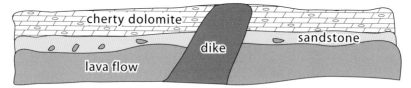

What are the oldest and youngest rocks in this figure? The lava flow is oldest. The sandstone is younger than the lava flow because it contains pebbles of the lava that mixed with sand when it was deposited. The dolomite is younger than the sandstone because it was deposited above it. The dike is the youngest because it cuts across the other three. The age of the sedimentary rocks is therefore bracketed by the radiometric ages of the lava flow and the dike.

elements because those mineral grains formed much earlier than the time when they were deposited as sediment. However, radiometric ages can be used to date igneous rocks that intrude or cover sedimentary rocks. For example, if an igneous dike cuts through a sequence of sedimentary rocks, those rocks have to be older than the dike.

Geologists working around the world have now found enough igneous rocks cutting across sedimentary rocks to be able to place absolute dates at the boundaries between the named geologic periods, as well as many of their subdivisions. But geologists still rely on fossils to know in which geologic period a sedimentary rock was deposited.

THE GEOLOGIC STORY OF MISSOURI

PROTEROZOIC EON
2.5 billion to 542 million years ago

The geologic story of Missouri begins in the Proterzoic Eon, several billion years after the Earth formed. In Proterozoic time photosynthetic algae first appeared in the Earth's oceans, and Proterozoic rocks contain the earliest fossils—mainly single- and multicelled organisms such as bacteria. Proterozoic life-forms aren't preserved in any of Missouri's oldest rocks because they are nearly all igneous or volcanic in origin, solidified from molten rock in which life could not have existed.

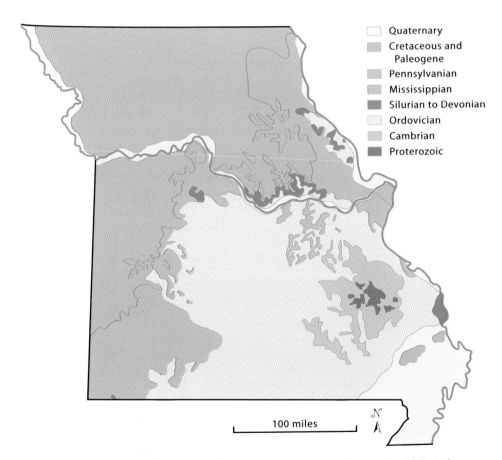

Quaternary
Cretaceous and Paleogene
Pennsylvanian
Mississippian
Silurian to Devonian
Ordovician
Cambrian
Proterozoic

100 miles

The bedrock geologic map of Missouri shows the general areas in which bedrock of various ages is exposed at the surface or is present just beneath soil or unconsolidated sediments. Various colors are used for each time interval, and a map key lets you know which color corresponds to which rocks. More detailed geologic maps accompany the road guides in later chapters.

During the Proterozoic Eon, the continents all continued to grow larger through plate tectonic collisions. Between about 1.8 and 1.6 billion years ago, there were a series of plate tectonic collisions along the southern edge of the ancient North American craton, which geologists call Laurentia. Several off-shore volcanic island chains were sequentially wedged against southern Laurentia. Many of the igneous rocks were metamorphosed by burial and pressure and now form the basement rock of North America in a swath from New Mexico northeast to the Great Lakes region. One of the tectonic collisions, the Central Plains mountain building episode between 1.7 and 1.6 billion years ago, added the rocks found beneath much of Missouri. Those igneous and metamorphic rocks are now buried under thousands of feet of sedimentary rocks but are encountered in deep drill holes across the northern part of the state.

The basement rocks beneath southern Missouri are younger. During the period between about 1.5 and 1.4 billion years ago, magma formed deep in the crust. It moved toward the surface, intruded the older basement rocks, collected in large, shallow magma chambers, and eventually caused a series of huge volcanic eruptions along the southern Laurentian coast. Today, the results of that igneous activity can be seen in outcrops of granite, volcanic rock, and lava flows in the St. Francois Mountains.

The origin of the magma that formed these rocks is still debated. Most geologists think the source of magma was not a plate tectonic subduction zone, but rather a column of hot, rising mantle rock called a *mantle plume* or *hot spot*. The volcanic rocks in Yellowstone National Park also formed above a mantle hot spot, though much more recently.

When the hot, rising mantle rock reached the base of the crust, the rocks there partly melted, and that magma eventually moved toward the surface. The molten rock seems to have moved mostly along older fault zones in the deep crust, some of which are likely former boundaries between small crust plates. Two such zones, the Grand River and Central Missouri Tectonic Zones, extend northwest-southeast across central Missouri in the Middle Proterozoic basement rocks.

Between those two tectonic zones is a feature known as the Missouri Gravity Low (MGL). It got its name because the MGL includes the Missouri batholith, a mass of granite that shows up in gravity surveys as lower density rock than the surrounding igneous and metamorphic rocks. The MGL crosses the state from northwest to southeast and is about 370 miles long and more than 60 miles wide. The age of the granite in the MGL has not been definitely determined, although the influence of the MGL structure on volcanic rocks erupted 1.47 billion years ago suggests the granite is at least that old.

At the end of the eruptive volcanic episode, around 1.3 billion years ago, a final surge of magma intruded the recently crystallized rhyolites and granites, forming dikes and sills cutting through older rocks. This magma had a much different composition from the magmas that formed the slightly older rhyolites and granites. It crystallized as diabase, a rock with dark green, iron- and magnesium-bearing minerals and no quartz. Why and where this magma formed is somewhat of a puzzle. It's possible that it was left over from the earlier igneous activity and took longer to get to the surface. A possible source may have been magma upwelling from the lower crust and upper mantle. The Midcontinent Rift System, which formed between 1.2 and 1.0 billion years ago, extends from the western shores of Lake Superior southwest through Iowa and into northeast Kansas. Huge volumes of iron- and magnesium-rich lava erupted into and filled the rift before tectonic activity stopped. The rift did not cross Missouri, and it formed later than the diabase and associated dikes in the St. Francois Mountains, but perhaps some magma forming at great depth moved through the basement rocks to southeastern Missouri and reached the surface earlier.

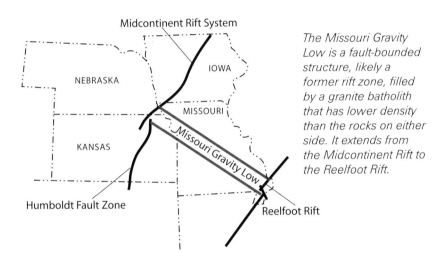

The Missouri Gravity Low is a fault-bounded structure, likely a former rift zone, filled by a granite batholith that has lower density than the rocks on either side. It extends from the Midcontinent Rift to the Reelfoot Rift.

There are no rocks in Missouri formed between 1 billion and 542 million years ago, during the last part of Proterozoic time. That is not to say that nothing was happening, and geologists have a reasonable idea of what was going on based on rocks studied elsewhere in North America. Between about 1.1 billion and 750 million years ago, the ancient North American craton was part of a larger landmass, the supercontinent Rodinia. Geologists think Rodinia began to rift apart sometime around 750 million years ago. About 600 million years ago a branching rift failed to completely split the continent. Known as the Reelfoot Rift, it lies deep below the Mississippi Embayment in Missouri's southeast lowlands. The intersection of the Reelfoot Rift and the Missouri Gravity Low is the location of major earthquake activity in the New Madrid Seismic Zone.

What happened after the Rodinia supercontinent rifted is still being studied. Initially, North America, northern Europe, and parts of Asia stayed together as a single landmass that remained near the equator. Meanwhile, the other continents drifted toward the south pole and rejoined to form another major continent.

Recently some researchers have suggested that during Late Proterozoic time the entire planet was gripped by a great ice age. In fact, some propose that the entire planet—including the tropical oceans—became ice covered at some point between about 850 and 635 million years ago, a period they call Snowball Earth. This is hotly debated, but there is good evidence for a prolonged period of ice sheet glaciers, especially on the southern hemisphere continents.

Whenever ice sheets grow, sea level falls, so the last few hundred million years of Proterozoic time were marked by weathering and erosion. Over a broad swath extending from New York to New Mexico, North America was leveled to a surface of rather uniform elevation, interrupted only by scattered knobs of igneous rock that formed hills a few hundred feet high. There was no land-based vegetation yet, so the landscape was barren. Geologists call this gently sloping surface the *continental platform*.

At the end of Proterozoic time, the ice sheets began to melt, leading to rising seas that flooded the newly formed platform for the first time. Eventually the seas reached Missouri's location on the platform, ushering in the deposition of the state's oldest sedimentary rocks.

PALEOZOIC ERA
542 to 251 million years ago

Rocks from the Paleozoic Era are well represented in Missouri. Paleozoic means "ancient life," and most of the sedimentary rocks in Missouri are composed of seafloor sediment on and in which abundant critters once crawled, burrowed, or anchored themselves. Some rocks are composed almost entirely of fossil debris. Limestone beds are generally the best places to look for fossils, but some shale and dolomite beds also contain abundant fossils.

Sea level fluctuated throughout Paleozoic time. Several major cycles of fluctuations are recognized in Missouri's rocks, with each cycle lasting about 100 million years. During the first half of each cycle, sea level rose, flooding the continental platform. The last half of each cycle was characterized by sea level falling. Following each fall in sea level, those parts of the continental platform exposed above sea level were eroded, which created an unconformity between the rocks of one cycle and the next. These large-scale patterns of sea level change recorded in North America's sedimentary rocks were first described by geologist Lawrence Sloss and are known as *Sloss sequences*. Four Sloss sequences—the Sauk, Tippecanoe, Kaskaskia, and Absaroka—controlled the prolonged episodes of deposition and erosion seen in Missouri's Paleozoic sedimentary rocks.

Sloss sequences are thought to result from a combination of large-scale plate tectonic activity and the formation and melting of large ice sheets. Seafloor spreading, the plate tectonic mechanism that forms new oceanic crust and pushes continents away from one another, causes changes in the volume of ocean basins. During periods of active seafloor spreading, the hot rocks near the rift zones are buoyant and rise to form mid-ocean ridges, thus decreasing the volume of an overlying ocean basin. Therefore, active periods of seafloor spreading result in smaller ocean basins to hold the same amount of water, so sea level rises. When seafloor spreading stops or slows down, sea level falls.

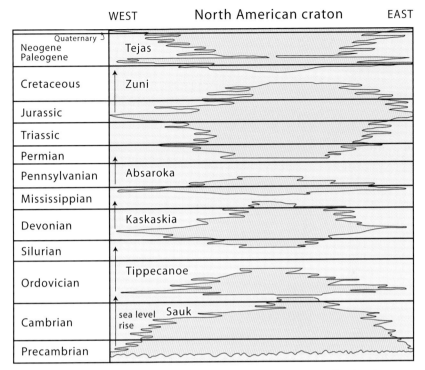

WEST   North American craton   EAST

Quaternary ↺ Neogene Paleogene	Tejas
Cretaceous	Zuni
Jurassic	
Triassic	
Permian	
Pennsylvanian	Absaroka
Mississippian	
Devonian	Kaskaskia
Silurian	
Ordovician	Tippecanoe
Cambrian	sea level rise Sauk
Precambrian	

Six major sea level cycles, called Sloss sequences, account for the depo-sition of sedimentary rocks in North America. The drawing depicts the North American craton from west to east and shows how much of the craton was exposed (tan) or submerged (blue) during the past 600 mil-lion years (vertical scale). The names in the blue area on the left side of the drawing are those geologist Lawrence Sloss gave to each major rise in sea level. —Modified from Sloss,1964

The formation of continental-scale ice sheets requires prolonged precipita-tion in climates where snowfall builds up from year to year. Because evapo-ration from oceans is the primary source of the water that forms snow, the accumulation of snow and ice on land lowers sea level. When melting resumes, the stored water returns to the oceans and sea level rises.

Added to these major causes of sea level changes were hundreds of smaller, shorter-lived fluctuations caused by a number of other factors. For example, the elevation of the North American platform oscillated now and then due to forces created during mountain building associated with collisions between North America and other continents, most notably Africa and South America during Pennsylvanian time.

Exerting a more local influence was deposition of deltas along Paleozoic coastlines. The weight of thousands of feet of sediment caused the platform to sink, which in turn caused coastal subsidence and inundation. This process probably accounts for many of the more rapid changes in sea level that shifted the coastline across Missouri during Paleozoic time.

ERA	PERIOD	AGE (million years)	SLOSS SEQUENCE	SEDIMENTARY ROCKS (discussed in book)	FOSSILS
PALEOZOIC	PERMIAN	— 299 —	ABSAROKA	no rocks in Missouri	
	PENNSYLVANIAN — Late			Wabaunsee, Shawnee, Douglas, Lansing, and Pedee Groups	crinoids, corals, pelecypods, echinoid spines brachiopods, cephalopods, trilobites, bryozoans, gastropods, and plant leaves and roots
				Kansas City Group (includes Lane, Chanute, Bonner Springs, Wea, and, Liberty Memorial Shales; Bethany Falls Limestone; and Argentine Limestone Mbr. of Wyandotte Fm.)	
				Pleasanton Group (includes Shale Hill Fm.)	
	PENNSYLVANIAN — Middle			Moberly and Warrensburg Channel Sandstones	
		— 325 —		Marmaton Group	
				Cherokee Group (includes Warner Sandstone)	
	MISSISSIPPIAN — Late		KASKASKIA	sandstone, shale and limestone in southeastern Missouri	
	MISSISSIPPIAN — Middle			Ste. Genevieve Formation	crinoids, echinoids, fish teeth, brachiopods, corals, bryozoans, blastoids, gastropods, and trilobites
				St. Louis Limestone	
				Salem Limestone	
				Warsaw Formation	
				Keokuk Limestone (Short Creek Oolite Mbr.)	
				Burlington Limestone	
				Reeds Spring–Elsey Formation (SW Missouri)	
				Pierson Limestone (SW, central, and maybe NE)	
				Fern Glen Formation (east-central and SE)	
	MISSISSIPPIAN — Early			Chouteau Group — Northview Shale / Sedalia Limestone / Compton Limestone	
				Hannibal Shale (NE Missouri)	
		— 359 —		Bachelor Formation	
	DEVONIAN			Formations in eastern Missouri include Louisiana Limestone, Saverton Shale, Grassy Creek Shale, Bailey Limestone, and Bushberg Sandstone	brachiopods, fish teeth, cephalopods, corals, and gastropods
				Cedar Valley Limestone (central Missouri)	
		— 416 —		Chattanooga Shale (SW Missouri)	
	SILURIAN	— 444 —	TIPPECANOE	Bowling Green Dolomite (NE Missouri)	trilobites, corals, and brachiopods
				Bainbridge Formation (SE Missouri)	
	ORDOVICIAN — Late			Noix Limestone (NE Missouri)	brachiopods, colony corals, graptolites, gastropods, and trilobites
				Maquoketa Shale	
				Girardeau Limestone (SE Missouri)	
				Kimmswick Limestone	
				Decorah Shale	
				Plattin Limestone	
				Joachim Dolomite	
	ORDOVICIAN — Middle			St. Peter Sandstone	
	ORDOVICIAN — Early		SAUK	Jefferson City Dolomite — Everton Formation / Smithville or Powell Dolomite / Cotter Dolomite / Jefferson City Dolomite	stromatolites
				Roubidoux Formation	
				Gasconade Dolomite (with Gunter Sandstone Member at base)	
	CAMBRIAN — Late	— 488 —		Eminence Dolomite	fossils rare; some brachiopods and trilobites
				Potosi Dolomite	
				Derby–Doe Run Dolomite	
				Davis Formation	
				Bonneterre Dolomite	
	CAMBRIAN — Middle			Lamotte Sandstone Great Unconformity	
PROTEROZOIC				igneous rock	

Paleozoic sedimentary rocks discussed in this book. Not all formations that occur in the state are shown here, particularly for Mississippian and Pennsylvanian times, and not all rocks shown here occur everywhere in Missouri. Major unconformities, formed during periods of erosion, are shown with wavy lines.

Cambrian and Ordovician Time

The distribution of continents in Cambrian time is not well established, but Missouri was likely positioned in the southern midlatitudes. The Sauk sequence, the first major rise in sea level to slowly inundate the North American platform, reached the weathered hills of Proterozoic rhyolite and granite in Missouri in Late Cambrian time. For a while the hills remained lifeless islands surrounded by beaches composed of sand accumulated over millions of years of weathering of the igneous rocks. The sand deposited at this time solidified into the 520-million-year-old Lamotte Sandstone, Missouri's oldest sedimentary rock. The contact between it and the granite beneath is an unconformity representing a gap of 900 million years of geologic time, called the Great Unconformity in Missouri.

But the hills soon disappeared beneath the waves, and as sea level rose the type of sediment deposited on the continental platform changed, first to mud delivered by rivers from dry land farther away on the continent, and finally to carbonate sediment as organisms colonized the seafloor.

Carbonate sediment was produced in the warm, clear water by plants and animals that extract calcium and carbon dioxide from seawater to form

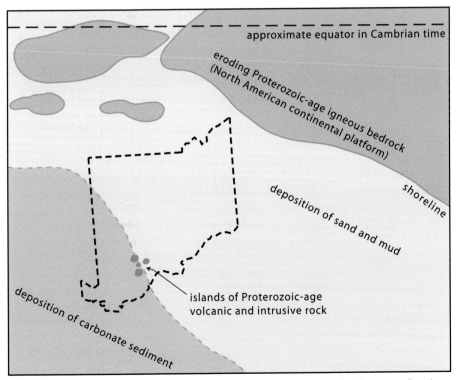

By Late Cambrian time, Missouri lay beneath the shallow sea that began to flood the continental platform at the end of Proterozoic time. Sand and mud were replaced by carbonate sediment as sea level rose and the shoreline moved north. By Ordovician time, carbonate sediment covered the entire state.

protective shells or skeletons made of the mineral calcite. Tiny grains of calcite dislodged from seafloor-growing algae and the shells of microscopic organisms collected in thick layers on the ocean floor. This mixture of sediment and water is called *carbonate mud*, or *lime mud*, to distinguish it from clay-rich sediment formed from weathered rock or soil. Larger organisms contributed their shells, now preserved as fossils.

Carbonate rocks dominate the Cambrian rock sequence in Missouri. The boundary between Cambrian and Ordovician time—about 488 million years ago—is found a few feet below the top of a largely carbonate rock layer called the Eminence Dolomite. Sea level was falling during this time and more sand was being deposited, so the uppermost few feet of the Eminence Dolomite is actually a sandstone in many places. Earliest Ordovician time saw deposition of more sand along the shoreline, which hardened into the Gunter Sandstone, the oldest member of the Gasconade Dolomite.

Sea level rose during Early Ordovician time, largely favoring carbonate sediment deposition, but it fluctuated enough that sand deposits formed a few relatively thin sandstone beds within the Gasconade, Roubidoux, Jefferson City, and Cotter Dolomites. The latter two, along with other very similar formations deposited in Early Ordovician time, are combined under the Jefferson City name on road guide maps in this book.

The carbonate beds deposited in Cambrian and Early Ordovician time exhibit several interesting and curious features. First, many of them are composed of the mineral dolomite rather than calcite. Dolomite is similar in chemical composition to calcite but with magnesium taking the place of about half of the calcium atoms. Dolomite is not used by modern marine organisms to form their shells. There just isn't enough magnesium in seawater, and it is chemically easier for creatures to extract calcium. The mineral is known to precipitate directly from seawater only in very shallow, saline, warm water isolated from circulation with the open sea and subject to high evaporation rates. The Red Sea has such conditions today.

Why are nearly all of the oldest carbonate rocks in Missouri dolomite instead of limestone? A few dolomite beds do have the chemical and physical characteristics of sediment precipitated in restricted, saline basins. But those conditions are not thought to have persisted over large areas in the ancient oceans throughout Cambrian and Ordovician time. The consensus of opinion today is that most of the dolomite beds originally were limestone and were later altered to dolomite by the replacement of calcium with magnesium by circulating groundwater or hot fluids originating in underlying Proterozoic basement rocks. The magnesium-bearing fluids might have seeped through the calcite sediment or through fractures in already hardened limestone beds. It is not clear when or how many times this happened.

Only a few dolomite beds are younger than Middle Ordovician age, including the Late Ordovician Joachim Dolomite. Some Mississippian limestone beds are dolomitic where they are fractured in fault zones, which seems to point to the importance of pathways along which magnesium-rich fluids could move.

Limestone and dolomite can be difficult to distinguish without chemical tests. The best way to tell which rock type you are seeing along a highway is

The rounded mounds in the rock layers are bioherms, Cambrian and Ordovician reeflike structures composed of stromatolites. Bedding planes often wrap around the structures, as in this roadcut along the southbound lanes of I-55 at mile marker 171.6 in Jefferson County.

your location. Nearly all of Missouri's dolomite beds are found south of the Missouri River, in the Ozarks and adjacent border regions, and are Cambrian or Ordovician in age.

Another fascinating characteristic of the Paleozoic dolomite beds is the abundance of reeflike structures called *bioherms*. These are masses of rock constructed nearly entirely of the remains of marine organisms. They typically are round or oval in shape and are separated from surrounding rock by distinct bedding planes. Bioherms are found in many Paleozoic carbonate rocks in Missouri and often are composed of piles of fossil corals, crinoids, or brachiopods. During Cambrian and Ordovician time they consisted mostly of mounds of thinly layered carbonate sediment trapped by colonies of algae that grew in very shallow water and projected above the seafloor. The fossilized algae colonies are called *stromatolites*.

Nearly all of Missouri's dolomite beds, as well as most of the limestone beds deposited in Mississippian and Pennsylvanian time, contain chert, a rock made of silica. It is found as nodules up to 1 foot across, or in thin irregular beds or seams that alternate with carbonate beds. The chert formed from the shells and skeletal structures of microscopic floating organisms known as *radiolaria* that extract silica from seawater. When the organisms died, their siliceous skeletons collected on the seafloor.

During Middle Ordovician time the eastern margin of the North American craton began converging with a tectonic plate to its east, and the rocks of the continental platform began to feel the effects of forces generated by the impending collision of the continent with a volcanic island arc. The platform initially rose slightly, which alone might not have dewatered Missouri entirely.

But at the same time, ice sheets formed on the southern hemisphere continent, which was positioned over the south pole. The combined effects led to a major fall in sea level and a period of erosion that likely lasted several million years. The Middle Ordovician unconformity is found everywhere in Missouri.

The Tippecanoe sequence, the second major cycle of sea level rise across the platform, followed this erosion episode. The first sediment deposited atop the unconformity was nearly pure quartz sand—the St. Peter Sandstone. The formation extends from Missouri to Minnesota and from Illinois to South Dakota and was deposited sometime between about 480 and 450 million years ago. It varies in thickness between 10 and 100 feet in Missouri. The interesting thing about the sand is that the surfaces of the grains are pitted, like frosted glass, which indicates that the sand was at one time transported by wind. Pitting of sand grains occurs when they collide with one another, which typically doesn't occur if water cushions the impacts. The source of the sand was probably a coastal dune field that collected during the arid climate of Middle Ordovician time. The sand in those dunes came from weathering and erosion of Proterozoic igneous rocks and Cambrian and Early Ordovician sandstones.

Marine conditions persisted for a while, and both mud and carbonate sediments were layered across the platform. The increased amount of mud at this time most likely came from erosion of the Taconic Highlands, a range of hills that began forming as the volcanic island arc collided with North America. A subduction zone formed off the northeast coast of North America, at least for a short time, and volcanic eruptions produced clouds of ash that blew west. The ash settled onto the seafloor, creating layers of clay, called *bentonite*, that are preserved in a few Late Ordovician limestone and shale beds in Missouri.

The ice sheets on the southern continent increased in size again late in Ordovician time, and that, coupled with the continuing tectonic movements of the midcontinent platform, once more caused sea level to fall.

Silurian and Devonian Time

A shallow sea might have covered much of Missouri in Silurian time but was likely most persistent across the northwest part of the state, where today drill holes encounter the thickest layers of Silurian rocks, as well as some Devonian rocks, in the Forest City Basin. Thinner beds of limestone, dolomite, and shale were deposited elsewhere in the state.

The collision between the volcanic arc and North America culminated in Early Silurian time, about 440 million years ago, with the uplift of the Taconic Mountains along the collision zone in what is now New England and southeastern Canada. The mountain building forces reactivated faults in basement rocks of Proterozoic age and caused large blocks of those rocks to shift. These movements influenced deposition in the southeast part of Missouri, where both Silurian and Devonian rocks appear to have been deposited in a basin created by the sagging of the underlying Cambrian and Ordovician rocks. A major fault system, the Ste. Genevieve, also formed or was reactivated in the Cambrian and Ordovician rocks, and movement of rocks along this fault continued periodically into Pennsylvanian time.

The best outcrops of Silurian rocks are found near the cities of Bowling Green (in northeastern Missouri) and Cape Girardeau (in the southeast). Where Silurian rocks are exposed, they exist in isolated patches, which means either the ocean was very shallow and filled only scattered low spots on the platform, or thicker and more widespread layers of Silurian sediments have eroded, leaving only those protected in structural low spots. There is indeed an unconformity separating Silurian and Devonian rocks throughout Missouri, so a period of erosion did occur.

The Kaskaskia sequence, the third Sloss cycle, began in Early Devonian time, around 410 million years ago. As the sea advanced over the platform, it flooded the eroded Silurian landscape across Missouri. Inundation probably occurred first in the southeast part of the state, where carbonate sediment was deposited into a structural basin that formed in Silurian time. Up to 1,000 feet of rock, mostly cherty or sandy limestone, hardened from those sediments. The one notable exception to carbonate deposits was a bed of quartz sand eroded from the Ordovician St. Peter Sandstone. But don't expect to see much Devonian rock. At some point in Middle Devonian time, maybe about 380 million years ago, sea level fell long enough for erosion to remove much of the recently deposited carbonate sediment. All of Missouri was likely resubmerged by Late Devonian time.

Land plants began to flourish in Devonian time. By Late Devonian time, abundant plant debris mixed with mud was carried off the land and deposited across the continental platform. Lack of oxygen prevented the organic material from decomposing entirely, and the sediment became the Chattanooga Shale, a

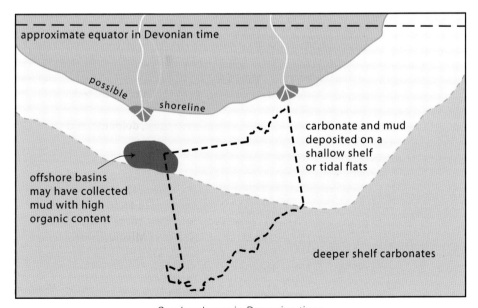

Sea level rose in Devonian time.

dense, black shale bed. It outcrops from Indiana to Oklahoma, but in Missouri the only outcrop of any thickness is in the southwest corner of the state near the Arkansas border. Elsewhere the shale is either very thin (and in those places its identification is disputed) or entirely absent. Deposition of the Chattanooga Shale in Missouri may have been restricted to low spots on the platform, or it may have occurred more widely but was later eroded.

At the end of Devonian time, a minor drop in sea level caused the ocean to retreat off some, though not all, parts of the platform, allowing Late Devonian sediments and rocks to be eroded. Throughout Missouri, an unconformity separates Devonian from Mississippian rocks, so the entire state was above sea level for some period of time.

The volcanic activity that created the Avon Diatremes, and unusual structure in southeastern Missouri, occurred during Devonian time. Fragments of sedimentary rock with Devonian fossils are found within some of the breccias, and radiometric dates obtained on the volcanic rocks confirm a Devonian age. Why the volcanic activity erupted then is not established.

Mississippian, Pennsylvanian, and Permian Time

A rising sea again flooded the platform and Missouri in Early Mississippian time, although this was just another rise within the Kaskaskia sequence. For several million years the entire state lay beneath a clear, warm, shallow sea in which plants and animals thrived. Picture the Bahama Banks stretched across the middle of North America. Some of the most abundant organisms were crinoids, also called *sea lilies*. These filter-feeding animals, cousins to sea stars and sea urchins, form a stalk of calcite disks with a cup at the top in which the animal lives. Five sets of arms wave above the cup, trapping and delivering food to

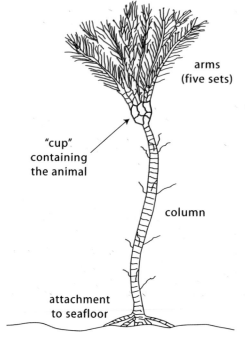

arms
(five sets)

"cup"
containing
the animal

column

attachment
to seafloor

Crinoids were abundant seafloor-dwelling animals in Mississippian and Pennsylvanian seas. Because of the plantlike appearance of their calcite skeletal structure, they are also known as sea lilies.

Fossils, such as these crinoids exposed on a weathered joint surface of Burlington-Keokuk Limestone, are slightly more resistant to weathering than the encasing limestone, so they stand in relief. Crinoid fossils are particularly abundant in Mississippian rocks.

the animal. The Mississippian seafloor was a forest of crinoids for millions of years, and some limestone beds are made almost entirely of their fossils. Thick beds of Mississippian limestone once covered the entire state. Today they are exposed in a band across Missouri from southwest to northeast and also on the east side of the Ozarks. They are present belowground in west-central and northwest Missouri.

The end of the Kaskaskia sequence was marked by a rapid drop in sea level toward the end of Mississippian time. No Late Mississippian rocks are found in northern Missouri either in outcrops or belowground; any sediment that was deposited eroded away. There are Late Mississippian rocks in southwest and southeast Missouri, and they show signs of the shallowing water. Crossbedded limestone beds composed of calcite grains, formed in reefs or shoals, alternate with sandstone and shale beds composed of sediment deposited by deltas building westward off the continent. Eventually the entire state was above water and subjected to erosion, which formed an unconformity between rocks of Mississippian and Pennsylvanian age.

During Pennsylvanian time, North America collided with Europe, Africa, and South America, completing the assembly of Pangea, the last supercontinent. During the plate collisions, Pangea rotated, and while the North American part remained near the equator, the southern half, including what is now southern South America, Africa, India, Australia, and Antarctica, slid over the south pole. Ice sheets formed on those southern hemisphere continents but not

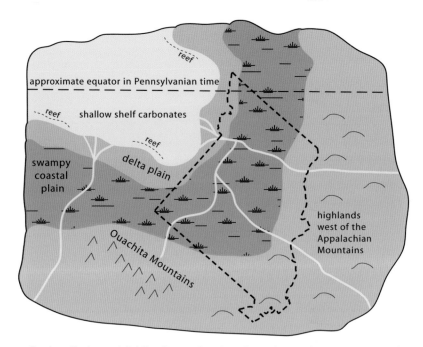

During Early to Middle Pennsylvanian time, large rivers transported sediment eroded off the uplifting Ouachita and Appalachian Mountains onto the continental platform. Mud and sand were deposited in broad, swampy deltas that merged to form a coastal plain.

in one continuous event. The ice collected and melted in cycles spanning tens to hundreds of thousands of years, which led to repeated fluctuations in sea level across the platform. For this and other reasons, the Absaroka sequence, the fourth major rise in sea level across North America, was unlike the previous three cycles. Combine the tectonic oscillations and sea level fluctuations with the enormous amounts of mud and sand that rivers were carrying from the eroding mountain ranges, and you have the recipe for frequent changes in depositional environments. In repeated cycles averaging perhaps 100,000 years, deposition at any one place on the platform changed from deep water to reef to delta to swampy coastal plain and back again.

The rocks formed as a result of these repeated cycles of deposition in Pennsylvanian time are called *cyclothems.* They contain limestone, shale, sandstone, and coal beds. By Middle Pennsylvanian time, roughly 318 to 310 million years ago, the coastline lay either across or just east of Missouri, and deltas of big rivers built across the state frequently, often merging with one another to form a broad coastal plain. Dense stands of giant tree ferns and other plants grew in the swamps. The mud in which the plants grew formed shale beds called *underclays.* Fossilized plant roots are often found in these shale beds, and some of the roots are so large that they were originally mistaken for tree limbs. Dead leaves and trunks that collected and decomposed in the stagnant water became layers of coal on top of the underclay beds. When sea level rose slightly, the coastal

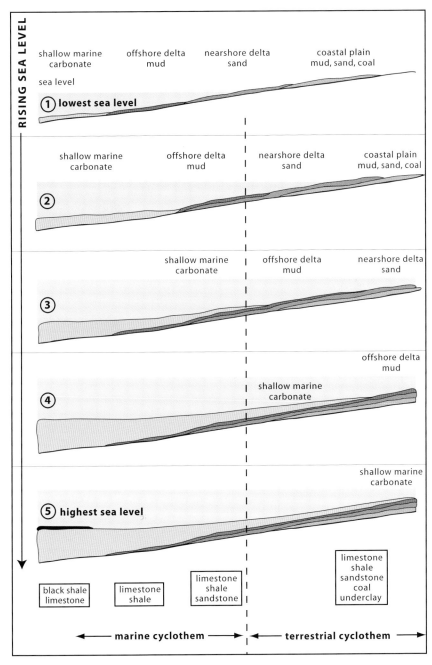

This drawing shows how sediment type might change during the first half of a cyclothem: the time interval in which sea level rose. The kind of sediment deposited at any given location depended on distance from the shoreline, which changed as water level rose. As sea level fell (not shown) a second sequence of sediments was deposited although not in a mirror image because sea level fall occurred more slowly. A complete cyclothem consists of rocks that represent one cycle of sea level rise and fall.

plain was inundated and the coal swamp sediments were buried under sand or mud as the delta shifted away. If the shoreline moved far enough to clear the water, organisms that produced carbonate sediment moved in. Most coal beds in the state are covered by shale or sandstone, but a few are capped by a thin limestone bed.

Pennsylvanian swamps were home to an abundance of tree ferns and other plants, including club moss trees called Sigillaria. *Its fossilized roots (a portion of one is shown here) are known by the name* Stigmaria. *This fossil is about 12 inches long and 4 inches in diameter. The dimples are places where rootlets attached.*

The cycle of sea level rise and fall happened more than forty times. The rapidity with which the coal swamps came and went prevented extensive accumulation of plant debris, so Missouri's coal seams of Middle Pennsylvanian age are generally no more than 1 or 2 feet thick. Coal-bearing cyclothems are exposed from west-central to north-central Missouri, and both areas were once coal-mining regions.

Some Pennsylvanian sandstones were deposited in stream channels that meandered across the delta plain. In western Missouri, a number of these channel-fill sandstones later became reservoirs that trapped oil. Because of their sinuous shape and somewhat unpredictable changes in location, both vertically and horizontally, drillers came to call them "shoestring sands" or "squirrel sands."

Sea level rose in Late Pennsylvanian time, beginning about 295 million years ago, and the coast shifted farther to the east and south. Clearer water allowed organisms to thrive, yielding thick layers of carbonate sediment. The ocean was not very deep, and wave action sometimes pushed sediment and shell debris around to form crossbeds in the limestone. Another type of sediment that formed in the shallow water was sand-sized calcite grains called *ooliths*. These spherical grains formed by deposition of concentric layers of calcite around a core grain. Gentle waves rolled the grains on the seafloor, enhancing oolith formation.

Every so often, no doubt in response to wetter conditions on the nearby continent, rivers delivered more mud into the ocean. This sediment drifted away from the coast and settled into the deeper water offshore. The quantity of mud varied significantly. Small amounts produced thin shale seams on bedding planes in limestone. Greater amounts formed thicker shale beds that often contain a little mixed-in carbonate mud and fossils of creatures that tolerated murkier water and muddy bottoms (some clams, for example). These beds are typically a few feet thick at most and are sometimes called *marine shales* because they were deposited on the seafloor. Some of them contain phosphate-rich nodules that hardened around fish bones, shark teeth, and other fossils. *Nonmarine shales* up to 80 feet thick formed in the river deltas, often containing sandstone layers or channel fill sands.

One rather unusual type of shale bed is found in the Pennsylvanian cyclothems. Known as *black shales*, they vary in thickness from about 4 to 8 feet and mostly consist of soft clay-rich shale or mudstone but also include beds of hard, brittle, black, organic carbon-rich shale, maybe a foot or two thick. Although their color is like that of the older Chattanooga Shale of Devonian age, they look much different and split into hard, thin sheets that can be mistaken for slate. They also contain almost minable concentrations of metallic elements like zinc, molybdenum, copper, and uranium. The preservation of the organic carbon in these shale beds required a lack of oxygen, and the consensus of opinion among geologists is that those conditions were found in very deep, cold-water ocean basins in which currents could not circulate. In this prevailing view, the black shale beds represent the deepest-water deposit of the cyclothems in which they are found.

Some geologists take a contrary position, arguing that since the characteristics of the other rocks in the black shale cyclothems all seem to indicate

In western Missouri, tall roadcuts—like this one along the westbound lanes of I-70 at the MO 131 overpass in Lafayette County—reveal nonmarine shale beds deposited in a river delta.

Hard, brittle, thin-bedded black shale beds were deposited in Middle Pennsylvanian time. Opinions differ about whether this type of organic-rich mud collected on the deep seafloor or in bayous on a coastal plain. —Ken Stalder photo

shallow-water environments, why should the black shales be different? Low-oxygen water conditions also exist in bayous. So it could it be possible that the black shale beds were, in fact, the result of mud deposition into a shallow, stagnant backwater. In either case, mineral-rich groundwater could have contributed the metals.

During the last several million years of Pennsylvanian time the ocean retreated from Missouri. Delta shale and sandstone beds are the predominant rocks from this time interval, with a few thin limestone beds sandwiched amongst them. These rocks are exposed in northwest Missouri in the Forest City Basin.

There are no rocks in Missouri dated to Permian time. Pangea straddled the equator then, and North America was in a dry, tropical climate. By the end of this period, the supercontinent Pangea began to split apart, forming the continents we know today. This was a period of erosion in Missouri, during which time considerable amounts of older rocks were removed.

Folds and Faults in Paleozoic Rocks

Missouri's Paleozoic sedimentary beds are rarely flat lying. Tectonic forces have pushed, pulled, and warped the platform almost constantly since Proterozoic time. Sometimes the tectonics influenced the location in which sediments were deposited, while at other times rock layers were folded and faulted. Some of the resulting geologic structures influence the outcrop pattern of rocks over large areas, and others are more local in scale.

Although there have been many episodes of folding and faulting of sedimentary beds from Cambrian through Pliocene time, the single largest event occurred after Middle Pennsylvanian time during the collisions that formed Pangea. First, Europe and Africa rammed the east coast of North America, causing the uplift of the Appalachian Mountains. Then, South America collided with North America, producing the Ouachita Mountains in Oklahoma and Arkansas. Both ranges reached elevations at least as high as the modern Rocky Mountains. The rocks on the platform west and north of the collision zones were squeezed by two sets of forces that caused both lateral compression and vertical motion.

Paleozoic sedimentary layers responded to these forces by faulting and folding. The largest folds in Missouri—the Ozark Dome, Forest City Basin, Lincoln Fold, and St. Louis Basin—are but a few of a large number of similar structures found in the midcontinent, including the Illinois Basin, Cincinnati Arch, and Nashville Dome, that formed at about the same time.

Major fault zones that disrupt Paleozoic rocks were reactivated by the nearby mountain building. The rocks along these faults slid both sideways and vertically.

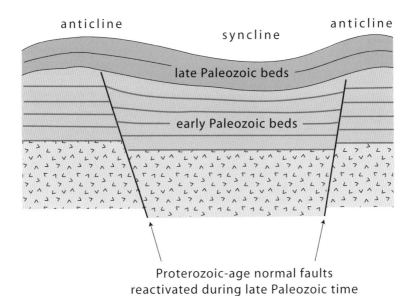

Vertical shifting of Proterozoic basement rocks far below the surface caused Cambrian and Ordovician dolomite beds to break and Mississippian and Pennsylvanian beds to settle over the deep faults in large, gentle folds.

The Chesapeake, Bolivar-Mansfield, and Cap au Gres Fault Zones were all formed at this time, and the Ste. Genevieve Fault was reactivated. But in other places the faults did not breach all of the overlying sedimentary rock layers. The deeper Cambrian and Ordovician dolomite beds did indeed break and move, but the overlying beds of more flexible Mississippian and Pennsylvanian shale, sandstone, and limestone slowly arched and sagged into broad, linear anticlines and synclines. These types of structures are known as *drape folds* because the rock layers are following changes in elevation of the rocks that they cover. The axes of the folds are oriented primarily northwest-southeast, and the beds on their flanks dip only a degree or two.

Most folded beds in Missouri tilt at angles of only a couple of degrees, which is difficult or impossible to see in outcrops and roadcuts. The most obvious expression of the folds is the outcrop pattern they produce over larger distances. Because structural basins and synclines cause downwarping of beds, when the structures are subsequently eroded, younger beds remain at their center. The

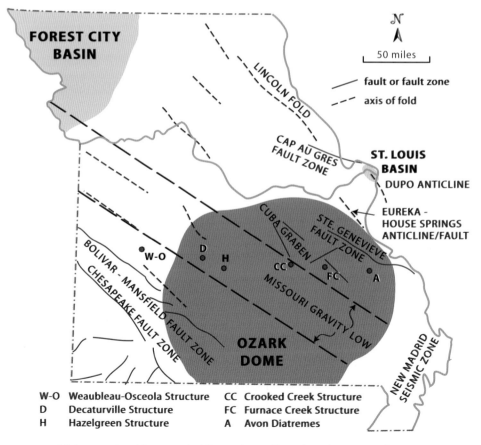

Major structural features in Missouri are aligned northwest-southeast, a direction parallel to deeply buried faults in the Proterozoic crust.

opposite is true of upward-arched domes and anticlines, in which older beds are exposed by erosion at the middle of the structure.

The Thirty-Eighth Parallel Lineament

One of the most peculiar regional geologic features in Missouri is a 10- to 20-mile-wide band in which numerous folds, faults, and areas of shattered and jumbled bedrock appear to line up across the state from the Kansas state line in Vernon County to the Mississippi River in Ste. Genevieve County. Geologists, who tend to get suspicious when more than two of anything line up so nicely, call such groupings *lineaments*. And because this one roughly coincides with the thirty-eighth degree parallel of latitude, it is known as the Thirty-Eighth Parallel Lineament. In western Missouri, the axes of folds bend where they cross the lineament, and within it there are clusters of faults in the Paleozoic rocks. In eastern Missouri it contains the Ste. Genevieve Fault, one of the longest surface fault zones in the state. The presence of many of these structures can be explained by the fact that the lineament is located more or less above an east-west-trending fault in the basement rock.

The lineament is most famous for its less readily explained and most enigmatic structural features: a string of eight small, roughly circular areas in which Paleozoic sedimentary rocks are broken and rearranged. In several of them, the sedimentary rocks are mixed together with pieces of igneous rocks. Six of these structures are in Missouri: from west to east, the Weaubleau-Osceola, Decaturville, Hazelgreen, Crooked Creek and Furnace Creek Structures and the Avon Diatremes.

What first drew the attention of geologists was the igneous rocks that outcropped or were present in the subsurface within four of the structures. Granite closely resembling that found in the St. Francois Mountains is in the middle of the Decaturville Structure, volcanic rocks are found in the Hazelgreen and Furnace Creek Structures, and fragments of diabase are in the Avon Diatremes. This led geologists to conclude that some type of volcanic activity was involved, so they called the features *cryptoexplosive*, or *cryptovolcanic*, structures.

Because these structures are above the basement rock fault system and also seem to be located where other faults cross the main fault, a hypothesis was put forth that gases emitted from magma intruding along the faults made its way to the surface and exploded through overlying Paleozoic rocks, bringing with it some pieces of previously buried igneous basement rocks.

More recently, an extraterrestrial explanation was proposed. The multiple impacts that occurred during the collision of Comet Shoemaker-Levy with Jupiter in 1994, sent geologists looking for evidence of similar strings of impacts on Earth. It didn't take them long to find the Thirty-Eighth Parallel Lineament. The igneous rocks found in the structures might be basement rocks brought to the surface in the central rebound area of an impact crater or crystallized from melting caused by the heat of impact. If these are indeed impact craters, their association with the folds and faults of Thirty-Eighth Parallel Lineament would be a coincidence.

However, the multiple impact explanation for all of the structures, though attractive and exotic, is not supported by studies of the rocks involved. For example, fossils found in rocks disrupted by the Weaubleau-Osceola Structure are of Middle Mississippian age, while undisturbed Cambrian rocks cap the Furnace Creek Structure. In other words, the Weaubleau is post-Mississippian and the Furnace Creek Structure predates Cambrian time.

As it turns out, the structures may in fact have different origins. The rocks in the Avon Diatremes consist of clusters of diabase dikes and volcanic diatremes, or vents, that intruded Paleozoic rocks, and the structure lacks any features of an impact crater. Its volcanic origin seems undebatable. The Furnace Creek Structure also appears to have an igneous origin. The origin of the Hazelgreen Structure has yet to be determined, although it may well be volcanic, too.

But all is not lost for impact lovers. The Weaubleau-Osceola, Decaturville, and Crooked Creek Structures all exhibit characteristics of meteorite impact craters, including circular shapes, central uplifts, elevated rims, and certain types of shattering in mineral grains. Many geologists lean toward an impact origin for these three structures. Research conducted by geologists at Missouri State University also supports an impact origin for the Weaubleau-Osceola Structure. However, the debate continues.

Get the Lead (and Zinc) Out!

Another product of Paleozoic time is Missouri's official state mineral—galena (lead sulfide). It is the single most economically significant ore mineral in the state. French explorers began mining lead deposits in the area around Mine La Motte in Madison County in the 1720s. By the early years of the twentieth century, Missouri produced more lead than any other state, a position that it maintained as recently as 2008, the last year for which records were available at the time of writing. Sphalerite, another economically important sulfide mineral, is the principle ore of zinc and occurs with the galena in Missouri.

The occurrences of lead and zinc ores in Missouri and other places in the midcontinent define Mississippi Valley–Type Deposits, so named because they were first studied in the Mississippi Valley. They occur many other places in the

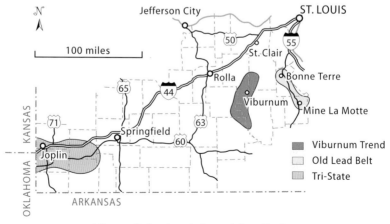

Missouri's lead and zinc mining districts.

Galena, the Missouri state mineral, was found as gray, cubic crystals in the Tri-State District lead and zinc mines. It was commonly accompanied by calcite (top edge).

Sphalerite (the dark masses on this specimen) was a primary ore mineral in the Tri-State District. Pink crystals of dolomite (upon which the sphalerite rests in this photo) were also common there.

Galena from the Viburnum Trend typically occurs as crystals in which cube corners are modified by additional crystal faces.

In the Old Lead Belt in Washington County, crystals of barite and quartz are found filling voids in fossilized stromatolites.

world and yield a large percentage of global lead and zinc production; however, those in the drainage basin of the Mississippi River are the world's largest. All Mississippi Valley–Type Deposits share some characteristics: they were deposited by hydrothermal solutions at temperatures of about 200 to 300 degrees Fahrenheit; the solutions contained very high concentrations of dissolved salts, essentially brines; the deposits occur in fractured limestone or dolomite in situations where the flow of the water became restricted; and the minerals barite and fluorite are commonly present.

The most widely accepted explanation for the origin of Missouri's Mississippi Valley–Type Deposits is that they were deposited by hydrothermal solutions that migrated north and east out of deeply buried rocks during the Ouachita mountain building in northern Oklahoma and Arkansas in Pennsylvanian time. The solutions most likely moved in several separate surges.

Galena occurs in minable quantities in three separate areas of Missouri. The Old Lead Belt and the Tri-State District were mined first, but after World War II exploration for new galena deposits began in southeast Missouri. Geologists suspected they existed because the same rocks that were mined in the Old Lead Belt also were exposed along the western side of the Ozark Dome. Sure enough, in the mid-1950s the richest lead deposit in the United States, and one of the largest in the world, was discovered in a region west of the St. Francois Mountains.

Named the Viburnum Trend after the small town of Viburnum in the northern part of the district in northwest Iron County, its ore deposits occur in a very narrow north-south band through Iron and Reynolds Counties. Production of lead and zinc and, to lesser extents, copper, silver, and cadmium began in the mid-1960s and continues today. All of the mines in "the Trend" are room-and-

The elevator headframe and other surface buildings at the Buick Mine in the Viburnum Trend near Bixby.

pillar. Most range from 600 to 1,200 feet belowground, but the deepest extends down 1,500 feet. Up to 27 million gallons of groundwater must be pumped from the mines every day to keep the shafts dry. The ore extracted from Cambrian-age dolomite beds in the Viburnum Trend is processed underground, avoiding piles of waste rock on the surface.

The ore minerals in the Old Lead Belt and Viburnum Trend are found primarily in the Bonneterre Dolomite, a rock formed from sediment deposited in a barrier reef that built up on the continental platform in Late Cambrian time. Loosely compacted stromatolite mats trapped carbonate sediment transported by wave action, and the porosity of the algal structures later allowed the mineralizing brines to easily penetrate the rock mass. Less permeable beds above the reef rock—the Derby–Doe Run Dolomite and Davis Formation—kept the mineral-bearing fluids from seeping to the surface, thus creating a chemical environment in which rich ores formed.

MESOZOIC ERA
251 to 65 million years ago

The Mesozoic Era is subdivided into the Triassic, Jurassic, and Cretaceous Periods. During Early Triassic time Pangea began drifting north, moving Missouri out of the tropics and eventually into the temperate latitudes it occupies today. Triassic Missouri consisted of highlands about halfway between the Appalachian Mountains and the west coast, which then ran roughly north-south along the Nevada-Utah border. The ocean continued to drain from the platform, and by Early Jurassic time most of North America was high and dry.

The fifth major sea level rise, the Zuni sequence, inundated parts of the continent from Middle Jurassic through Cretaceous time. The ocean submerged the craton in a swath from Texas to Montana. This shallow sea, which teemed with marine reptiles such as plesiosaurs, mosasaurs, and ichthyosaurs, is known as the Interior Seaway, and Missouri likely was near its east coast. Did dinosaurs such as *Allosaurus*, *Diplodocus*, and *Stegosaurus* walk the coastal plains of Missouri? Maybe. A few dinosaur fossils have been found in isolated clay deposits, but there just aren't enough rocks left from this time period to complete the story.

If and how much of Missouri was inundated during Cretaceous time is also unknown. If most of the state was underwater, as some geologists think, nearly all of the sediments deposited have been eroded. The only widespread deposits from Cretaceous time are beds of marine and delta sand and clay, not yet really hardened into rock, found in the Southeast Lowlands beneath Pleistocene alluvium, and in outcrops in the Benton Hills. These sediments were deposited into the upper part of the Mississippi Embayment, a slowly sinking structure that once accommodated a northern extension of the Gulf of Mexico. The beds get thicker to the south, where they are present only in the subsurface and contain more marine sediment, due to increasing distance from the delta. Persistent subsidence in the embayment has exposed the edge of Cretaceous sediment to erosion at the embayment's northern end.

There are also some scattered outcrops of Cretaceous clay found in the Ozarks just north of the Southeast Lowlands. Their circular shape and isolated distribution led geologists originally to interpret them as filled sinkholes in Ordovician dolomite. But recent excavations at one site have revealed a suite of fossils that suggests the sediments were deposited either in freshwater lakes or an estuary. If the latter, these deposits would be the only evidence that the Cretaceous sea extended into Missouri beyond the Mississippi Embayment. What is most exciting about this discovery is that among the fossils are several kinds of reptiles, including duck-billed and tyrannosaurid dinosaurs.

CENOZOIC ERA
65 million years ago to the present

The traditional subdivisions of Cenozoic time were the Tertiary and Quaternary Periods. The Tertiary was subdivided into the Paleocene, Eocene, Oligocene, Miocene, and Pliocene Epochs, and the Quaternary into the Pleistocene (ice age) and Holocene (modern) Epochs. In 2004, the International Commission on Stratigraphy, which recommends nomenclature to the worldwide geologic community, proposed that the traditional Cenozoic subdivisions be replaced with the Paleogene Period (Paleocene, Eocene, and Oligcene Epochs) and Neogene Period (Miocene and Pliocene Epochs, plus the Quaternary, which was demoted from period status). Not everyone liked the idea, particularly geologists who specialized in studying the ice sheet glaciations of the last ice age. A compromise was proposed in 2006 to retain the Quaternary Period following the Neogene and starting it about 2.6 million years ago. That is where things stand today.

Paleogene and Neogene Time

The Tejas sequence, the final major rise in sea level, began in early Paleogene time. Rocks of Paleogene age are absent in Missouri except for beds of delta and marine sandstone and clay exposed on Crowley's Ridge in the Southeast Lowlands. These sediments were deposited into the slowly sinking Mississippi Embayment under conditions quite similar to those in Cretaceous time. The Midway Group of Paleocene time consists primarily of bentonite-rich clay, while the Wilcox Group of Eocene time contains much nonmarine sandstone and plant-fossil bearing clay.

Neogene deposits in Missouri are restricted to patchy exposures of Mounds Gravel, thought to be of Pliocene age, found on ridges and hilltops across the unglaciated parts of the state and beneath Quaternary deposits in northern Missouri. They rest unconformably on pre-Pliocene rocks and sediment. The traditional interpretation is that they are remnants of an alluvial plain deposited by streams flowing west to east from the uplifting Rocky Mountains to the Mississippi River valley. To the east the main river flowed into the Teays River, a large stream that drained the area west of the Appalachian Mountains and entered the Mississippi Embayment north of present-day St. Louis.

Recently an alternative, though somewhat controversial, explanation for the gravels has been proposed. Researchers suggest that rather than being deposited by east-flowing streams, these gravels were deposited by streams that were eroding the Central Highlands, a continuous area of elevated topography that extended from Oklahoma to Maine. Prior to Middle to Late Pleistocene time, rivers on the north side of the Central Highlands drained to a west-flowing river that turned southward through Kansas and Oklahoma before eventually draining to the Gulf of Mexico. That drainage pattern persisted until a drainage divide near the north end of the Mississippi Embayment was breached in Pleistocene time, possibly during the Illinoian glacial stage, diverting flow southward into the present Mississippi River valley. Streams in Missouri then established their present courses as tributaries to the modern Missouri and Mississippi Rivers. The Mounds Gravel, therefore, came from erosion of the Central Highlands to the east and south of the present-day Ozarks. There are some intriguing lines of evidence to support this hypothesis. For example, biologists report that certain species of fish found north and south of the proposed Central Highlands province appear to have evolved from separated populations; what's more, they are species that thrive in fast-moving water, which streams draining the Ozarks part of the highlands would have had.

Under either scenario, by late in Pliocene time Missouri was likely buried under stream-deposited sediment. Beginning either at the end of Pliocene time or the beginning of Pleistocene time, some changes occurred that caused streams to switch from deposition to erosion. First, there was renewed tectonic uplift and tilting in the midcontinent, including the rise of the Ozark Dome and perhaps the southern Appalachians. Exactly what caused it is not clear. One view is that it may have been caused by density changes in the underlying mantle rocks, perhaps related to a mantle hot spot, that pushed up the crust very slowly. An alternative explanation is that it might have been caused by changes in tectonic plate motions on the west coast of North America, where a subduction zone was morphing into the San Andreas Fault. Strong evidence for either mechanism—or any other—is lacking at the moment. The uplift was accompanied by renewed subsidence in the Mississippi Embayment, which allowed streams draining toward it to erode more actively.

A second factor involved in the switch from deposition to erosion was that glaciers began to build up on northern hemisphere continents, lowering sea level. That allowed all streams draining to the Gulf of Mexico to start downcutting. In addition, the climate became cooler and drier, which also altered stream behavior. This renewed stream erosion removed most of the pre-Pleistocene alluvium from Missouri.

Quaternary Time and the Pleistocene Ice Age

The consensus in the geologic community is to place the start of the Quaternary Period (the Pleistocene Epoch) at just under 2.6 million years ago, roughly corresponding to the initial advance of ice sheets across North America. The Laurentide Ice Sheet slowly flowed out from its collection zone in northern and eastern Canada and eventually reached as far south as central Missouri. At the edge of the ice sheet, giant lobes of ice moved, or advanced, creeping forward in different places at different times. Details of Missouri's Pleistocene geology are still being unraveled because the evidence—sediment deposited during early incursions of ice—is either buried beneath younger sediment or eroded away altogether.

The early classification of North America's Pleistocene Ice Age identified four major episodes of ice sheet growth, or glacial stages, named the Nebraskan, Kansan, Illinoian, and Wisconsinan glaciations, after the states in which deposits were found. These glacial episodes were separated by interglacial stages, warmer climates during which ice melted and the glaciers retreated.

However, subsequent studies have revealed that many more cycles of ice formation and melting occurred through Pleistocene time, perhaps as many as fifty. In each cycle the volume of glacier ice in the northern hemisphere waxed and waned, although not necessarily everywhere simultaneously. The resulting advances and retreats of ice sheets did not fit well within the traditional four glaciation model. What's more, ice-deposited sediment older than the Nebraskan glaciation was discovered in drill holes buried beneath younger deposits in the midcontinent. Today the period covered by the two older traditional glacial stages (Nebraskan and Kansan), plus all pre-Nebraskan deposits, are identified as pre-Illinoian. Nearly all of Missouri's glacial deposits are from pre-Illinoian glaciations.

When ice sheets advance, they scrape up pieces of rock and incorporate them into the ice. Then, as they melt, they deposit the rocks and ground-up sediment in a jumbled mix called *till*. Recent studies have identified as many as five, and possibly seven, distinct pre-Illinoian till layers in north-central Missouri, each representing a separate ice lobe incursion. The oldest dates to about 2.4 million years ago and is thought to be part of the oldest till deposit in North America. The youngest widespread till in Missouri is about 600,000 years old, although an ice lobe briefly pushed across the Mississippi River valley near St. Louis about 200,000 years ago.

The pre-Illinoian glacial stages ended about 250,000 years ago. As the ice sheet covering Missouri began to melt, huge volumes of sediment-laden meltwater flowed away from the retreating edge of the glacier. Glacial sediment deposited by flowing meltwater is called *outwash* and can be distinguished from till by the presence of stratified layers.

Along the western edge of the retreating ice, meltwater scoured out the valley of a stream that had been a south-flowing tributary to the Ancestral Kansas River, a major waterway that traversed Kansas from west to east in pre-Pleistocene time. The tributary valley, widened and deepened by the incredible amount of water moving through it, became a primary conduit for meltwater for the remainder of Pleistocene time and is now home to the modern Missouri River. The tremendous discharges of water entered the Ancestral Kansas River valley at Kansas City and flowed east across the state, eroding deeper into the bedrock. By the end of Pleistocene time, the entire valley was filled with sediment; first with boulders and gravel dumped off the melting glacier, then with sand and mud deposited by the meltwater river.

Across northern Missouri the retreating glacier left behind several hundred feet of till, the thickest amounts of which are found in buried preglacial stream valleys. Missouri's till is typically tan to reddish brown where exposed in weathered outcrops or roadcuts. It is composed mostly of clay and also contains lenses of sand, permeable sediment that produces water if a well driller is lucky enough to find it. The till also contains some cobbles and boulders of various rock types. These large rocks are called *erratics* if the glacier transported

This erratic boulder of granite is in a roadside park along US 136 in eastern Scotland County. An ice sheet probably transported it to the area from granite outcrops in Minnesota.

them from outcrops located far from their final resting spot. The largest glacial erratic so far uncovered in Missouri (in central Sullivan County, northwest of Milan) is more than 20 feet across, but most are much smaller.

Most of Missouri remained ice free in late Pleistocene time, except for a small area in St. Louis, where about 200,000 years ago one or more small lobes of ice briefly pushed across the Mississippi River valley from Illinois. At least one lake formed behind the ice dam and several channels developed as water overflowed from the lake.

During the last 100,000 years or so of Pleistocene time, as ice sheets dwindled far to the north, windblown deposits of clay and silt, called *loess*, blanketed much of Missouri. The grinding action of the ice sheets pulverized much of the rock and sediment they transported into powdery material. As glaciers melted, the clay and silt were carried away by outwash streams and deposited in large lakes or on river floodplains. Eventually these deposits dried out and were picked up by the prevailing winds. In Missouri, the thickest loess deposits are found along the valleys of the Missouri and Mississippi Rivers. Soil has formed on top of the loess across much of the state.

In the time since the final northward retreat of ice sheets, tributaries flowing to the Missouri and Mississippi Rivers eroded till, loess, and outwash valley fill

Road excavations through loess, such as this one along Missouri 210 just west of Interstate 435 in Kansas City, will stand in vertical cuts, most likely due to the interlocking of sand and silt grains. However, the base of the cuts must be allowed to drain freely to prevent the collapse of saturated sediment. Lower slope angles can erode if water runs across the loosely consolidated sediment.

Glacially scratched and polished limestone is exposed along MO 169 on the north bluff of the Missouri River. The scratches, called striations, are aligned along the direction of ice movement.

sediment. Because of the thick deposits of till across northern Missouri, many of the streams there occupy valleys that are in different locations from the valleys buried by the advancing ice sheet. Elsewhere, and especially in west-central Missouri, streams are flowing in preglacial valleys filled with glacial lake or outwash sediment. The modern rivers also have yet to cut down to pre-Pleistocene elevations and lack the discharge or slope to do so. As a result, they meander across wide floodplains. Drill holes in these valleys pass through thick layers of sand and gravel before encountering bedrock.

Glaciers also erode the terrain across which they advance, but glacial erosion features are hard to find in Missouri because the subsequent deposition of till, outwash, and loess conceals them. However, scratched bedrock surfaces have been uncovered at some construction sites.

Fossils of plants and animals living at the end of Pleistocene time are found throughout Missouri, as are arrowheads and tools of the people living in the region at the time. Mastodon teeth and bones are regularly dredged from the channel of the Missouri River and have been found along other stream valleys in the state. Caves in southern Missouri contain fossils of ground sloths, bears, and other animals.

Mastodon State Historic Site, just south of St. Louis, preserves the state's most productive deposit of Pleistocene fossils: a formation called the Kimmswick Bone Bed. One of the most interesting discoveries at the site, which was first excavated in 1839, occurred in 1979 when a Clovis Culture spear point was found among mastodon bones. This artifact was the first solid evidence for the interaction of humans and mastodons in eastern North America. The presence of the spear point indicates the site was occupied between 14,000 and 10,000 years ago. The bone bed has been buried, preserving any remaining artifacts and fossils for future research, but the museum at the visitor center displays many of the fossils found there.

Although climate and vegetation have certainly changed since Pleistocene time, the topography is much the same as that over which mastodons and their ancient hunters roamed more than 11,000 years ago.

Caves, Springs, and Sinkholes

Because the bedrock across so much of Missouri consists of limestone and dolomite, the state contains a wide range of features related to erosion of those rocks by groundwater. In fact, one of the state's nicknames is the Cave State. Although all of the carbonate rocks in Missouri are affected by groundwater erosion, the state's caves, springs, and sinkholes are concentrated in the outcrop areas of Ordovician dolomite and Mississippian limestone. Areas in which such features are present are said to have *karst topography*.

Precipitation is naturally slightly acidic because it contains dissolved carbon dioxide gas picked up from the atmosphere. Once rain and snowmelt percolate into the soil, the water picks up even more of the gas. Limestone and dolomite are soluble in acidic solutions, so when groundwater moves through these rocks it can dissolve or remove the rock mass through dissolution. It is a slow process that requires thousands upon thousands of years to create openings of any size in the rock.

The most obvious karst features along Missouri highways are solution-widened joints that appear in roadcuts. They formed long before the road was there, as water seeped down through the fractures. Many of them are filled with clay, which either washed into them from the overlying soil or was left behind when carbonate was dissolved from a clay-rich limestone or dolomite bed.

Though other states might have bigger caves, and maybe more total miles of passageways, Missouri boasts the greatest number of caves (6,300 and counting), and the most caves open to the public (more than 20). Though most of the "show caves" are commercial operations, a few are in state parks.

Missouri caves consist of networks of passageways, many of which eroded along joints in dolomite and limestone beds. Where passages intersect, vertical shafts and larger rooms formed. All caves formed below the water table, where the rock was in prolonged contact with moving groundwater. The fact that most of Missouri's caves are no longer submerged is due to a combination of factors. The uplift at the end of Pliocene time elevated the cave-bearing bedrock layers. At the same time, streams eroded their valleys deeper, creating lower discharge

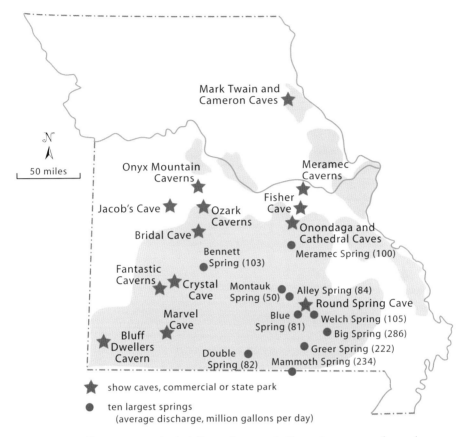

Karst topography in Missouri occurs in the outcrop areas (green) of Ordovician dolomite and Mississippian limestone beds.

points for the groundwater system, and the water table dropped, dewatering the caves.

But that is not to say that Missouri caves are dry. Water does percolate down from the surface, entering the caves through fractures, dripping from the ceilings, or oozing down the walls. The water carries in it calcium carbonate dissolved from the soil and rock through which it has seeped. When the water encounters the void of a cave, the mineral is deposited, forming stalagmites, stalactites, and other intricate cave formations. The relative humidity in most caves is near 100 percent, so these calcite formations are not the result of evaporating water. Rather, dissolved carbon dioxide gas in the seeping water is returning to the cave air, which has a lower concentration of the gas. Because the water contains less carbon dioxide, it's less acidic and therefore less capable of holding calcium carbonate in solution, which results in deposition of calcite.

The water entering a cave has to go somewhere, and it generally finds a way out along one or more passages. Eventually it ends up discharging back to the ground surface in a spring, often in the bed of a river. The Ozarks have

Big Spring in Carter County is Missouri's largest, discharging an average of nearly 300 million gallons of water per day into the Current River. Groundwater issues from the base of the Eminence Dolomite of Cambrian age.

hundreds of springs that are fed through underground passages. The largest springs collect water from hundreds of square miles on the Salem Plateau. Studies of Big Spring, the state's largest, reveal that its water comes from as far as 50 miles away.

The large springs generally discharge their water under pressure from inclined or vertical tunnels that can be thousands of feet long and hundreds of feet deep. The ten largest springs in the state have a combined average flow of over 1 billion gallons of water every day. Mammoth Spring is usually included in lists of Missouri springs because about 90 percent of its flow comes from Missouri, even though it is located about 500 feet into Arkansas.

Although caves and springs are popular attractions, sinkholes are also common karst features in Missouri. These circular or elliptical depressions in the ground surface form either above a collapsed cave or where the overlying soil has thinned because water has carried clay particles into an underlying cavern. Sinkholes are most noticeable when they contain water and form small lakes. Usually these sinkhole ponds form because water cannot drain out through the clay that washes into them. Otherwise, the water drains into the underlying cave or eroded fracture.

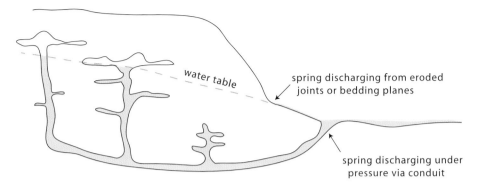

Missouri springs flow to the surface along eroded joints or bedding planes in limestone and dolomite. The largest springs, the outlets for water in submerged cave systems, flow under pressure. The higher elevation of the water table on the plateau at the far end of the spring's collection area produces the pressure at the point of discharge.

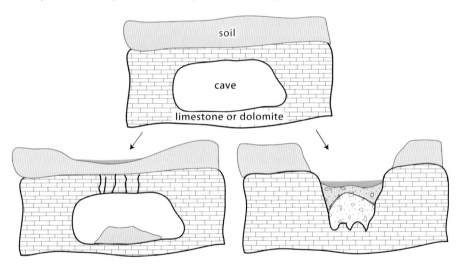

Sinkholes can form wherever a cave in limestone or dolomite is close to the surface. Sinkholes form either when seeping water carries soil down into a cave or open joint (bottom left), or the roof of a cave collapses (bottom right).

A Tale of Two Rivers

On August 1, 1993, a historically unprecedented event unfolded at the confluence of the Missouri and Mississippi Rivers when record-high floods on both rivers arrived simultaneously. The Missouri was unable to drain quickly enough, and flooding extended upstream across the entire state. From its mouth to Jefferson City the river remained above flood stage for over three months. The flood of 1993 was the most destructive to date in Missouri. Damage costs in Missouri alone exceeded three billion dollars, and repairs to breached levees took half a year. Ironically, these two rivers are the most flood-controlled

During the 1993 flood, the Missouri River remained at flood stage at Jefferson City for more than three months. This aerial view of Jefferson City shows the Missouri state capitol and flooded land around it. The parallel lines of trees across the center of the photo mark the river channel. —Missouri Department of Natural Resources photo

streams in the United States. Eighty years of engineering and billions of dollars spent on levees, dams, and channel modifications failed to prevent an event for which they were designed.

Missouri's two largest cities were settled near the confluences of rivers. St. Louis was founded as a fur trading settlement in 1764 at a location about 18 miles south of the confluence of the Missouri and Mississippi Rivers. By the time of the Louisiana Purchase in 1804, the town was the major hub of fur trading and commerce along the Mississippi River. In 1817 the era of riverboat traffic began with the arrival of the first steamboat. A natural ledge of limestone, which protruded from the bank along the entire riverfront, was used as a wharf. That ledge is no longer visible, having been either removed or buried by subsequent construction along the waterfront. By the middle of the nineteenth century, St. Louis was the eastern portal for people traveling along the Missouri River and the trails west, thus earning the name Gateway to the West. The riverbank location of the original settlement is within the Jefferson National Expansion Memorial, where now stands the city's iconic symbol, the Gateway Arch.

On the other side of the state, Kansas City began in 1821 as a trading post on the south bank of the Missouri River. The original location, 3 miles downstream from the confluence of the Kansas River, was flooded out, and the town was relocated to the present location on the bluffs in 1826. About the same time, an entrepreneur who had established a trading post on the Santa Fe Trail discovered a ledge of limestone jutting out into the Missouri River channel at the base of the south bluff. As in St. Louis, this natural formation was used as a wharf. Called Westport Landing, the site became a primary point of departure for folks headed west. The limestone ledge remained visible above the waterline until concealed by construction along the riverfront in the 1990s.

St. Louis and Kansas City soon became important centers of commerce, relying on the two rivers as their primary transportation routes. The rivers were used by barge traffic moving grain and other commodities to and from agricultural and industrial centers in the Midwest. But neither river was all that predictable or dependable. Water levels varied with droughts and floods, shallow channels eroded only to fill again with sand, and fallen trees often clogged the tight bends. Once the floodplains were filled with businesses and homes, floods became a problem, and something had to be done to confine the rivers to permanent channels.

The subsequent changes that humans have made to the appearance and behavior of the two rivers are so great that neither river remotely resembles what it looked like two centuries ago. Some of the changes were brought about to facilitate transportation, but most were intended to tame the floodwaters.

HARNESSING THE MIGHTY MISSISSIPPI. The first flood control levee on the Mississippi River was built in the early 1700s by the French to protect their settlement in New Orleans. Floods in the latter half of the nineteenth century began to get the attention of policy makers, and in 1879 the Mississippi River Commission was established with the charge of determining how best to control floods and maintain navigation on the river. The prospects of success were not great, according to one well-known analyst of human endeavors:

> You turn one of those little European rivers over to this Commission, with its hard bottom and clear water, and it would just be a holiday job for them to wall it, and pile it, and dike it, and tame it down, and boss it around, and make it go wherever they wanted it to, and stay where they put it, and do just as they said, every time. But this ain't that kind of a river.
>
> —Mark Twain, from *Life on the Mississippi*

The Mississippi River has the fourth largest drainage basin of all rivers in the world, draining nearly all the land in the United States between the Rocky Mountains and the Appalachians. It was not to be taken lightly. In 1852 Congress appropriated fifty thousand dollars for the U.S. Army Corps of Engineers to study the causes of flooding on the river. One of the study's surprising conclusions was that levees might actually make flooding worse by preventing the floodwaters from spreading out as they naturally would do. But the suggestions were ignored, and beginning in 1882, the Corps of Engineers, which still has the responsibility of maintaining the nation's navigable waterways, embarked on a levee construction program that extended the levee system from Cairo, Illinois, all the way to the mouth of the river. Through the first two and half decades of the twentieth century, the levees did the job. Then failure came in spectacular fashion.

The year 1926 ended with the Missouri, Ohio, and Arkansas Rivers, which drain the upper part of the Mississippi River basin, all at record flood stages. The rain continued into the spring of 1927, and record rainfalls over large portions of the lower Mississippi River watershed sent the Mississippi out of its banks. The levees failed.

The greatest damage occurred in the lower half of the Mississippi River basin. The river caused damage as far north as the Missouri Bootheel but expended most of its wrath upon river towns from Memphis to New Orleans. Nearly 30,000 square miles of land were flooded, hundreds of thousands of people were driven from their homes, and damage estimates reached 350 million dollars, nearly five billion in today's dollars. The Mississippi was reported to be 80 miles across in some places. One levee breach in a small Mississippi town sent floodwaters up to 60 miles away from the channel. In another place water reportedly reached 100 feet deep, no doubt assisted by local topography in addition to the flood. It was arguably the greatest natural disaster of any kind to that time, and certainly the biggest recorded flood in North America.

Although the flood did not directly impact most of Missouri, the response most certainly did. The U.S. Congress passed the Flood Control Act of 1928, authorizing the Corps of Engineers to do whatever it took to prevent a similar flood from occurring again. The Corps set into motion an engineering project unlike any ever attempted to that date: they would tame one of the largest rivers in the world.

On the upper Mississippi, the Corps built a series of locks and dams as control structures. The dams regulate water depth and discharge rates, while the locks permit barges and boats to pass. Seven of these structures are located along Missouri's eastern border between Canton and St. Louis and make the river more a chain of large lakes, called *slackwater pools*, rather than a free-flowing stream.

Between St. Louis and the Arkansas state line, the Mississippi River is confined by flood control levees over more than 80 percent of its course. Workers must dredge the channel, removing accumulated sand, to maintain sufficient water depths for navigation. More than one thousand wing dams, earth and rock structures that protrude from the banks to divert the current, were constructed along the length of the river to help move sediment through its channel.

NARROWING THE WIDE MISSOURI. When Lewis and Clark paddled up the Missouri River in 1804, they navigated a muddy river flowing in a shallow, sandy channel with many twists and turns. The river's discharge was capricious, depending on the season. Water levels were historically highest in the spring and lowest in winter and tended to fluctuate quickly in response to precipitation. At flood stage the water rapidly topped the natural banks of the river and spread out over the floodplain, which in many places was covered with swamps and marshes.

By the mid-nineteenth century, the river and its tributaries were the principal avenues for settlers headed west. The murky waters were said to be "too thick to drink and too thin to plow," earning the river the nickname the Big Muddy. Like many of the streams crossing the plains, the Missouri is muddy

At Cape Girardeau, floodgates in the levee are closed to protect the city when the Mississippi River rises.

because the land it drains has clay- and silt-rich soil and sediment that become suspended in the stream flow.

Curves in the river channel were so tight that they posed challenges to navigation, as did the tangles of limbs and brush that often clogged the stream and the submerged trunks of dead trees, called *snags*. Just upstream from Kansas City, the paddle-wheel steamboat *Arabia* hit a snag in 1856 and went down with its cargo intact but no loss of life. Over the years, the shifting channel of the river buried the boat under nearly 50 feet of mud and sand. In 1988 it was located about 0.5 mile from the modern river channel. The artifacts recovered from the excavation are preserved in the Arabia Steamboat Museum in downtown Kansas City.

Dredging and straightening of the channel to improve and maintain navigability began as early as 1832, but concerted federally funded efforts began in the early twentieth century. Just before World War I, Congress authorized the Corps of Engineers to establish and maintain a 6-foot-deep navigation channel from Kansas City to St. Louis. The war temporarily halted the project, but it was later revived and modified to provide for a 9-foot-deep channel. The Corps dredged the channel and reinforced the riverbanks to encourage the natural flow to scour the streambed and maintain the depth.

The tight bends of the Missouri River, called *meanders*, were always a headache for rivercraft. Meanders are almost organic creatures. They grow longer and sweep downstream over time and occasionally are breached at their narrowest points by raging floodwaters. The breaches are called *meander cutoffs*. Beginning in the 1930s, the Corps of Engineers set out to straighten the channel, breaching their fair share of meanders. Whether natural or engineered, the meander cutoffs are rather easy to find on photos or maps. Because political boundaries don't change much, any place where the modern river channel and the state or county lines no longer match is almost always a meandor cutoff. The abandoned part of the meander is called an *oxbow.*

Straightening of a river channel increases its gradient, or drop in elevation per distance traveled, so it also increases the river's ability to erode. The Missouri's riverbanks had to be reinforced with rock to limit erosion and prevent future meandering. Flood control levees were constructed to protect urban

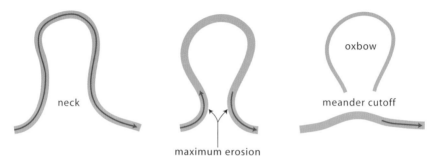

Meanders change shape over time due to erosion on the outsides of the curved channel. If the neck becomes too narrow, it can be breached by a flood, or by human intervention, resulting in a meander cutoff and an oxbow.

Despite decades of flood control measures, the historic 1993 flood breached levees all along the Missouri River's channel. This levee breach occurred in St. Charles County, near St. Louis. —Missouri Department of Natural Resources photo

areas and fertile farmland on the floodplain. All of these human alterations to a stream's channel are known as *channelization*.

Management of the Missouri River has involved more than flood control and navigation concerns. Irrigation and hydroelectric power needs in the northern Great Plains prompted construction of six large reservoirs on the upper Missouri River between 1937 and 1963. The dams were designed to impound water for upstream uses and release water as needed to maintain water levels for navigation in the downstream parts of the river, particularly between Omaha, Nebraska, and St. Louis.

The river's flow is now almost completely artificially controlled, and according to the Missouri Department of Conservation, the total water surface area of the river is only half of what it was before channelization. In what may seem to be a contradiction, the modern flood control levee system along the Missouri River probably made the 1993 flood worse than it would otherwise have been. The protection offered by the levees encouraged dense development on the floodplain, resulting in greater economic losses. In addition, channeling floodwaters between levees in one place often creates larger floods downstream where levees are either absent or lower. Damage around Kansas City and for miles downstream was limited in 1993 because of levees built after that area's catastrophic 1951 flood. Because those levees prevented floodwaters from spreading out over the floodplain, the floodwaters were higher downstream in central and eastern Missouri, breaching levees there.

THE GLACIATED PLAINS

Roads in northern Missouri provide opportunities to view the work of ice sheets, or at least the sediment they left behind. The relatively flat area north of the Missouri River is a large till plain, an extensive deposit of glacial sediment left by melting ice sheets in Pleistocene time. Till once covered all of northern Missouri, but some of it has been removed, or dissected, by stream erosion, primarily in places close to the Missouri and Mississippi Rivers and their bigger tributaries. With the exception of some younger till near St. Louis, the youngest till in northern Missouri is about 600,000 years old. The till plain slopes gently to the south from the Iowa border to the Missouri River valley, reflecting the thinning of till deposits toward the southern edge of the ice sheet.

There aren't many roadcuts in this region, and even where road construction has required some excavation, the highway department has planted vegetation on the slopes to prevent erosion. Generally speaking, you will get only occasional glimpses of till on eroded slopes. If you see pebbles or larger stones scattered in the soil of a sloping roadcut, it is likely till, although not all of the glacial sediment is till. A layer of sand or gravel is more likely glacial outwash, sediment deposited by streams that carried water away from melting glaciers.

Shaded-relief image of northern Missouri. Note the parallel streams that flow south down the gently sloping till plain. —Shaded-relief base map from EROS Date Center

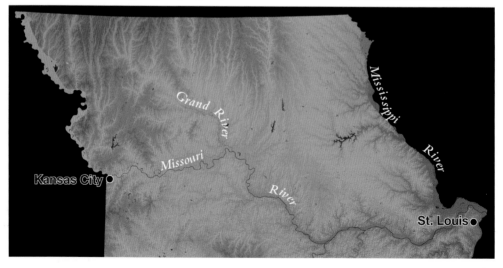

This roadcut in Mercer County about 7 miles south of the Iowa border on US 65 exposes till deposits. The pinkish cobble at left-center of the insert is Sioux Quartzite that was transported by the ice sheet from outcrops near Sioux Falls, South Dakota.

Loess (windblown silt) covers the glacial sediment in most places in northern Missouri, but it can be even harder to pick out in roadcuts than glacial till. The thickest and best exposed deposits are found along the bluffs of the Missouri and Mississippi Rivers, where the loess is nearly 100 feet thick. Elsewhere it is only a few feet thick, and because it is the uppermost deposit in Missouri, it is the first to weather into soil or erode.

One aspect of Missouri's till plain makes it a bit different from other places in the midcontinent: it lacks ridges of till called *end moraines*. These piles of till collect along the edge of an ice sheet when the ice is melting as fast as it is advancing, causing the edge of the ice to remain stationary for a period of time. Geologists know that the Pleistocene glaciers moved in fits and starts, and end moraines are all over the place in Illinois, Michigan, and Wisconsin. The reason there are no end moraines in northern Missouri is not clear, although it could be that it is simply a matter of time. Missouri's till is several hundred thousand years older than that found to the north and east, and it is quite plausible that erosion during late Pleistocene time removed end moraines formed during the final glacier retreat. There may be end moraines in older till, buried beneath younger deposits.

Pennsylvanian bedrock underlies most of the till in northern Missouri. The sedimentary rock layers dip very slightly to the west-northwest, toward the Forest City Basin, so the ages of beds get progressively younger from east to west. The best outcrops of Pennsylvanian rocks are near the valleys of larger streams that have eroded more of the overlying till. Mississippian bedrock, the same limestone and shale beds that outcrop on the Springfield Plateau, is exposed along the Mississippi River valley in northeastern Missouri. The Lincoln Fold brings these older rocks to the surface there. The Forest City Basin and Lincoln Fold, two of Missouri's large-scale folds, formed in response to crustal warping associated with the collision in Late Pennsylvanian time between the North and South American tectonic plates, which raised the Ouachita Mountains.

Drainage Patterns, Then and Now

During a drought in the 1950s, the Missouri Geological Survey embarked on an investigation to find groundwater sources within the glacial deposits in northwestern Missouri. Till does not contain much groundwater because the clay in it plugs the gaps between the sand and gravel. However, the sand and gravel of glacial outwash does contain water, so over 1,200 holes were drilled in nineteen counties between 1955 and 1960 to find groundwater in glacial

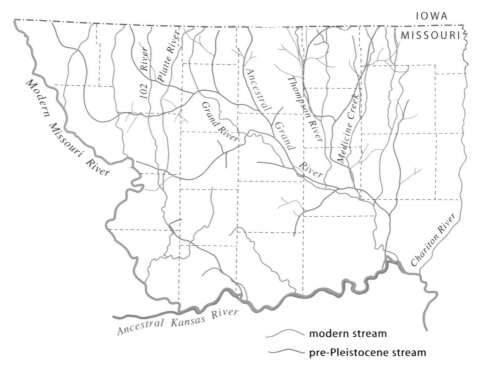

Pre-Pleistocene rivers in northwestern Missouri occupied valleys that frequently bear little relationship to the locations of modern streams. The modern Missouri River is very wide at Waverly (south of Carrollton) because the Ancestral Grand River joined the Ancestral Kansas there. —Map modified from Anderson, 1979

outwash. In each hole, the depth at which bedrock was encountered beneath the till was noted. By plotting those elevations and drawing lines to connect points of the same elevation, maps were created that showed the shape of the buried bedrock surface—the land surface prior to Pleistocene time. Back then, the topography in northwestern Missouri resembled that seen today in the Osage Plains south of the Missouri River. Prior to glaciation, rivers had been eroding Pennsylvanian bedrock for millions of years. A few big rivers flowed in well-developed valleys, collecting water from a branching network of tributaries, a pattern called *dendritic* because of its resemblance to branching tree limbs. The modern drainage system bears no resemblance to this older, buried system. In fact, the pre-Pleistocene river valleys were often in different places than the modern ones.

The largest preglacial river flowed east-southeast across northwestern Missouri. Because its valley sometimes coincides with that of the modern Grand River, the older stream is known as the Ancestral Grand River. Near Brunswick, the Ancestral Grand joined the east-flowing Ancestral Kansas River, which occupied the valley in which the Missouri River now flows between Kansas City and Brunswick. The Missouri River as we know it today did not exist. None of the pre-Pleistocene valleys, some of which were up to 200 feet deep, can be seen today because they are filled with glacial till and outwash. Sand and gravel aquifers in the buried valleys provide small quantities of water for domestic and livestock use.

During and after the retreat of ice sheets from northern Missouri, a completely different drainage pattern was created. The topography was flat but irregular, littered with mounds of till and shallow low spots and crossed by the occasional outwash stream channel. Eventually, a network of rivers and tributaries established their courses, but often in entirely different locations from where the streams existed prior to glaciation. The largest streams flow more or less south, toward the Missouri River. Their channels are roughly parallel to each other, a pattern called *parallel drainage*, which usually forms in an area of uniform slope (here sloping south to the Missouri) and homogenous rock type (here glacial till).

Swamps and bogs were widespread and persisted in many places until farmers drained them in the late 1800s. The farmers also straightened and deepened the streams.

Road Guides to the Glaciated Plains

St. Louis Metropolitan Area

The confluence of the Missouri and Mississippi Rivers is just north of the St. Louis metropolitan area. Because the velocity of the Missouri River is faster than that of the Mississippi River here, when the two flows mix, sediment drops out of the slowing Missouri River water. The sand deposit forms a point between the two rivers. In 2001 the land between the rivers was added to Missouri's park system as Jones–Confluence Point State Park. The park is reached by taking MO 367 north from I-270, then US 67 across the Missouri River to Riverlands Way at West Alton.

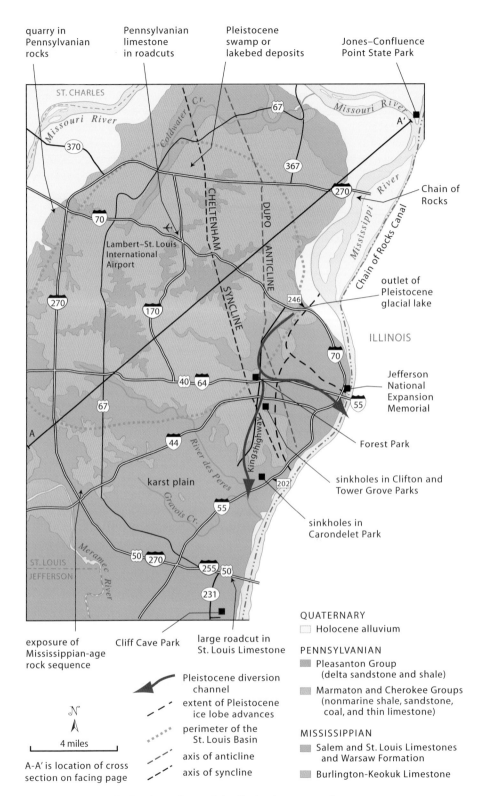

quarry in Pennsylvanian rocks

Pennsylvanian limestone in roadcuts

Pleistocene swamp or lakebed deposits

Jones–Confluence Point State Park

ST. CHARLES

Missouri River

370

67

Missouri River

A'

Coldwater Cr.

367

270

Chain of Rocks

CHELTENHAM SYNCLINE

DUPO ANTICLINE

Mississippi River

Chain of Rocks Canal

70

Lambert–St. Louis International Airport

270

170

246

outlet of Pleistocene glacial lake

ILLINOIS

70

A

40 – 64

Jefferson National Expansion Memorial

55

67

44

River des Peres

Kingshighway

202

Forest Park

sinkholes in Clifton and Tower Grove Parks

karst plain

Gravois Cr.

55

sinkholes in Carondelet Park

Meramec River

50 – 270

255 – 50

231

ST. LOUIS
JEFFERSON

exposure of Mississippian-age rock sequence

Cliff Cave Park

large roadcut in St. Louis Limestone

N°
⋀

4 miles

A–A' is location of cross section on facing page

Pleistocene diversion channel

extent of Pleistocene ice lobe advances

perimeter of the St. Louis Basin

axis of anticline

axis of syncline

QUATERNARY

☐ Holocene alluvium

PENNSYLVANIAN

▨ Pleasanton Group
(delta sandstone and shale)

▨ Marmaton and Cherokee Groups
(nonmarine shale, sandstone, coal, and thin limestone)

MISSISSIPPIAN

■ Salem and St. Louis Limestones
and Warsaw Formation

▨ Burlington-Keokuk Limestone

Bedrock geology of the St. Louis metropolitan area.

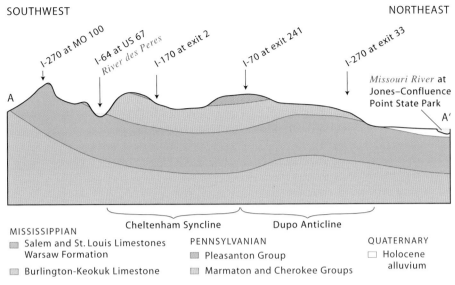

SOUTHWEST

NORTHEAST

I-270 at MO 100

I-64 at US 67
River des Peres

I-170 at exit 2

I-70 at exit 241

I-270 at exit 33

A

Missouri River at
Jones–Confluence
Point State Park

A′

Cheltenham Syncline   Dupo Anticline

MISSISSIPPIAN
◻ Salem and St. Louis Limestones
  Warsaw Formation
◻ Burlington-Keokuk Limestone

PENNSYLVANIAN
◻ Pleasanton Group
◻ Marmaton and Cherokee Groups

QUATERNARY
◻ Holocene
  alluvium

This cross section from southwest to northeast across the St. Louis metropolitan area shows the gently dipping rock layers in the St. Louis Basin. Topographic expression and dip of beds are exaggerated to show detail.

The site of the original settlement of St. Louis is within the Jefferson National Expansion Memorial, home to the Gateway Arch. A ledge of St. Louis Limestone once exposed along the riverbank was used as a wharf, but it was removed or buried through the years. Some of the stones used in the original flood control levee and riverfront roads have been incorporated into the modern sidewalk near the river. The rocks are primarily different colors of granite and rhyolite, most of which were mined in the St. Francois Mountains.

The city of St. Louis is built on the bluffs along the Mississippi River. The suburbs in St. Louis County, which does not include the city proper, radiate outward to the valleys of the Missouri and Meramec Rivers. Nearly all of the rocks exposed in the area are of Mississippian age and are best exposed along the interstate highways at the perimeter of the metropolitan area, generally along and outside of the I-270 loop. In the urban core, most roadcuts made during highway construction are now obscured by landscaping, sound barriers, frontage roads, lane dividers, or buildings.

The Dupo Anticline and Cheltenham Syncline influence the dip of beds and outcrop pattern of rocks across St. Louis and northern St. Louis County, and beds across the entire area are downwarped by the St. Louis Basin. Pennsylvanian rocks are preserved within the basin, and a limestone bed is exposed in roadcuts near the intersection of I-70 and I-170, east of Lambert–St. Louis International Airport. Fossils in these rocks date them to about the same age as Pennsylvanian rocks in western and northern Missouri. They are likely remnants of rocks that once covered the entire area.

The Mississippi riverfront at Jefferson National Expansion Memorial was the site of the original settlement of St. Louis. Most of the town was constructed on the low loess bluff to the west (right side of photo). View to the south at Eads Bridge.

East of Lambert–St. Louis International Airport, roadcuts along I-170 below the I-70 overpass reveal some of the few exposed Pennsylvanian rocks south of the Missouri River in eastern Missouri. These beds are preserved within the St. Louis Basin.

The aptly named St. Louis Fault cuts through the heart of the city almost parallel to the waterfront. The fault is completely buried beneath glacial deposits and alluvium but is thought to be a strike-slip fault that may be responsible for the occasional small tremors experienced in the area.

Mining Around St. Louis

Bedrock mining has been and continues to be a significant economic resource in the area. The Pennsylvanian beds in the St. Louis Basin were exploited for coal in the past, but those pits were long ago abandoned and covered. Today the primary resources are limestone and sandstone. There are many open-pit quarries and underground mines, mostly to the west and south of the urban core. The St. Peter Sandstone is mined in southern Jefferson County at Festus and Crystal City, the latter an underground operation. Four limestone beds are either quarried or mined underground: the Plattin and Kimmswick Limestones of Ordovician age, and the Burlington-Keokuk and St. Louis Limestones of Mississippian age. The largest quarry in the area, which has operated since the early 1900s, is visible to the southwest of the intersection of I-70 and I-270 on the northwest side of town. Some of the underground mines also have space converted to secondary uses, such as offices and warehouses.

Clay was also once an economically important resource mined in the area. Driving through the urban core, you will no doubt notice the abundance of old brick buildings. Clay bricks were manufactured locally, either from fire clay

The St. Louis Limestone, once exposed along the downtown riverfront, is one of the limestone beds mined in the metropolitan area. This roadcut is on the northeast corner of I-255 and Koch Road (exit 3). A quarry and underground mine are a short distance to the south of this location. The slightly different appearance of the lower and upper beds exposed here is due to composition. The lower bed is dolomitic and the upper one is crystalline limestone. They are separated by what is thought to be an unconformity.

mined from the Cheltenham Clay of Pennsylvanian age or from the loess that blankets the region. Bricks were also used as pavers for early streets, but the local clay did not have a good chemical composition for paving bricks, so the raw material (mostly shale) was imported from central and western Missouri and other Midwestern states.

Chain of Rocks

Chain of Rocks, a limestone ledge over which the Mississippi River flows north of St. Louis, forms a small waterfall at low water levels. At the end of Pleistocene time, the course of the river shifted to the west, where it encountered the bedrock. Chain of Rocks Canal was completed on the Illinois side of the river in the early 1960s to provide navigation around the bedrock ledge.

The bridge that takes I-270 across the Mississippi River is known as the New Chain of Rocks Bridge. To the south of the new bridge is Old Chain of Rocks Bridge, built in the 1920s with a 22-degree bend in it. The odd orientation was a compromise between navigational concerns (barges trying to line up with the current) and geologic ones (the need to build the foundation on solid bedrock). The old bridge was abandoned in 1967 when the new I-270 bridge was opened, and since 1999 it has been part of a bike and pedestrian trail.

Karst Topography

Sinkholes are common in the southern parts of St. Louis City and St. Louis County. As many as 100 per square mile have been counted in St. Louis County's undeveloped areas. More than 125 caves are documented in St. Louis County, though half are no more than widened joints or bedding planes in the

Ponds form when the bottoms of sinkholes become plugged with clay, preventing surface water from draining quickly into the groundwater system. These pond-filled sinkholes are on the bluffs above Cliff Cave in Cliff Cave County Park, in southern St. Louis County. —Kevin Conroy photo

limestone. Some of the local caves were used by breweries in the nineteenth century to store beer, a precursor to today's use of mines for underground storage space. Many of the small caves are sealed or obliterated by construction, but the largest known cave system is preserved in Cliff Cave County Park. To reach the park, take I-255 exit 2 south on Telegraph Road (MO 231) to Cliff Cave Road. Spelunking and tours are available by reservation only.

Many sinkholes in the urbanized part of St. Louis have been filled, but a few remain. Though not visible from the interstates, sinkholes (or lakes that fill plugged sinkholes) are features in Clifton Park (south of I-44 at exit 286), Tower Grove Park (south of I-44 at exit 287), and Carondelet Park (west of I-55 at exit 202).

Pleistocene Geology

During Pleistocene time, ice sheets advanced into the St. Louis area at least twice. The first incursion, most likely around 500,000 to 400,000 years ago, deposited the till found north of the Missouri River on the northwest side of the metropolitan area. As that ice melted, water flowed in streams in front of the ice, depositing an outwash plain. A lake or swamp formed at the present location of Florissant, north of the junction of I-170 and I-270. Fossilized spruce cones and the bones, teeth, and claws of several mammals have been found in the lakebed sediment.

About 200,000 years ago, the last lobe of glacier ice to enter Missouri pushed across the Mississippi River valley from Illinois. It advanced west to about the present alignment of Kingshighway and deposited the till found in downtown St. Louis.

The lobe also temporarily blocked and diverted the flow of the Mississippi River. When the ice first crossed the Mississippi Valley, it impounded a large lake that inundated the valleys of the Mississippi, Missouri, and Illinois Rivers

This lake, one of several along the east edge of Forest Park, occupies the former Pleistocene diversion channel that drained water from the lake created when an ice lobe blocked the Mississippi River about 200,000 years ago.

as far as 20 miles upstream. The lake drained through a low divide near O'Fallon Park (I-70 at exit 246) in north St. Louis. Water flowed south, approximately along the route of Kingshighway, through the eastern edge of Forest Park before returning to the Mississippi River in the valley of Mill Creek. St. Louis's Union Station (north of I-64 at exit 38D) is built in this valley. A later surge of the ice lobe blocked that drainage route and water was diverted farther west into the valley of the River des Peres.

Interstate 29
Iowa Border—Kansas City
129 MILES

Interstate 29 crosses the Forest City Basin, the major geologic structure in the sedimentary rocks in northwestern Missouri. The structure is named for a town located a few miles southwest of the interstate at exit 75 in Holt County. The basin, a large downwarp in Paleozoic sedimentary rocks, extends from northwestern Missouri into Kansas, Nebraska, and Iowa.

The youngest Pennsylvanian rocks in Missouri are found in the Forest City Basin. Studies suggest that formation of the basin was related to the presence of the Nemaha Anticline and Fault Zone, which runs north-south through eastern Kansas and Nebraska. The sedimentary rocks east of the Nemaha structures were pushed against a faulted escarpment and gently warped downward in Late Pennsylvanian time. The youngest Pennsylvanian sediments were deposited into a topographic basin created by the underlying structure.

Loess hills border the eastern side of the Missouri River valley between the Iowa border and Mound City. Erosion or excavations expose the windblown silt deposit, as here between mile markers 81 and 82 on Interstate 29. —Ken Stalder photo

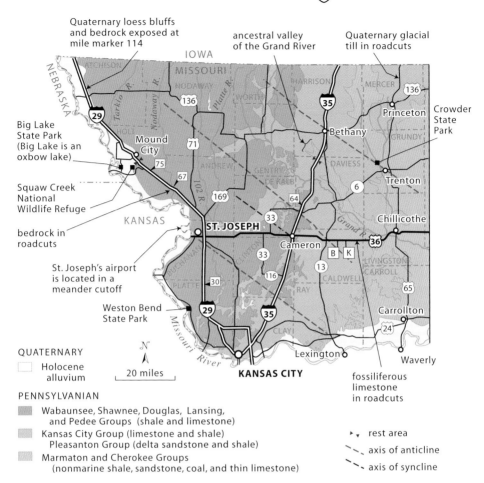

Pennsylvanian rocks in northwestern Missouri. Bedrock is covered by loess on the bluffs adjacent to the Missouri River, and by till over nearly all the rest of the region, except in and near stream valleys.

Interstate 29 crosses the centerline, or axis, of the basin at about the US 136 interchange (mile marker 110). The axis trends slightly northeast-southwest across the northwest corner of Missouri. Beds on the northwest side of the fold axis dip to southeast and those on the southeast side dip to the northwest, but at such a slight angle that they appear horizontal. All of the rocks exposed along the highway are Pennsylvanian age.

Between the Iowa state line and Mound City (exit 84), the interstate is built on the east side of the Missouri River's floodplain. The present position of the river channel runs along the western bluffs of the valley, which are occasionally visible low on the horizon a few miles away. Loess and till form the hills along the east side of the interstate. Late Pennsylvanian bedrock appears at the base of a few roadcuts along the northbound lanes between mile markers 114 and 112.

South of Mound City, I-29 is on the uplands. Loess is present in roadcuts between Mound City and the US 59 junction near mile marker 67. The Nodaway River and its tributaries have eroded into Late Pennsylvanian bedrock here. Limestone beds are present in roadcuts at exit 67 and south to about mile marker 58.

Big Lake State Park

If you're in the mood to get up close and personal with the meanderings of the Missouri River, head for Big Lake State Park, located about 10 miles off I-29 at exit 79. The park preserves Big Lake, the largest oxbow lake in Missouri, and marshland that resembles the river's floodplain during presettlement times. An oxbow lake is an abandoned meander of the river. The name comes from the looping shape, which resembles yokes once used on teams of oxen. Big Lake formed more than two hundred years ago when a flood breached the narrow neck of land separating the river channel on the upstream and downstream sides of a meander. It might be one of the lakes visited by Lewis and Clark. To reach the park, take either MO 118 (exit 84) or US 159 (exit 79) west to MO 111 and follow signs to the park entrance. Squaw Creek National Wildlife Refuge, a reclaimed wetland, is also located in the area. Prior to modification of the river channel and construction of flood control levees, wetlands like these served to contain spring floods.

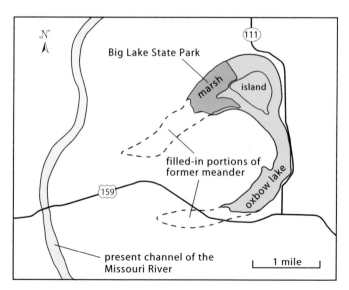

Big Lake fills part of an oxbow, a former meander of the Missouri River.

St. Joseph to Kansas City

St. Joseph, famous as the departure point for the Pony Express, is built atop a loess-covered bedrock ridge. The ridge separates two valleys through which tributaries of the Ancestral Grand River flowed before the Pleistocene ice sheet buried them in till. Interstate 29 crosses the northern valley near the Buchanan county line (just north of the US 169 interchange at exit 50) and the southern valley at US 36. Both valleys were filled with till and outwash as the glaciers retreated, so there is no topographic expression of them. Roadcuts along the interstate between mile markers 58 and 30 are mostly covered by vegetation but likely contain loess or soils derived from the glacial sediment.

Roadcuts between mile marker 30 and MO 45 (exit 5) expose either Pennsylvanian limestone and shale, or loess. South of MO 45, the interstate cuts through Kansas City Group formations, slightly older beds of Pennsylvanian limestone and shale than those to the north. Interstate 29 ends at downtown Kansas City, which is built atop loess, till, and bedrock on the south bluff of the Missouri River.

Weston Bend State Park

If the oxbow at Big Lake wasn't enough river for you, a nice view of the Big Muddy can be had at Weston Bend State Park. To reach the park, take MO 273 (exit 20) west to MO 45. Go about 0.5 mile south on MO 45 to the park entrance. A boardwalk leads to a panoramic overlook of the river. The town of Weston was established across the river from Ft. Leavenworth, Kansas, on a natural cove along the east bank.

Interstate 35
Iowa Border—Kansas City
114 MILES
See map on page 65.

Between the Iowa border and mile marker 64, vegetated slopes of roadcuts along I-35 conceal Pleistocene till, often with a thin cover of loess. You can catch glimpses of the reddish brown, gravel-bearing till in small gullies eroded on the slopes. The bedrock beneath the glacial deposits consists of Pennsylvanian limestone and shale, which are best exposed between Bethany and Kansas City. The Bethany Falls Limestone, the rock that is mined in the Kansas City area, got its name from outcrops here.

Interstate 35 is built on gently rolling till deposits of Pleistocene age from the Iowa border south to about mile marker 64. View looking south from mile marker 114 at the border.

Crowder State Park

At Crowder State Park, the Thompson River and its tributaries have carved unusually steep-walled valleys into glacial till, exposing the underlying Middle Pennsylvanian bedrock. The Thompson River is flowing in a valley that closely matches that of its pre-Pleistocene predecessor, which is filled with thick layers of glacial sediment. The meandering river contains numerous sandbars and gravel bars. The Weldon River, a meandering stream that flows almost due south down the slope of the till plain, joins the Thompson River on the northeastern boundary of the park. Prehistoric Native American mounds are found within the park boundaries. The state park is east of I-35 off MO 146 near Trenton.

The Thompson River flows south through Crowder State Park. Sand and gravel picked up from erosion of till is stored in the channel as gravel bars during times of normal stream flow, when water velocity is not fast enough to move larger sediment. The rocks along the left side of the stream are part of a flood control levee. This view is to the north from the MO 6 bridge.

Ancestral Grand River

The rest area at mile marker 81 is located in, or more accurately above, the buried valley of the Ancestral Grand River. There is no topographic clue to the valley's presence, but bedrock here is buried beneath 200 feet of glacial till, which fills the old valley. The modern Grand River is about 6 miles to the south, and its valley is nearly 2 miles wide where I-35 crosses it, bounded by very low bluffs. The river flows on a floodplain that is the upper surface of glacial and meltwater sediment that filled the valley of an east-flowing, pre-Pleistocene tributary to the Ancestral Grand River. The modern Grand River at this location is a classic example of an underfit stream—a modern river that flows in a valley that is much wider or deeper than the present-day river could possibly have created.

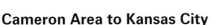

Cameron Area to Kansas City

Limestone beds appear in roadcuts between mile marker 64 and the end of the route at Kansas City. In many cuts in this interval, ledges of limestone are capped by sloping surfaces that indicate softer material. Unlike farther north, not all of these slopes are till. Some of them are soft shale beds that alternate with the limestone layers. Through Clay County, loess is present, although mostly covered with vegetation, in some roadcuts between I-435 and the merge with I-29.

Where the merged I-35 and I-29 cross the Missouri River in Kansas City, the bedrock floor of the valley is up to 150 feet below river channel and floodplain deposits. The valley here was eroded by massive volumes of water discharged from melting glaciers at the end of Pleistocene time. At the bottom of the valley, buried under the younger alluvium, is a boulder layer that could only have been deposited by water flowing at a much greater velocity and volume than any flow in the modern Missouri River. For information about Kansas City geology, see the Osage Plains and Springfield Plateau chapter.

Interstate 70
Columbia—Missouri River at St. Louis
123 MILES

Between Columbia and the valley of the Loutre River, roadcuts reveal mostly Pennsylvanian bedrock. However, on either side of Auxvasse Creek, roughly between mile markers 151 and 159, Mississippian limestone appears because of the presence of a northwest-southeast-oriented anticline. The Auxvasse Creek Anticline is typical of the small folds that influence the orientation of beds on the northern flank of the Ozark Dome. The interstate crosses the axis of the fold in the valley near mile marker 155. At the Loutre River, an anticline known as the Mineola Structure exposes Ordovician and Devonian rocks in roadcuts on either side of the valley. Because the beds were arched upward and then the upper layers eroded away, older rocks are now exposed along the fold axis.

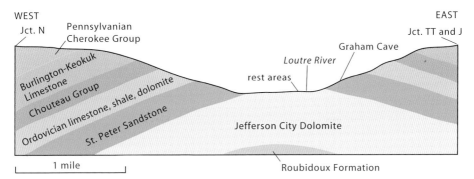

I-70 crosses the axis of an anticline at the Loutre River valley. The oldest Ordovician rocks are present along the axis, buried beneath alluvium. Graham Cave is on the east bluff of the valley, north of the highway. The vertical scale is greatly exaggerated to show topography and bed dips.

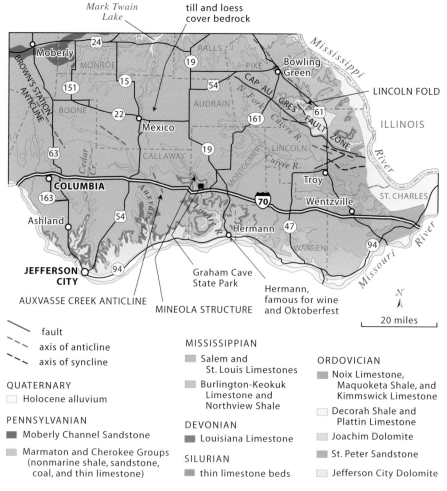

Paleozoic bedrock beneath the till in east-central Missouri along I-70 between Columbia and the Missouri River at St. Louis.

The correlation between fold axes and stream valleys is probably more than coincidence. When rock layers are folded, fractures form along the axis of the fold. Those cracks allow water to penetrate more easily into the rock mass, accelerating weathering and making the rocks easier to erode.

On the hill north of I-70 east of the Loutre River is Graham Cave State Park, an archaeological site in St. Peter Sandstone of Ordovician age. We don't usually think of caves in sandstone, and they certainly do not form in the same way as those in carbonate rocks. Graham Cave formed as groundwater seeped out of the sandstone rock face, carrying with it sand grains loosened by freeze-thaw cycles. The floor of the cave was originally the top of the underlying Jefferson City Dolomite, although sediment obscures the rock. Evidence of human habitation of the cave dates to as far back as 10,000 years ago and includes petroglyphs and

Graham Cave formed when groundwater seeping from the base of the St. Peter Sandstone loosened and eroded sand grains. Prehistoric peoples occupied the cave, which is a protected archaeological site today.

stone circles, which are visible through a fence that secures the site. To reach the park, take exit 170 and turn north. Immediately turn west onto Route TT, the north frontage road parallel to I-70. Stay on this road for 2 miles to the park entrance and continue until the road ends at a cul-de-sac. The parking lot is on your left. A paved walkway leads uphill to the cave.

Between the Loutre River valley and the north bluff of the Missouri River, I-70 crosses a band of Mississippian limestone. The junction with MO 370 (exit 223) approximately marks the eastern edge of pre-Illinoian till deposits. Between there and the Missouri River, loess covers the bedrock.

US 36
St. Joseph—Hannibal
193 MILES
See map on page 65 for the western part of the route.

The St. Joseph airport, Rosecrans Memorial Airport, is located west of the city. In fact, it is located west of the Missouri River. Just why is part of Missouri located where Kansas ought to be? Following a damaging flood in 1952, the U.S. Army Corps of Engineers excavated a cutoff through the neck of the Missouri River meander that surrounded the airport.

Through St. Joseph and for several miles to the east, in northern Buchanan and southern DeKalb Counties, US 36 follows the southern of two buried pre-Pleistocene river valleys that bracket the city. The buried valley bends to the northeast about where US 36 crosses the Platte River, one of the modern streams that flows south across the southward-sloping till plain.

The flat area through DeKalb County, roughly between MO 31 and I-35, is the divide separating the drainage basins of the Platte and Grand Rivers. In the stretch of highway between the I-35 junction at Cameron and Caldwell County Route B, pale brown till is visible in gullies in the roadcuts, some of which have been stabilized against erosion by placement of limestone rubble.

Pennsylvanian limestone and shale beds of the Kansas City Group appear along both sides of US 36 in several roadcuts between Caldwell County Route K and the Grand River valley west of Chillicothe in Livingston County. The rocks contain lots of fossils, including brachiopods, crinoids, and fossilized algae, which appear as wavy seams in the limestone beds. In some of the roadcuts, the limestone contains cavities formed by groundwater erosion. At Hamilton (MO 13), the highway crosses the southern end of the fold axis of the Hamilton–King City–Quitman Anticline, which extends from about 12 miles southeast of the intersection over 80 miles to the northwest. There are no roadcuts exposing beds affected by this structure, but in the cuts 2.8 miles east of Route K (1.2 miles west of Routes M/A) in Caldwell County, rock layers dipping slightly to the west are influenced by an unnamed fold.

US 36 crosses the buried valley of the Ancestral Grand River, here occupied by the modern Grand, between Utica and Chillicothe. A thick bed of Pennsylvanian shale, probably part of the Pleasanton Group, is exposed in the roadcut just west of Utica. This bedrock forms the valley wall of both the modern and Ancestral Grand Rivers.

The top of a limestone bed in a roadcut along the eastbound lanes of US 36, 0.5 mile west of Route K in Caldwell County, is scalloped due to groundwater erosion. The wavy bedding in the rock is fossilized algae (39.735N 93.880W).

Dipping beds in Pennsylvanian limestone and shale along the westbound lanes of US 36 in eastern Caldwell County mark the flank of a small fold (39.441N 93.818W).

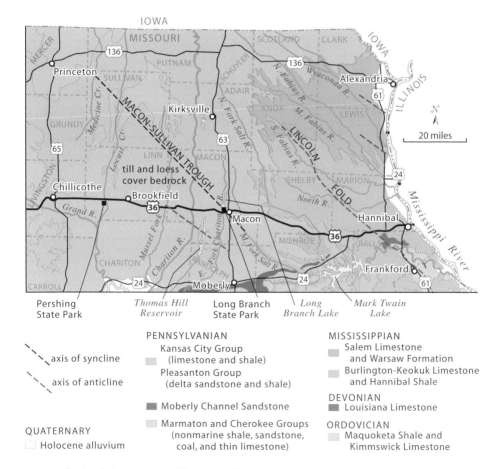

Bedrock beneath the till along US 36 between Chillicothe and Hannibal.

Between Chillicothe (US 65) and Macon (US 63), US 36 crosses the roughly parallel valleys of several south-flowing streams: from west to east, Medicine Creek, Locust Creek, Mussel Fork, the Chariton River, the Little Chariton River, and East Fork Chariton River. Take particular note of the very broad, shallow shape of the Chariton River's valley between MO 149 and MO 3. The valley walls are mostly composed of glacial sediments rather than resistant rock layers. The river has been here for a geologically short period of time, only since the retreat of ice sheets in Pleistocene time.

The lake at Long Branch State Park, 2 miles west of US 63, was formed by damming of the East Fork Chariton River to provide flood control in the lower parts of the Chariton River drainage basin. The park preserves an example of the upland prairie grassland that developed on the till plain following Pleistocene time. The highway also crosses the axis of the Macon-Sullivan Trough here. This structure is a broad syncline, probably a drape fold, that extends to the northwest about 65 miles. At Macon, US 36 crosses Missouri's Grand Divide, the drainage divide separating the watersheds of the Missouri and Mississippi Rivers in this part of the state.

Although the bedrock is buried, US 36 crosses the contact between Pennsylvanian and Mississippian rocks between Marion County Route U and Ralls County Route DD (about 6 miles east of Monroe City). Between there and

The channel of Medicine Creek in eastern Livingston County, like the channels of most of the streams in this part of Missouri, was straightened to improve runoff from farmland. As is typical of channelized streams, the force of moving water soon creates sandbars and gravel bars around which the flow diverges. A meandering channel will eventually form. View looking south from the US 36 bridge.

the Mississippi River, the bedrock is Mississippian shale and limestone. The appearance of older rocks here is due to the influence of the Lincoln Fold, an asymmetrical anticline produced during continental collisions in Pennsylvanian time.

Between the US 61 interchange and the Mississippi River, US 36 is also called I-72. Plans are in place for the entire length of US 36 to be converted to interstate and called I-72; watch for new roadcuts!

The Chariton River in Macon County flows in a broad, shallow valley that the river is presently eroding into the glacial sediment. The floodplain shown here, looking to the west from the east side of the valley, is alluvium. Till and loess cover the uplands.

This swampy area is near Locust Creek at the turnoff to Pershing State Park on the southwest corner of US 36 and MO 130 in Linn County. It resembles the postglacial vegetation of much of northern Missouri prior to the modification of streams to create farmland.

US 61
Alexandria—Hannibal
60 MILES

Between Alexandria and Canton, US 61 is on the floodplain near the western bluffs of the Mississippi River valley. At Canton, a short trip east on MO 16 takes you to Lock and Dam No. 20, the northernmost of these structures in Missouri. Take MO 16 off US 61 and go 1.2 miles east to US 61 Business, which runs parallel to the river. Turn north for two blocks and turn east on Henderson, where a sign points to Mississippi Park RV Campground. Go east another two blocks to Front Street and turn north. You can park at the RV campground or in the U.S. Army Corps of Engineers lot next to the lock.

Between Canton and La Grange, US 61 runs atop the bluff. The Warsaw Formation and Salem Limestone of Mississippian age appear in several roadcuts and are particularly well exposed about 1 mile north of the Wyaconda River. This corner of Missouri, as well as adjacent areas of Iowa and Illinois, is renowned for the geodes found in the Warsaw Formation. Geodes are roughly spherical rocks that are hollow and contain quartz crystals. How they formed is still the subject of some speculation, but one hypothesis is that they began as rounded masses of calcite in the shale that were later dissolved by groundwater, forming a void. Silica-bearing groundwater then deposited a rind of chalcedony, a type of quartz. Crystals of quartz grew into the remaining void.

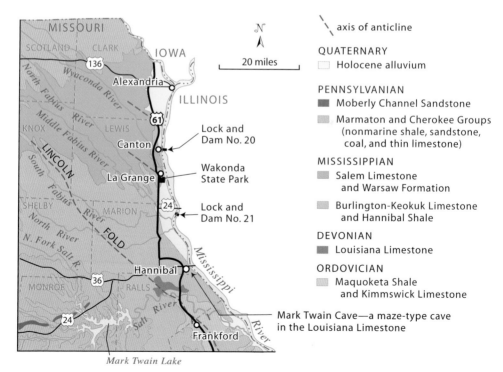

Bedrock geology along US 61 between Alexandria and Hannibal.

Lock and Dam No. 20 at Canton. Water level in the lock (foreground) is raised and lowered for watercraft. The westernmost gates of the dam are in the background; gates are opened or closed to regulate the discharge of the river downstream.

Roadcuts along the northbound lanes of US 61 between Lewis County Route P and the Wyaconda River reveal Warsaw Formation (bottom) and Salem Limestone (top) of Middle Mississippian age. This cut is 1 mile north of the Wyaconda River.

Geodes from the Warsaw Formation in northeastern Missouri have a thick rind of chalcedony enclosing a cavity into which quartz crystals grew. This specimen is about 6 inches in diameter, but geodes more than 1 foot across have been found!

Just south of La Grange, US 61 is back on the floodplain, crossing sand and gravel deposited at the end of Pleistocene time by floods of glacier meltwater. More than 26 million tons of gravel were excavated for use in statewide road construction from pits just east of the highway. That quarry is now Wakonda State Park, accessed from US 61 at Route B in southern Lewis County. The landscape in the park is entirely artificial. The lakes are former sand and gravel pits, and the hills are spoil piles.

Hannibal, once home to writer Mark Twain, features many sites related to the author and his stories, including Mark Twain Cave, just south of town. It became Missouri's first commercial cave in 1886 and is now a national landmark. To reach the cave, take MO 79 south from US 36. A bit less than 2 miles south is the turn to Lovers Leap, a bluff that provides panoramic views of the town and the Mississippi River.

Tall roadcuts bracket the turn-in to Lovers Leap. The Burlington-Keokuk Limestone is at the top. The Keokuk Limestone is on top but is rarely differentiated from the Burlington Limestone because they are almost identical. The same limestone is exposed southwestward across the state to the Springfield Plateau. However, the thick shale bed at road level, known as the Hannibal Shale, does not because varying depositional environments existed in Missouri during earliest Mississippian time. In central Missouri, the same time interval is represented by a limestone bed, and on the Springfield Plateau by a sequence of sandstone, limestone, and shale.

The turnoff to Mark Twain Cave is a little over 1 mile south of the Lovers Leap entrance. The cave was dissolved along a network of joints in the Louisiana Limestone of Devonian age. Young Mark Twain explored the cave and gave a perfect description of this maze-type cave in *The Adventures of Tom Sawyer*:

> The cave was but a labyrinth of crooked aisles that ran into each other and out again and led nowhere. It was said that one might wander days and nights together through its intricate tangle of rifts and chasms and never find the end of the cave.

On the hill across the parking lot from Mark Twain Cave is Cameron Cave. The two cave systems were originally connected, but the erosion that formed the valley between them severed the connecting passageways and also created the cave entrances.

View looking upstream at Hannibal, the Mississippi River, and the US 36 bridge from the top of Lovers Leap, a bluff topped with Burlington-Keokuk Limestone.

The Burlington-Keokuk Limestone caps the bluff at Lovers Leap in Hannibal. The Hannibal Shale, at road level here along the northbound lane of MO 79, is the oldest Mississippian rock deposited in this part of Missouri.

US 61
Hannibal—Missouri River at St. Louis
116 MILES

Between Hannibal and Troy, Ordovician bedrock is exposed on the Lincoln Fold. The axis of the fold extends for about 170 miles through northeastern Missouri, trending northwesterly from where it enters the state near Winfield in Lincoln County. US 61 follows the crest of the fold between the MO 19 junction at New London and the Auburn area.

Although the fold warps bedrock layers into the overall pattern of an anticline, the structure is actually a group of related folds and faults. The broad arching of rock layers is nestled between the Forest City Basin to the west and the Illinois Basin to the east. Folding may have begun as early as about 425 million years ago, in Silurian time, but most of the regional uplift and deformation was likely produced during the collision of the South American and North American continents during Pennsylvanian time.

The Lincoln Fold is an asymmetrical anticline—beds dip at different angles on either side of the axis. On the southwest flank of the fold, beds dip at angles of between 10 and 15 degrees toward the southwest; beds on the northeast flank dip at less than 5 degrees to the northeast. The asymmetry is an indication that the entire fold was tilted to the west, either during or after the initial buckling of beds.

Limestone, shale, and dolomite beds dating from Late Ordovician time appear in many roadcuts on the crest of the fold both north and south of the Ralls-Pike county line. These beds are also exposed farther south near Cape Girardeau, where their total thickness is about four times what it is here.

The Kimmswick Limestone is very fossiliferous, and local roadcuts have long been popular destinations for collectors. Unique to the Kimmswick are its fossilized calcareous algae colonies called *Fisherites* (pronounced *fish-er-ITE-eez*). Although the fossil is also known as sunflower coral for its resemblance to a flower head, it is not a member of the coral family.

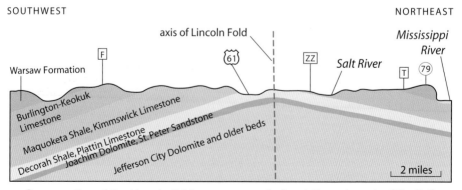

Cross section of the Lincoln Fold, an asymmetrical anticline, along the Pike-Ralls county line. Beds on the west dip at about twice the angle as beds on the east.

The Kimmswick and Plattin Limestones are pitted and perforated by holes and tubes. These cavities formed through a process called *differential weathering*, in which parts of the rock were more readily dissolved by water than the rest of the rock mass. Some type of animal likely burrowed through the soft lime mud on the seafloor, and as the rock lithified, these churned-up areas of sediment became rock that was less dense, and thus less resistant to weathering, than the rest of the limestone. Similar features are found in these formations elsewhere in the state.

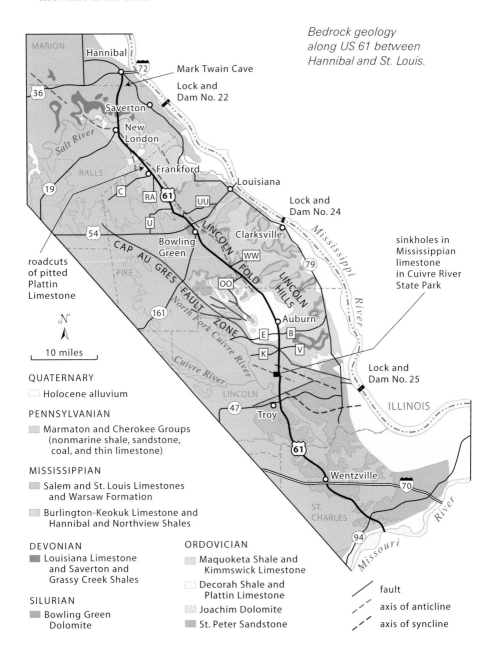

Bedrock geology along US 61 between Hannibal and St. Louis.

QUATERNARY

▢ Holocene alluvium

PENNSYLVANIAN

▨ Marmaton and Cherokee Groups (nonmarine shale, sandstone, coal, and thin limestone)

MISSISSIPPIAN

▨ Salem and St. Louis Limestones and Warsaw Formation

▨ Burlington-Keokuk Limestone and Hannibal and Northview Shales

DEVONIAN

▨ Louisiana Limestone and Saverton and Grassy Creek Shales

SILURIAN

▨ Bowling Green Dolomite

ORDOVICIAN

▨ Maquoketa Shale and Kimmswick Limestone

▢ Decorah Shale and Plattin Limestone

▨ Joachim Dolomite

▨ St. Peter Sandstone

╱ fault

╱ axis of anticline

╱ axis of syncline

The Kimmswick Limestone contains many fossils, including those of algae colonies called Fisherites. The algae secreted calcite plates that were arrange in a spiraling-outward pattern. This fossil is about 6 inches across.

Along the ramps of the Pike County Route C interchange at Frankford, Plattin Limestone of Ordovician age is pitted due to differential weathering.

*To prevent erosion, the Maquoketa Shale of Ordo-
vician age is covered with limestone gravel in this
roadcut along the northbound lanes of US 61 halfway
between Pike County Routes RA and U. The limestone
at the top of the cut is most likely the Bowling Green
Dolomite of Silurian age. Inset: The Maquoketa Shale
contains fossils of graptolites.*

The contact between the Kimmswick Limestone and the overlying Maquoketa
Shale (pronounced mah-COKE-et-uh) is an unconformity—the limestone was
eroded for a short period prior to the deposition of silty mud that later became
the shale. The Maquoketa Shale contains fossils of graptolites, which were floating animals fossilized as carbon silhouettes that look like pencil markings on
the shale. This type of animal evolved so quickly that its different species can
be used to identify beds deposited during Ordovician and Silurian times. Such
fossils are called *index fossils.* The shale is best exposed in roadcuts between Pike
County Routes RA and U. South of Route U, glacial till caps the bedrock and is
exposed in a few roadcuts.

Side Trip to Louisiana

Many rocks are exposed along US 54 east of Bowling Green as it follows the valley of Noix Creek to the Mississippi River at Louisiana. The age of bedrock layers
gets older to the east as elevation decreases, but also remember that you are driving down the dip of beds on the east flank of the Lincoln Fold. Louisiana Limestone of Devonian age and Hannibal Shale of Mississippian age are in roadcuts
just east of US 61. Going east, Silurian limestone beds are sometimes visible
below the road elevation along the south side of the wooded creek valley. Near
the junction with MO 79 is an outcrop of the Burlington-Keokuk Limestone.

Hannibal Shale of Early Mississippian age (top) overlies Louisiana Limestone of Late Devonian age (bottom) in the roadcut along westbound US 54 about 1.2 miles east of US 61 in Pike County.

Bowling Green to Missouri River

Roadcuts between the US 54 junction at Bowling Green and about Pike County Route WW expose the Burlington-Keokuk Limestone. Ordovician rocks are present in the roadcuts in southernmost Pike County and northern Lincoln County. Erosion of the Ordovician beds by the Cuivre River and its tributaries is responsible for the topographic relief in northern Lincoln County known as the Lincoln Hills

The Cap au Gres Fault Zone, crossed about halfway between the Lincoln County Routes E/B and K/V intersections, truncates the southern end of the Lincoln Fold. Beds on the north side of the fault zone are as much as 1,000 feet

Gravel-filled clay till covers rocks on the uplands in southern Pike County. This cut is along the northbound lanes of US 61 about 0.4 mile north of Route OO (91.042N 39.253W).

higher than they are on the south side and shifted as much as 30 miles to the west. The sideways movement on the fault offset what was originally a much longer fold. The southern part, called the Dupo Anticline, extends from east of St. Louis southeast across the Mississippi River into Illinois.

Mississippian limestone and shale form the bedrock from the Cap au Gres Fault Zone across the Missouri River and all the way to I-270 in St. Louis. Cuivre River State Park features a few sinkholes formed in the Burlington-Keokuk Limestone beds on the flanks of the Lincoln Fold. Between I-70 and the MO 94 junction, till is present atop the bedrock. Loess is the surface deposit between MO 94 and Research Park Circle on the north bluff of the Missouri River valley, and between Long Road and Chesterfield Parkway on the south bluff.

US 63
Iowa Border—Jefferson City
150 MILES

The till plain lives up to its name between the Iowa border and the northern Boone county line south of Moberly. There are few roadcuts, and even the best of those reveal only glimpses of rusty brown soil developed in loess or till. But the road occupies a unique topographic position in Missouri: it runs atop Missouri's Grand Divide, a broad ridge that separates the drainage basins of the Missouri and Mississippi Rivers. The flat plain slopes away to the west and east only slightly, but enough to influence the direction in which streams flow. West of the highway they drain south toward the Missouri River, while to the east they flow toward the Mississippi.

As in most other parts of northern Missouri, till and loess cover the bedrock, which here consists of Pennsylvanian limestone, shale, sandstone, and coal. The depth to bedrock ranges from around 50 to more than 200 feet, depending on how much till and loess are present. Where till is thinnest, bedrock is occasionally exposed in stream valleys. At Thousand Hills State Park, west of US 63

View to the south of the till plain along US 63 about halfway between Macon County Routes NN and J, where the highway runs along Missouri's Grand Divide.

on MO 6 just north of Kirksville, a sandstone ledge near the Chariton River contains petroglyphs carved into a sandstone bed of the Marmaton Group by Native Americans 1,500 years ago. Around Moberly, where bedrock is still covered by 50 to 100 feet of till and up to 10 feet of loess, there are several limestone quarries and former coal mines.

Coal mines near Moberly, the most productive coal field in Missouri, began operations as early as the 1850s. The thin coal beds are interspersed within a couple hundred feet of sandstone and shale belonging to the Cherokee and Marmaton Groups. One of the largest mines encompassed 25,000 acres and produced more than 30 million tons of coal for the Thomas Hill Power Plant

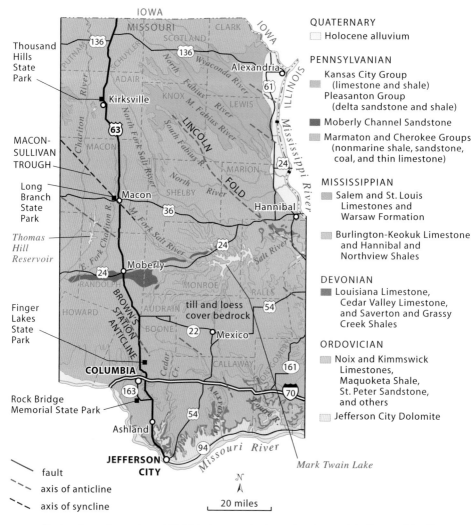

Bedrock geology along US 63 between the Iowa border and Jefferson City. The highway runs along the Grand Divide, which separates the drainage basins of the Missouri and Mississippi Rivers in northern Missouri from the Iowa border to about Columbia.

a few miles west of Moberly. The plant no longer uses the local coal, however, due to its high sulfur content. Low-sulfur coal is imported from elsewhere to fuel Missouri's coal-fired plants.

The intersection of US 63 and East Rollins Street in Moberly marks the middle of the Moberly Channel Sandstone. The sand was deposited in the channel of a large river that flowed across the landscape at the beginning of Middle Pennsylvanian time, eroding its channel into Marmaton and Cherokee Group sediments. This river may have joined another large river in west-central Missouri before emptying into a shallow sea. The Moberly Channel Sandstone has been traced over a continuous distance of about 55 miles, from the area of Mark Twain Lake (40 miles east of Moberly) to a point about 15 miles to the west of the city. It ranges in width from less than 1 mile at its eastern end to more than 5 miles just east of Moberly. It is about 2 miles wide where US 63 crosses it, but unfortunately it is not exposed in roadcuts.

In northern Boone County, Mississippian limestone beds appear in roadcuts. These rocks are on the axis of the Brown's Station Anticline, which strikes northwest-southeast. US 63 crosses the fold axis north of the junction with MO 124 West.

At the turnoff to Finger Lakes State Park, 10 miles north of I-70, limestone, shale, and coal typical of Middle Pennsylvanian cyclothems are in the roadcut on the northeast corner of the intersection. The park is the former site of the Mark Twain Mine, where over 1 million tons of coal were removed from strip pits during the mid-1960s. The mine, which operated prior to the passage of

US 63 crosses the axis of the Brown's Station Anticline near this outcrop of Mississippian limestone along the northbound lane of US 63 about 0.25 mile north of the MO 124 West junction. The layers dip very slightly toward the south here (from left to right in the photo).

Rocks of a Pennsylvanian cyclothem are exposed at the turnoff to Finger Lakes State Park. The darker layer in the lower part of the cut, which is mostly shale, is a coal seam. A limestone bed is in the ditch next to the road (not seen in this picture).

federal and state mine reclamation laws, was simply abandoned. The property was deeded to the State of Missouri, which obtained a federal grant to test the concept of converting former strip mines to recreational uses. The piles of rock and soil excavated to get to the coal bed, called *spoil piles*, remain, and the pits were allowed to fill with water and then were stocked with fish.

Between the park turnoff and Columbia, bedrock is better exposed due to more stream erosion closer to the Missouri River valley. Till and loess are still present, capping the hills and ridges. South of Columbia, Mississippian limestone beds are in the roadcuts on both sides of US 63 to about 14 miles south of I-70.

Rock Bridge Memorial State Park

The centerpiece of Rock Bridge Memorial State Park is a cave system partly exposed by the collapse of its roof. To reach the park from US 63, turn west onto MO 163 (about 7 miles south of I-70) and proceed 3.6 miles to the parking lot at the trailhead. This route takes you across a karst plain on which many circular depressions and ponds mark the locations of sinkholes. Precipitation falling onto this plain ends up flowing through the cave system in the park.

From the parking lot, a 0.5-mile round-trip trail takes visitors first to the rock bridge, which is the remains of the cave roof. A staircase leads to the top of the bridge, and the trail continues around the limestone promontory, following the path of joints widened by groundwater erosion long before they were exposed here. The deep ravine upstream of the bridge was once part of the cave. The creek under the bridge flows from Connor's Cave, a short distance up the trail, which in turn collects water from the karst plain.

Continuing on the trail and boardwalk from the bridge brings you to the lip of the collapsed cave, and at the bottom you can walk into the cave system. The upstream part of the cave is known as the Devil's Icebox for the cool air that issues from it. This cave is gated and access is allowed only in the company of park naturalists. The Missouri gray bat, an endangered species, uses the Devil's Icebox as a summer roosting site.

The creek that flows from Devil's Icebox continues through Connor's Cave and eventually through the ravine outside. You can follow the stream for about 150 feet through the cave. A flashlight, waterproof boots, and a hard hat are useful. The cave height is generally adequate for walking, but be aware that there are some rocks projecting from the roof that you will come upon unexpectedly. Do not enter the cave if there is any imminent likelihood of rain. The flow of the stream increases substantially soon after any significant rainfall.

Connor's Cave does not have stalactites or stalagmites like many other caves in Missouri (although Devil's Icebox has a few), but the walls, ceiling, and rocks projecting from the roof are coated with calcite deposits. At the back of the cave, a slippery, muddy slope allows access to a vertical shaft that formed where two fractures intersect. (Warning: When I say "muddy" I mean *muddy*, and the mud is hard to clean out of clothing!)

View on the upstream side of the rock bridge at Rock Bridge Memorial State Park. Since a rockfall in 2006, the boardwalk under the bridge has been closed.

A staircase leads down into a collapsed cavern passage that provides access to Connor's Cave and Devil's Icebox in Rock Bridge Memorial State Park.

Connor's Cave at Rock Bridge Memorial State Park contains ceiling channels eroded by water moving along fractures in the limestone. The channels are coated with a calcite deposit precipitated from the flowing water. The channel pictured here is about 2 feet deep.

Ashland to Jefferson City

Between Ashland, at the US 63 junction with Boone County Routes M and Y, and the north bluff of the Missouri River in southwestern Callaway County, most of the rocks in roadcuts are the Burlington-Keokuk Limestone of Mississippian age. But a roadcut about 1 mile north of the Boone-Callaway county line exposes rocks ranging from that Mississippian limestone (at the top of cut on the north end) to Ordovician St. Peter Sandstone and Jefferson City Dolomite (at the bottom of the cut on the south end). Unconformities are present between the beds of different ages, and the Middle Devonian unconformity also occurs here. Near the south end of this roadcut is a bed of conglomerate composed of chert pebbles that probably were deposited in a shallow stream channel. The rock below this bed is Ordovician St. Peter Sandstone, and the one above it is Middle Devonian Cedar Valley Limestone.

In Middle Devonian time, erosion removed previously deposited limestone, creating an unconformity, an irregular surface onto which Late Devonian sediment was deposited (black arrows). Another unconformity separates Devonian rocks (white) from overlying Mississippian limestone (brown). The Devonian limestone was weathered into pinnacles (yellow arrows) around which carbonate mud was deposited as horizontal beds in Mississippian time. This roadcut is along US 63 in southern Boone County.

An unusual conglomerate composed of rounded chert pebbles lies between the underlying Ordovician St. Peter Sandstone and the overlying Devonian Cedar Valley Limestone in a roadcut along the east side of US 63 about 1 mile north of the Boone-Callaway county line in southern Boone County.

The route crosses the southernmost position of Pleistocene glaciers at the Boone-Callaway county line. US 54 joins US 63 north of the Missouri River, and the combined highways cross the river at Jefferson City. North of Jefferson City, US 54 slices through the Devonian limestone and Ordovician dolomite that form the north bluff of the Missouri River.

THE OSAGE PLAINS AND SPRINGFIELD PLATEAU

West of the Ozarks and south of the Missouri River is an area of relatively low relief with rolling hills, wide valleys, and flat prairies. The northern part is called the Osage Plains (also called the Western Plains), and the southern part is called the Springfield Plateau.

The Osage Plains, named for the Osage Indians, who once lived in the region, extend from Missouri to north Texas. The area was never glaciated, and streams have cut into the bedrock, exposing Middle Pennsylvanian limestone, shale, sandstone, and coal beds. The northern part of the Osage Plains in Missouri has more limestone bedrock, which is resistant enough to erosion to produce hilly topography with moderately steep slopes and rounded hilltops and ridges. Driving south, you will notice that the plains topography gets much flatter, reflecting the more easily eroded sandstone and shale beds there.

The Springfield Plateau, in the southwest corner of Missouri, is named after the largest city built upon it. The bedrock at the surface of the Springfield Plateau is of Mississippian age, mostly limestone beds that dip to the west-northwest off the Ozark Dome. The topographic transition from the Osage Plains to the Springfield Plateau is gradual because erosion has leveled off the southern edge of Pennsylvanian rocks. On its eastern and southern margins, the edge of the Springfield Plateau is more abrupt, earning the name the Eureka Springs Escarpment. The rocks there stand a couple hundred feet higher in elevation than the Ordovician and Cambrian rocks of the adjacent Salem Plateau because the Mississippian limestones are somewhat more resistant to erosion. The escarpment is inching its way to the north and west as erosion continues to remove rock. The limestone bedrock of the Springfield Plateau is permeated by caves and other groundwater erosion features. Much of the precipitation that falls on the plateau percolates directly into the groundwater system before it can reach stream channels.

The Southern Edge of the Ice

The edge of the final ice sheet in Missouri pushed some distance south of the present-day Missouri River in western Missouri, and to a line a bit north of the river's valley in the eastern half of the state. Between about 780,000 and 620,000 years ago, glacial ice advanced through western Missouri across the valley of the east-flowing Ancestral Kansas River, a stream that drained the region prior to Pleistocene time. The Ancestral Kansas River occupied the east-west segment of

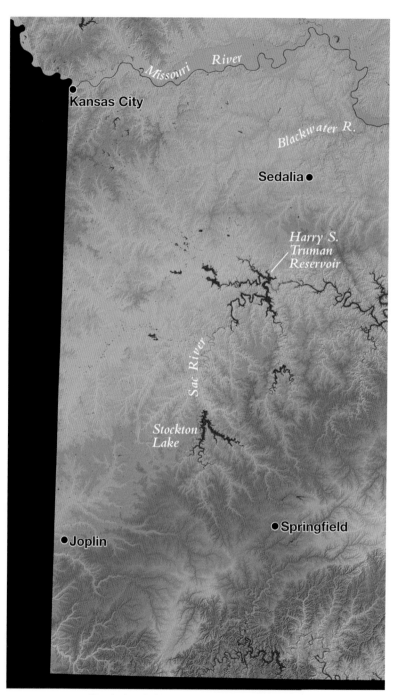

Shaded-relief image of western Missouri.
—Shaded-relief base map from EROS Data Center

the valley in which the modern Missouri River now flows between Kansas City and Brunswick. As the glacier advanced southward, lobes of ice temporarily blocked the valley of the Ancestral Kansas at several locations (now in Jackson, Lafayette, and Saline Counties). Lakes impounded behind the ice dams eventually overflowed into the valleys of adjacent streams, which carried the water around the ice lobes and back to the main river. These valleys, which are much wider and deeper than they would otherwise be, are called *diversion channels*.

Evidence also indicates that ice blocked the mouths of several north-flowing tributaries to the Ancestral Kansas River. The valleys of the Blackwater and Lamine Rivers both have one or more characteristics that suggest they were blocked, at least for a short time. Because the streams could no longer flow into the Ancestral Kansas River, their valleys filled with water, forming lakes that received mud, sand, and gravel outwash.

We know that ice-dammed lakes existed in central Missouri valleys because of the evidence they left behind. Stream terraces that contain outwash gravel deposits are found high on valley walls. Silt deposits that resemble modern lakebed deposits are found on top of modern drainage divides. Water wells drilled in the valleys have encountered glacial outwash sediments. Finally, the modern streams do not have sufficient velocity, discharge, or sediment load to be capable of eroding (or filling) the width and depth of the valleys they occupy. The underfit nature of the Blackwater River valley west of Warrensburg on US 50 is the easiest to see from the highways included in the road guides.

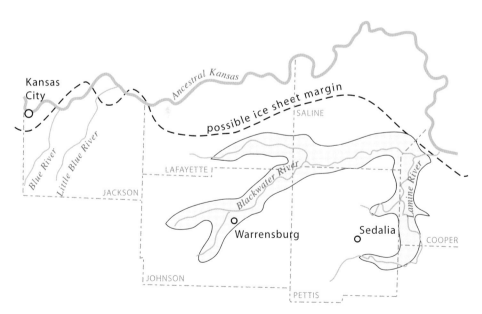

A Pleistocene ice sheet crossed the valley of the east-flowing Ancestral Kansas River and, for at least a short time, blocked the mouths of several north-flowing tributaries, forming glacial lakes. Since Pleistocene time modern streams established their courses atop the lakebed sediments.

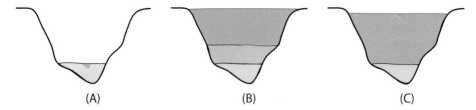

How did the Blackwater River valley get to look like it does today? (A) Prior to Pleistocene time, the Blackwater was a north-flowing tributary of the Ancestral Kansas River and had carved a deep valley. (b) The ice sheet blocked the mouth of the river, and sediment deposited in the resulting ice-dammed lake filled the valley. (C) After the ice sheet retreated and the lake drained, the river was left flowing at higher elevation, across a much wider floodplain. The Blackwater is an underfit stream because it is not responsible for the shape of the valley we see today.

Gravel and clay deposits are found on hilltops in southern Jackson County, miles south of the farthest identified advance of ice. Some of the cobbles and gravel are composed of rocks not native to the state. Some of the rocks have scratched surfaces that formed when they were pushed along at the base of the glacier. But if the glacier never reached that far south, how did the rounded rocks get on top of the hills there? It is possible that the valley divides were submerged at some point, and that blocks of ice carrying the gravel and cobbles broke away from the edge of the ice sheet and floated south before melting and dropping their load. More likely, the area may have been a flat plain over which large meltwater streams issuing from the edge of the glacier flowed, transporting and depositing the sediment. Most of this plain was subsequently eroded as modern rivers, like the Blue River and Little Blue River, established their courses after the ice sheet retreated. Some patches of silt and clay on the hilltops were probably mud deposited in outwash plain lakes.

Road Guides to the Osage Plains and Springfield Plateau

Kansas City Metropolitan Area

Many people find it a bit confusing that the second largest city in Missouri is named after the state next door. The explanation lies in the naming chronology. The original settlement was called Town of Kansa, after the local Native American tribe. The name later morphed to the Town of Kansas, and ultimately Kansas City. By the time Kansas Territory was created in 1854, the name of the city was firmly entrenched and left unchanged.

Kansas City was built at the confluence of the Kansas and Missouri Rivers. Although downtown Kansas City is constructed on the south bluffs of the Missouri River, much of the industrial area is located on the floodplains of local

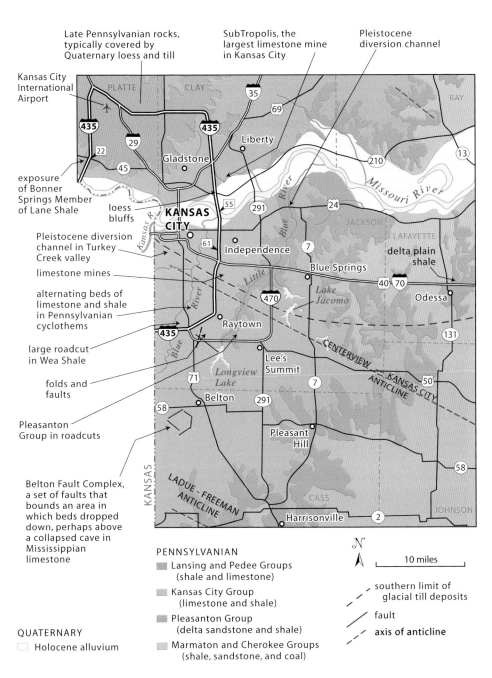

Late Pennsylvanian rocks, typically covered by Quaternary loess and till

SubTropolis, the largest limestone mine in Kansas City

Pleistocene diversion channel

Kansas City International Airport

exposure of Bonner Springs Member of Lane Shale

Pleistocene diversion channel in Turkey Creek valley

limestone mines

alternating beds of limestone and shale in Pennsylvanian cyclothems

large roadcut in Wea Shale

folds and faults

Pleasanton Group in roadcuts

Belton Fault Complex, a set of faults that bounds an area in which beds dropped down, perhaps above a collapsed cave in Mississippian limestone

PLATTE   CLAY   RAY

Liberty

Gladstone

loess bluffs

KANSAS CITY

Independence

Blue Springs

JACKSON   LAFAYETTE

delta plain shale

Odessa

Raytown

Lee's Summit

Longview Lake

Belton

Lake Jacomo

CENTERVIEW   KANSAS CITY ANTICLINE

Pleasant Hill

LADUE - FREEMAN ANTICLINE

KANSAS

CASS

JOHNSON

Harrisonville

PENNSYLVANIAN

Lansing and Pedee Groups (shale and limestone)

Kansas City Group (limestone and shale)

Pleasanton Group (delta sandstone and shale)

Marmaton and Cherokee Groups (shale, sandstone, and coal)

QUATERNARY

Holocene alluvium

N

10 miles

southern limit of glacial till deposits

fault

axis of anticline

Bedrock geology of the Kansas City metropolitan area.

streams. Levees built by the U.S. Army Corps of Engineers protect those areas from flooding—most of the time. In July of 1951, record rainfall in Kansas contributed to an already swollen Kansas River. The resulting flood destroyed many businesses in Kansas City's west bottoms, including the city's economically important stockyards, which never recovered. The flood of 1993 also breached levees, but mostly along the north bank of the Missouri River.

The highways around Kansas City provide ample opportunities to view Middle Pennsylvanian rocks, which consist of cyclothem sequences of alternating beds of limestone, shale, and sandstone deposited during cycles of rising and falling sea level. In general, the rock layers dip to the northwest, so the rocks on the south side of town are just a bit older than those on the north side. The fastest way to see almost all of the local rocks is to drive the I-435 loop.

In roadcuts you can see that the thicknesses of the shale and limestone beds vary considerably. Some limestones consist of massive ledges of rock, 20 or more feet thick, which formed during long periods of relatively undisturbed production of carbonate sediment. Others contain sets of thin limestone beds, a few inches to 1 foot thick, that alternate with thin seams of shale resulting from periodic deposition of mud on the submerged continental platform.

The alternating beds of limestone and shale typical of Middle Pennsylvanian marine cyclothems are exposed in many Kansas City area roadcuts, including this one along Eighty-Seventh Street east of US 71, near the Blue River in south Kansas City. Three major cycles of deposition are represented. The three thick limestone beds—the massive, vertically cut ledges of rock—were each deposited during a prolonged period of sea level fall. The grassy slopes obscure shale beds, including black shales thought by most geologists to be the deepest water deposits in the cyclothems.

Other limestone beds contain ooliths and shell debris worked by wave action on shallow reefs.

Shale beds can be anywhere from a few inches to 80 feet thick. The thickest beds are composed of mud and sand deposited in deltas or delta plains that built across the region. Five deltaic shales appear along roads on the Missouri side of the Kansas City metropolitan area. They are descibed below from youngest to oldest.

LANE SHALE, BONNER SPRINGS MEMBER (KANSAS CITY GROUP). This shale is exposed along I-435 at MO 45 (exit 22) west of Parkville. This usage of the name Lane Shale Formation was adopted by the Missouri Division of Geology and Land Survey (DGLS) in 2004. It replaces the previous use of the formation name (see next paragraph) and includes the three beds above the underlying Wyandotte Formation.

LIBERTY MEMORIAL SHALE (KANSAS CITY GROUP). This shale is not well exposed in any roadcuts along metro highways in Missouri, but a crinoid collected from this shale during construction of a downtown building in 1889 became Missouri's state fossil: *Delocrinus missouriensis.* The name of this formation was reinstated by DGLS in 2004 and refers to the shale bed just below the Wyandotte Formation. This shale previously was known as the Lane Shale. The name was revised because the original mapping and correlation of beds in Kansas, where it was named, were incorrectly done.

This fossil of the crinoid Delocrinus missouriensis *was excavated from the Liberty Memorial Shale in downtown Kansas City. It was used to establish the species as Missouri's state fossil.* —Raymond M. Coveney photo

The Wea Shale, named after a town in eastern Kansas, is a delta deposit that is usually 15 to 20 feet thick in west-central Missouri. Along US 50/I-435 at mile marker 72.5, it is about twice that thick.

CHANUTE SHALE (KANSAS CITY GROUP). This shale often sports a nice maroon or pale green color in roadcuts, due to varying oxidation states of iron in the mud. It is not well exposed along the highways discussed here. The best exposures are in roadcuts north of the Missouri River, near the intersection of US 169 with MO 9, where the shale contains abundant fossils of the snail *Worthenia*.

WEA SHALE (KANSAS CITY GROUP). Many roadcuts along US 50/I-435 and US 50/I-470 expose the thick Wea Shale. The thickness varies quite a bit across the area. The shale often contains rounded nodules of iron carbonate minerals, called *concretions*, that probably formed where the water table in the delta fluctuated up and down.

SHALE HILL FORMATION (PLEASANTON GROUP). The oldest rocks in the Kansas City metro area are exposed in a few roadcuts, most notably along US 50/I-470 east of the Little Blue River (east of mile marker 5). The formation name was adopted in 2004; previously these beds were identified as simply the Pleasanton Group.

Kansas City Underground

The Kansas City Underground is not a subversive political organization, nor a subway system. It is limestone mines. Limestone has been mined in and near Kansas City, primarily for use as crushed aggregate, since the 1880s, and the metropolitan area has the largest amount of mined-out space devoted to secondary uses in the country. More than 200 million square feet of office and storage spaces, including refrigerated and freezer rooms, have been constructed in more than twenty local mines. While the earliest of these uses simply took advantage of the space left behind by mining the limestone, in the 1950s mining methods were changed to specifically accommodate secondary usage of the space. Today, the mined space is more valuable than the rock removed to create it.

The limestone mines in Kansas City, as well as in other places in Missouri, are created using what is called *room-and-pillar mining*. In this method, rock is removed in parallel tunnels about 30 feet wide, with 20 to 30 feet of rock left between the tunnels. A second set of similarly spaced tunnels is excavated at right angles to the first. The rock left in place forms square or rectangular pillars that support the weight of the overlying rock and soil. The space created can be used for roadways or walled off to form warehouse and office spaces. Companies move most of their products into and out of the mines with tractor-trailer trucks, but a few mines have railroad spurs.

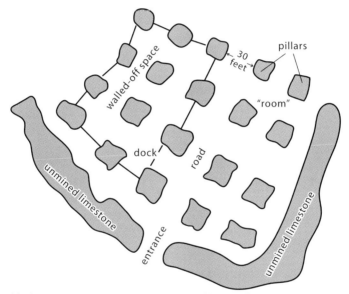

Underground limestone mines in the Kansas City area use room-and-pillar mining to produce space that is easily adapted to secondary uses, such as offices and warehouses. Pillars (gray squares) are about 20 feet square.

With one exception, the mines in the Kansas City area are in the uniformly thick Bethany Falls Limestone, which yields crushed rock aggregate for local construction. In addition to being a valuable resource, the Bethany Falls is the most readily identifiable limestone in the area. It is a prominent hill-capping rock that weathers along two major joint sets into large, square blocks that slowly slide downhill. These tilted blocks of rock appear along many highways south of the Missouri River. Another unique feature is that the upper 2 to 3 feet of the rock is made of gravel that probably formed when waves in shallow water ripped up recently deposited carbonate sediment 300 million years ago.

Tunnels cut into the Bethany Falls Limestone provide access to SubTropolis, the largest limestone mine in the Kansas City area devoted to secondary uses. It is located east of I-435 (at exit 55) on MO 210.

You can see limestone mines along the east side of I-435 near mile marker 61, north and south of Twenty-Third Street, and on either side of MO 291 north of Truman Road in Independence. SubTropolis, the largest mine in the region, is located east of I-435 on MO 210, just north of the Missouri River. Park University, located a few miles west of I-29 on MO 45 (in Platte County), owns and operates two mines. Classrooms, offices, and the library occupy space in the Argentine Limestone at the top of the hill on which the campus sits. About 200 feet below, the Bethany Falls Limestone is being mined, although the space there cannot be used because it is below the water table.

Geologic Structures

The single largest geologic structure in the Kansas City metropolitan area is the Centerview–Kansas City Anticline, the axis of which trends northwest-southeast. Although beds on either side of the axis dip in opposite directions, the angles of dip are so slight as to be undetectable in roadcuts. The structure is probably a drape fold that formed in Pennsylvanian time due to vertical shifting of Proterozoic basement rocks.

Other major structures include several sets of synclines and normal faults, the most visible of which are along US 50/I-470. At Raytown Road (exit 4), and continuing to the east for about 0.25 mile, a roadcut along the north side of US 50/I-470 contains a series of faults that create stairstep offsets of the Bethany Falls Limestone, as well as the limestone and shale beds above and below it. The fault with the greatest vertical displacement (about 6 feet) is in the cut along the ramp from westbound US 50/I-470 to Raytown Road. Just west of Raytown Road, the orientation of beds is influenced by two synclines that intersect here at about a right angle, each aligned with a predominant joint direction. Near the end of the roadcut along the north ramp from Raytown Road to westbound US 50/I-470, bedding planes in the exposed bedrock dip to the west at an angle of about 30 degrees.

The working hypothesis for the origin of these structures is that they formed when the roof of a cave collapsed, causing the overlying layers of Pennsylvanian rocks to sag, forming the synclines and faults. The cave was eroded along intersecting joints in Mississippian limestone beds several hundred feet below the surface.

A dipping bed of Wea Shale at the west end of the ramp from Raytown Road to westbound US 50/I-470 reveals the location of a syncline. These beds are slightly younger than those just east of Raytown Road.

A series of normal faults (two of which are at arrows in this photo) produce offsets in limestone and shale beds along the westbound lanes of US 50/I-470 at Raytown Road.

The Belton Fault Complex is another set of faults thought to have formed when Pennsylvanian rocks near the surface dropped into a collapsed cave in Mississippian rocks, but it is not exposed in roadcuts. It is one of about twenty similar small structures scattered across western and northwestern Missouri in Pennsylvanian rocks.

Pleistocene Geology

The Kansas City area straddles the boundary between the glaciated till plains to the north and the unglaciated Osage Plains to the south. Till covers the bedrock north of the Missouri River, but there are only thin deposits south of the river. Loess is widespread north and south of the river and is well exposed in roadcuts in and near the Missouri River valley, especially along I-435 and MO 210. The thickest deposits—up to 90 feet—make up the bluffs along the north side of the river. The age of these deposits is around 120,000 years, but the loess was not continuously deposited. At least one break in deposition occurred, during which weathering began to form soil. This ancient soil zone was buried beneath subsequent deposits but can be identified due to its slightly different texture.

Two prominent diversion channels formed in the Kansas City area when the ice sheet temporarily blocked the flow of the Ancestral Kansas River. Lakes formed upstream of the ice dams, and the lake levels eventually topped drainage divides. Water then flowed around the nose of the ice through preexisting stream valleys, eroding them up to 200 feet deep. The dams formed, perhaps simultaneously, at downtown Kansas City and in eastern Jackson County.

The western lake drained through the valley of Turkey Creek. Interstate 35 is built in this valley southwest of downtown, US 71 crosses it between about Eighteenth and Twenty-Seventh Streets, and I-70 passes over it roughly between

Kansas City's Union Station sits in the Turkey Creek valley, which served as a diversion channel during Pleistocene time. This view is to the north from the observation deck of the Liberty Memorial. In Pleistocene time, glacial meltwater flowed to the east in the valley (left to right in photo).

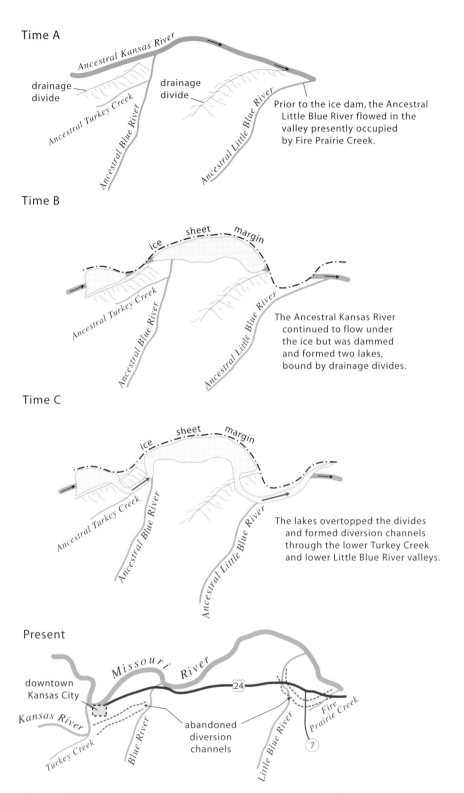

Time A

Ancestral Kansas River

drainage divide

drainage divide

Ancestral Turkey Creek

Ancestral Blue River

Ancestral Little Blue River

Prior to the ice dam, the Ancestral Little Blue River flowed in the valley presently occupied by Fire Prairie Creek.

Time B

ice sheet margin

Ancestral Turkey Creek

Ancestral Blue River

Ancestral Little Blue River

The Ancestral Kansas River continued to flow under the ice but was dammed and formed two lakes, bound by drainage divides.

Time C

ice sheet margin

Ancestral Turkey Creek

Ancestral Blue River

Ancestral Little Blue River

The lakes overtopped the divides and formed diversion channels through the lower Turkey Creek and lower Little Blue River valleys.

Present

Missouri River

downtown Kansas City

Kansas River

24

abandoned diversion channels

Turkey Creek

Blue River

Little Blue River

Fire Prairie Creek

7

During Pleistocene time, the flow of the Ancestral Kansas River was blocked by ice lobes at two places in Jackson County (Time B). The river's flow was diverted around the ice and eroded deep valleys called diversion channels (Time C). It is not known if the two channels formed at the same time.

mile markers 4 and 6. But don't expect to see a deep defile because most of the valley was filled with boulders, gravel, sand, and clay as the volume of flow in the diversion channel diminished. The best view of the valley is from the observation deck at the Liberty Memorial, located at the north end of Penn Valley Park, just southeast of Twenty-Third Street and I-35 (also home to the National World War I Museum). Kansas City's Union Station is located in this diversion channel valley.

The second diversion channel formed in eastern Jackson County where water found a path around an ice lobe through the valleys of the Little Blue River and one of its small tributaries. The intersection of US 24 and MO 7 sits atop the bedrock knob that remained at the center of this loop and was under ice at the time. The broad valley that circles around the knob is occupied by the Little Blue River and Fire Prairie Creek.

About 5 miles east of MO 291, US 24 crosses a Pleistocene diversion channel that loops around a bedrock remnant. This photo is of the west side of the loop looking to the east toward the central high ground. Glacial meltwater flowed south here (left to right).

Interstate 44
Oklahoma Border—Northview
96 MILES

Grand Falls near Joplin

The rocks along I-44 on the Springfield Plateau are nearly all Mississippian limestone beds that contain considerable amounts of white chert in seams and nodules. However, a single 20- to 30-foot-thick bed of pure chert outcrops beneath the highway near mile marker 6 at the valley of Shoal Creek. Known as the Grand Falls Chert, it is found nowhere else in Missouri. The bed is not laterally continuous but correlates in time to the Reeds Spring–Elsey Formation, a chert-rich limestone deposited in early Mississippian time. One of the best places to see it is at its namesake—Grand Falls on Shoal Creek. The chert bed, which is extremely resistant to erosion because it is made of silica, forms what is said to be the state's broadest continuously flowing waterfall.

To reach Grand Falls, take exit 6 (MO 43/86) off I-44 and turn south on MO 86. Immediately south of the interchange, turn west onto Glendale Road and proceed west for about 0.8 mile to Jackson Road. Turn south (left) on Jackson and just after crossing the Shoal Creek Bridge, turn right on Riverside Drive/Murphy Boulevard. Continue for about 1.1 miles to parking areas on both sides of the road.

The Grand Falls Chert forms the widest perennial natural waterfall (lower falls in foreground) in Missouri on Shoal Creek near Joplin (37.032N 94.542W). The smaller falls in the background flows over a low dam.

Tri-State Lead and Zinc District

Over a period of nearly one hundred years, approximately 1850 to 1950, the Tri-State District produced about 50 percent of the zinc and 10 percent of the lead output of the United States. It was called the Tri-State District because it covers adjacent parts of southwestern Missouri, southeastern Kansas, and northeastern Oklahoma. The ore minerals are Mississippi Valley Type deposits and are found in highly fractured beds of Early Mississippian limestone. The ore minerals, which precipitated from hot fluids circulating through the rocks in Pennsylvanian time, fill openings between rock fragments and cover the surfaces of fractures in the rocks. Many of the richest ore bodies were found in roughly cylindrical areas of broken rock that may have formed when caves in older beds collapsed. Because of the shape of the cross section of these deposits, they came to be known as "circle deposits."

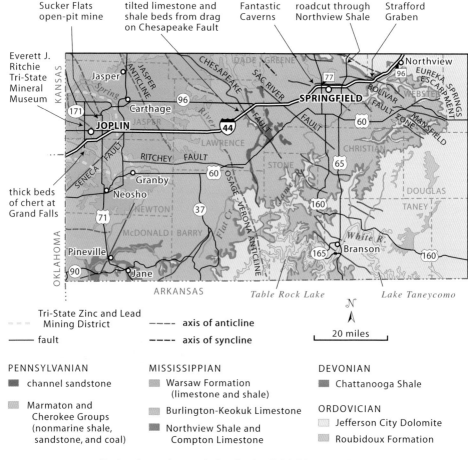

Bedrock geology of the Springfield Plateau along I-44 between the Oklahoma border and Northview.

Although zinc was the primary metal produced overall, the first deposits discovered in southwestern Missouri were lead, and that metal was the principle product of the region into the late 1880s. The ore-bearing beds are near or at the surface on the Missouri side of the district, and many of the smaller mines around Joplin consisted of shallow shafts and tunnels. All of the large commercial mines were open pits. Several pits and their associated large piles of cherty limestone waste rock, locally called "chat," remain.

The Everett J. Ritchie Tri-State Mineral Museum, which charges a very nominal admission fee, contains exhibits about the history of mining in the Tri-State District, as well as beautiful examples of the minerals extracted from the mines. To reach the museum, take MO 43 (also called I-44 Business Loop and South Main Street) north off I-44 at exit 6 for a little over 2.25 miles to Seventh Avenue (MO 66). Turn west and go about 2 miles to Schifferdecker Avenue, then turn right (north). Go about 0.1 mile north and turn left into the Joplin Museum Complex in Schifferdecker Park. The museum is the building closest to Schifferdecker Avenue.

A former open pit mine at Sucker Flats in Webb City is discussed in **US 71: Harrisonville—Arkansas border**.

Chesapeake Fault Zone and Other Faults

The interstate crosses several faults between Joplin and Springfield. Most of the faults on the plateau trend northwest-southeast, although a few trend in other directions. Some faults displace beds just a few feet, as in the small fault zone exposed at the west end of the roadcut along the westbound lanes at mile marker 27.0. Others are much more dramatic.

Fault zones are sometimes not all that obvious in roadcuts but can often be identified by weathered or eroded rock or by offset beds. Weathered rock is associated with several small faults (located approximately at the red lines) and offset beds of Short Creek Oolite (shown by arrows pointing to the top of the bed) in this roadcut along the westbound lanes of I-44 near mile marker 27. The Short Creek Oolite is the top bed of the Keokuk Limestone of Early Mississippian age.

The fault with the greatest known offset of rock layers along this stretch of road is the Chesapeake Fault, which I-44 crosses at mile marker 54. West of the fault, the nearly horizontal beds of Early Mississippian limestone are 150 feet higher in elevation than the same beds on the east side. Steeply dipping layers of rock, part of a drag fold, mark the fault zone. A drag fold forms when beds bend as they are slowly dragged in opposite directions by fault movement.

The Chesapeake Fault is one example of a surface rupture that formed above a fault zone in deeply buried rocks of Proterozoic age. Its age is post-Mississippian because those rocks are affected by it, and most—though perhaps not all—shifting along the fault likely occurred during the Pennsylvanian plate collision that formed the Ouachita Mountains. The Chesapeake Fault is associated with other faults and folds within its fault zone, which trends northwest-southeast from eastern Kansas into northern Arkansas.

Limestone beds in fault zones on the Springfield Plateau are often altered to dolomite. In fact, dolomitized limestone is used as an indication of the presence of a fault, even where the fault is hidden. Magnesium-rich groundwater moving through the broken rocks in fault zones may have altered the limestone to dolomite. It may have happened before the end of Pennsylvanian time, about the same time that ore minerals were deposited in the Joplin area.

Fantastic Caverns

Fantastic Caverns, a private commercial cave, was discovered in 1862. It contains nice examples of flowstone and dripstone deposits, but the most unusual feature is how you get around in it. Instead of the usual walking tour, guests

Beds of Jefferson City Dolomite of Early Ordovician age (bottom) and Compton Limestone (middle), Northview Shale, and Pierson Limestone (top) of Early Mississippian age are exposed in this roadcut along the westbound lanes of I-44 at mile marker 54.1. The beds are on the west, upthrown side of the Chesapeake Fault and were tilted due to drag folding along the fault.

One of the signature features of limestone weathering on the Springfield Plateau is turretlike karst pinnacles. These are along the westbound lanes of I-44 near mile marker 53.6.

are driven through the cave in natural-gas powered trams. To reach Fantastic Caverns from I-44, take exit 77 and go north on MO 13 a bit less than 2 miles. Turn west on West Farm Road 94 for 2.1 miles, then turn north on North Farm Road 125 for 1.2 miles. Follow the signs to the parking lot (about 2.9 miles off MO 13 on paved roads).

Limestone Pinnacles

One of the characteristics of the Burlington-Keokuk Limestone of Mississippian age on the Springfield Plateau is the pinnacles that form as it weathers. These are particularly abundant in roadcuts between mile markers 82 and 96. The pinnacles are remnants of rock left behind when water seeping downward along joints erodes the limestone.

Strafford Graben

Between mile markers 92 and 94, Mississippian rocks are about 100 feet lower than they are either to the east or west. The rocks in this interval have dropped down between two faults to form a structure called a *graben*. I-44 crosses the Strafford Fault, which marks the west side of the graben, at mile marker 92, but there are no roadcuts that might reveal its location. An unnamed fault near mile marker 94 is the east boundary. The faults and graben are part of the Bolivar-Mansfield Fault Zone, the largest fault system on the west side of the Ozark Dome.

The Bolivar-Mansfield Fault Zone lies parallel to, and northeast of, the Chesapeake Fault Zone. It consists of numerous faults and some folds, most striking northwest-southeast, in an area about 10 miles wide and 100 miles long. Vertical displacement on individual faults can be as much as 300 feet, though typically it is much less. As with the Chesapeake Fault Zone, the surface structures formed in late Paleozoic time due to reactivation of a fault zone in Proterozoic rocks.

A graben is a block of rocks that drops down between two normal faults. I-44 crosses the Strafford Graben in the Bolivar-Mansfield Fault Zone between mile markers 92 and 94.

Eureka Springs Escarpment

The stretch of interstate between mile markers 95.4 and 96.1 crosses the transition between the Springfield Plateau and its slightly lower neighbor to the east, the Salem Plateau. The Eureka Springs Escarpment, a sloping topographic feature, forms the boundary. The limestone beds that support the Springfield Plateau are a bit more resistant to erosion than the dolomite to the east, creating the topographic difference along the edge of the higher plateau.

Interstate 70
Kansas City—Columbia
128 MILES

Limestone bedrock of Pennsylvanian age is exposed in numerous roadcuts between Kansas City and Grain Valley (exit 24). Just east of MO 131 at Odessa (exit 37), a thick shale bed deposited in a delta is exposed on both sides of the interstate. Through eastern Lafayette County and all of Saline County, the topography opens up into a rolling plain with few bedrock exposures. The interstate is north of the farthest southward advance of the Pleistocene glacier in this stretch, and many roadcuts are through till.

I-70 crosses the Warrensburg Channel Sandstone at exit 49 (MO 13). The sandstone was deposited in a river channel in Pennsylvanian time. The highway cuts at a right angle across the channel, which extends a total of 50 miles and is bounded on each side and beneath by Middle Pennsylvanian rocks. You can see it at Cave Hollow Park on the west side of Warrensburg. It is discussed in **US 50: Kansas City—Sedalia.**

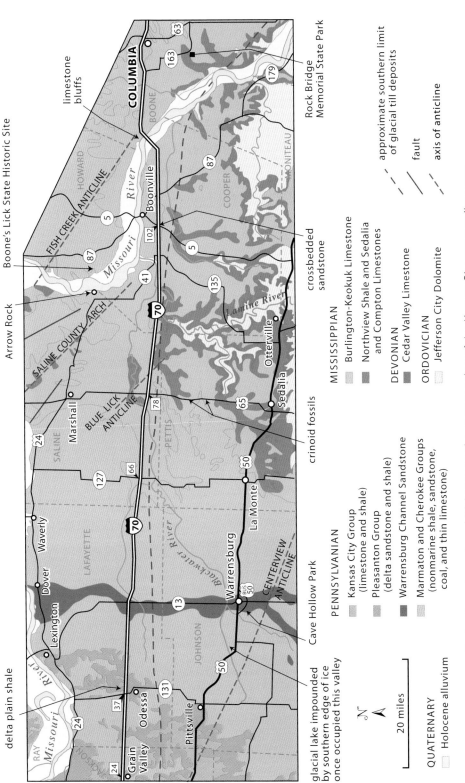

Bedrock geology along I-70 between the eastern edge of the Kansas City metropolitan area and Columbia and along US 50 between Kansas City metropolitan area and Sedalia.

limestone bluffs

Boone's Lick State Historic Site

Arrow Rock

delta plain shale

crossbedded sandstone

crinoid fossils

Cave Hollow Park

glacial lake impounded by southern edge of ice once occupied this valley

Rock Bridge Memorial State Park

COLUMBIA

Boonville

Marshall

Waverly

Dover

Lexington

Odessa

Grain Valley

Pittsville

Warrensburg

La Monte

Sedalia

Otterville

FISH CREEK ANTICLINE

SALINE COUNTY ARCH

BLUE LICK ANTICLINE

CENTERVIEW ANTICLINE

Missouri River

Lamine River

Blackwater River

BOONE

HOWARD

COOPER

MONITEAU

SALINE

PETTIS

LAFAYETTE

JOHNSON

RAY

N
20 miles

approximate southern limit of glacial till deposits

fault

axis of anticline

MISSISSIPPIAN
Burlington-Keokuk Limestone
Northview Shale and Sedalia and Compton Limestones

DEVONIAN
Cedar Valley Limestone

ORDOVICIAN
Jefferson City Dolomite

PENNSYLVANIAN
Kansas City Group (limestone and shale)
Pleasanton Group (delta sandstone and shale)
Warrensburg Channel Sandstone
Marmaton and Cherokee Groups (nonmarine shale, sandstone, coal, and thin limestone)

QUATERNARY
Holocene alluvium

MISSISSIPPIAN ROCKS ALONG US 65

North of I-70 at exit 78, Mississippian rocks are exposed in roadcuts along US 65 south of Marshall. Although not discernible in the cuts, the beds dip in slightly different directions on either side of the valley due to the Blue Lick Anticline.

Numerous cuts along US 65 between I-70 and about 4 miles south of Sedalia expose the Burlington-Keokuk Limestone, one of the most recognizable layers of Mississippian rock in Missouri due to its crinoid fossils and its tendency to weather readily along joints and bedding planes. It weathers to a deep red soil.

This roadcut through Mississippian rocks along US 65 is on the north bluff of the Blackwater River just south of Saline County Route UU.

This outcrop of Burlington-Keokuk Limestone is one of many along US 65 between I-70 and Sedalia. Crinoid fossils are abundant here.

Gently folded beds are common in the Mississippian limestone layers exposed along I-70 in central Missouri. This roadcut in Burlington-Keokuk Limestone is along the westbound lanes at mile marker 92.6.

The interstate crosses the eastern margin of the Osage Plains province near mile marker 67. The limestone beds in roadcuts between here and Columbia are in Mississippian rocks. The northernmost outcrops of Mississippian rocks in western Missouri are found in southern Saline County. Between the US 65 junction (exit 78) and Columbia, I-70 crosses the southern end of the Saline County Arch, a broad anticline. Several smaller folds and faults are found on the flanks of this structure.

Arrow Rock and Boone's Lick

Arrow Rock, named by the French in the early 1730s, is a landmark visible from the Missouri River. Archaeological studies reveal that Native American tribes used the bluff as a site for tool- and weapon-making for almost 12,000 years. An abundant supply of chert, which is sometimes referred to as flint locally, was available here, weathered from the bluff-forming Burlington-Keokuk Limestone. To reach Arrow Rock State Historic Site, take Cooper County Route K north from I-70 at exit 89. At the junction with MO 41 turn left and go north to the entrance.

After the War of 1812, settlers traveling west on what later became known as the Santa Fe Trail took advantage of a spring here to refill their water barrels. They also crossed from the south to the north bank of the Missouri River on a ferry built for that purpose, often to stop at Boone's Lick, a saline spring from which salt was produced by Nathan and Daniel Morgan Boone (sons of frontiersman Daniel) from 1805 to the mid-1830s. To reach Boone's Lick State

Historic Site, take MO 5 north at exit 101, through Boonville and across the river to MO 87. About 8 miles north on MO 87 is the junction with MO 187; turn west and go 2 miles to the site.

Boonville to Columbia

In a 10-mile stretch near Boonville, roughly between mile markers 98 and 108, Middle Pennsylvanian rocks are present along the highway. These are the same beds that are exposed in the western part of the Osage Plains, preserved here atop hills. The best roadcut is at mile marker 102, where crossbedded sandstone of the Cherokee Group appears along both lanes of the interstate.

Burlington-Keokuk Limestone of Mississippian age forms the cliffs along the east side of the Missouri River valley north and south of I-70 near mile marker 114. This view is to the south of the bridge.

US 50
Kansas City—Sedalia
80 MILES
See map on page 113.

US 50 crosses the northern portion of the Osage Plains from the Kansas City area to east of Sedalia. Rocks of the Kansas City Group are present in roadcuts along the highway for most of the way between the I-470 junction in Lee's Summit and Pittsville (MO 131). A short stretch of Pleasanton Group shale is present between Johnson County Routes Z/W and MO 131. East of Pittsville, Middle Pennsylvanian bedrock underlies the area. Marmaton Group rocks are in cuts from Pittsville to the valley of the South Fork Blackwater River, and Cherokee Group rocks from there to La Monte (MO 127).

A few miles west of Warrensburg, US 50 crosses the very wide valley of the Blackwater River. The valley was once submerged by a glacial lake that formed when the ice sheet crossed south of the Ancestral Kansas River and dammed a tributary stream. Take note of the hilltops bordering the Blackwater River; they have rather flat tops, all at about the same elevation. A lakebed, perhaps? When the ice retreated, the lake drained, and the Blackwater River was left to reexcavate its former valley. It's still trying, but it doesn't have enough water flowing fast enough to do much eroding these days.

Just east of La Monte, the road crosses into the outcrop area of Mississippian bedrock. The crinoid-rich Burlington-Keokuk Limestone appears in many roadcuts around Sedalia, particularly north and south of town on US 65.

Cave Hollow Park

Cave Hollow Park, at Warrensburg, preserves outcrops of the Warrensburg Channel Sandstone, which was deposited in a river channel in Middle Pennsylvanian time. The sandstone channel has been traced for more than 50 miles from the Missouri River bluffs near Dover nearly to Clinton, in Henry County. The outcrops in Cave Hollow Park are the best place to see it. The walking path to the east of the shelter house leads to several outcrops of the Warrensburg Channel Sandstone. The channel was eroded into the cyclothem rock layers. There is a nice hillside exposure of a cyclothem sequence of limestone, coal, and shale beds

The Warrensburg Channel Sandstone at Cave Hollow Park in Warrensburg contains well-defined crossbedding, visible in the bands of iron oxide stains in the rock.

just west of the shelter house. The shale at the top of the hill contains crystals of gypsum, a calcium sulfate mineral that crystallized in cracks in the mud.

The park's caves are overhangs in sandstone along the creek. Groundwater seepage loosened sand grains, which were then eroded by running water. To get to the park, turn on US 50 Business (west junction), go about 1 mile and turn south on Main Street. Proceed south to Gay Street, turn west, and follow it to the park entrance. Park in the first lot on the right as you enter.

US 54
Kansas Border—Preston
83 MILES

Between the Kansas border and MO 13 at Collins, US 54 crosses the southern part of the Osage Plains. Most of the rocks along the highway are Pennsylvanian shale and sandstone of the Cherokee Group, but the roadcuts are generally vegetated. US 54 cuts through the Southwest Coal Field, in which coal beds within the Pennsylvanian rocks were mined. See **US 71: Harrisonville—Arkansas Border** for more on the coal field.

About 4 miles east of the MO 32 junction at El Dorado Springs (37.861N 93.952W), roadcuts contain abundant chert gravel left behind by weathering of the Mississippian bedrock. US 54 crosses the northwestern end of the Bolivar-Mansfield Fault Zone here, and the Mississippian rocks outcrop on the upthrown (east) side of the fault. A bit farther east, Jefferson City Dolomite appears in the valley of the Sac River.

Weaubleau-Osceola Structure

At the intersection with MO 13, US 54 is on the southern edge of the Weaubleau-Osceola Structure, the westernmost of the state's six cryptoexplosive structures. This one most closely resembles a meteorite impact structure because it has a low ridge encircling its 12-mile-diameter circular lowland. If its impact origin is confirmed, it will be the fourth largest impact crater in the United States. Based on the age of the rocks disrupted by the structure, it probably formed in Middle to Late Mississippian time, about 340 million years ago. Within the structure, Early Mississippian rocks are broken and faulted. In places the shattering of the rocks was so great that it produced a breccia composed of angular pieces of rock debris from adjacent rock layers.

One odd feature of these disturbed rocks is clusters of spherical chert nodules called Weaubleau eggs, which are found in weathered joints. Although they resemble geodes in shape, they are solid and are thought to be concretions that formed when silica-rich groundwater deposited silica around buried fragments of shale. They weather out on local hillsides.

If you head north on MO 13, you will pass through the middle of ground zero of the impact crater, and many roadcuts along the highway expose rocks related to the structure. The first interesting roadcut is about 3.6 miles north of US 54, where a Pennsylvanian channel sandstone is exposed on both sides of the highway. This rock is a remnant of the sediments deposited atop the structure. Another 1.4 miles north begins a stretch of about 2 miles in which roadcuts reveal examples of the Mississippian limestone beds that were broken or displaced by the event.

A little farther north on MO 13, turn west onto MO 82 to drive about 2.5 miles to a roadside park on the west side of the road that overlooks the confluence of the Sac and Osage Rivers. Depending on the pool level of the Harry S. Truman Reservoir, the confluence may be inundated.

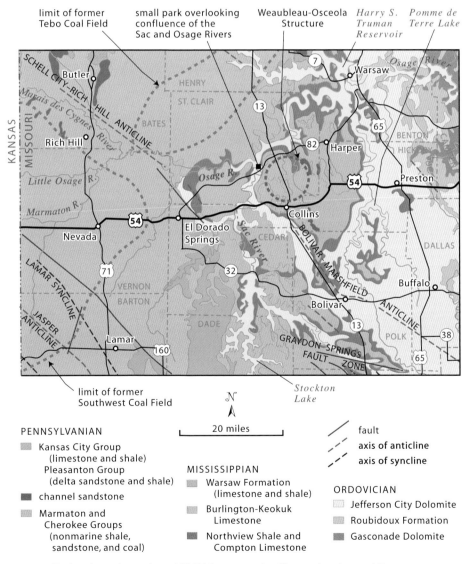

PENNSYLVANIAN

- Kansas City Group
  (limestone and shale)
  Pleasanton Group
  (delta sandstone and shale)
- channel sandstone
- Marmaton and
  Cherokee Groups
  (nonmarine shale,
  sandstone, and coal)

MISSISSIPPIAN

- Warsaw Formation
  (limestone and shale)
- Burlington-Keokuk
  Limestone
- Northview Shale and
  Compton Limestone

ORDOVICIAN

- Jefferson City Dolomite
- Roubidoux Formation
- Gasconade Dolomite

— fault
—- axis of anticline
—- axis of syncline

20 miles

Bedrock geology along US 54 between the Kansas border and Preston.

Weaubleau eggs, here embedded in a concrete wall, are chert concretions that grew around fragments of shattered shale. They are found within the Weaubleau-Osceola Structure.

This channel sandstone was deposited on top of the eroded Weaubleau-Osceola Structure during Middle Pennsylvanian time. This outcrop is along the northbound lanes of MO 13, 3.6 miles north of US 54 (37.943N 93.634W).
—Ken Stalder photo

*A roadside park on MO 82 overlooks the confluence of the Sac River (bot-
tom) and Osage River (left and back) in St. Clair County. The flood pool of
Harry S. Truman Reservoir inundates this valley. The rocks of the cliffs here
are Early Mississippian Pierson and Burlington-Keokuk Limestones.*

Collins to Preston

Between Collins and Hermitage, roadcuts expose mostly Mississippian limestone. Pennsylvanian rocks of the Cherokee Group cap the hills west of Weaubleau and Wheatland. These are not channel sandstone deposits, although there
are patchy outcrops of channel sandstone on either side of the highway in this
area, perhaps related to the one found along MO 13. Jefferson City Dolomite
of Ordovician age appears in the valley of Weaubleau Creek and in the 2-mile
stretch west of the Pomme de Terre River. This interval is the transition between
the Osage Plains and Salem Plateau. Between the Pomme de Terre River valley
and Preston, the rocks along the highway are primarily Jefferson City Dolomite,
with Mississippian limestone and shale capping the hills.

US 65
Springfield—Arkansas Border
55 MILES

North of Springfield near the junction with Greene County Routes KK and A,
US 65 crosses the transition between the Salem Plateau of the Ozarks and the
northern edge of the Springfield Plateau. The shale bed exposed in roadcuts
from just north of this intersection to just south of Routes AA and C is Northview Shale, one of the oldest Mississippian rocks in southwestern Missouri.

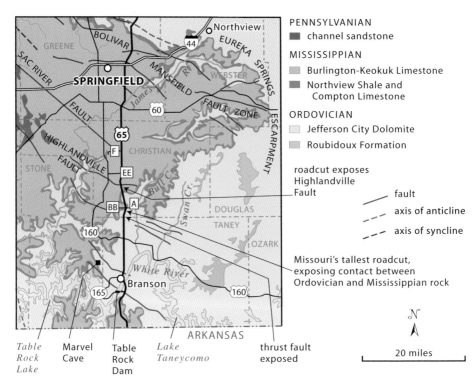

PENNSYLVANIAN
■ channel sandstone

MISSISSIPPIAN
▨ Burlington-Keokuk Limestone
■ Northview Shale and
   Compton Limestone

ORDOVICIAN
▨ Jefferson City Dolomite
▨ Roubidoux Formation

roadcut exposes
Highlandville
Fault

——— fault
– – – axis of anticline
–·– axis of syncline

Missouri's tallest roadcut,
exposing contact between
Ordovician and Mississippian rock

N

20 miles

Table
Rock
Lake

Marvel
Cave

Table
Rock
Dam

Lake
Taneycomo

thrust fault
exposed

Bedrock geology along US 65 between Springfield and the Arkansas border.

The Northview Shale of Early Mississippian age is exposed along US 65 north of Springfield. This roadcut is along the southbound lane about 0.7 mile south of Greene County Routes AA and C (37.292N 93.181W).

The Burlington-Keokuk Limestone is exposed in many roadcuts along US 65 on the Springfield Plateau. This cut is south of Finley Creek (0.5 mile north of County Route F) in Christian County.

The Burlington-Keokuk Limestone is the most prominent rock in roadcuts through Greene County. In new roadcuts the rock is almost white, but it quickly weathers to dark gray. Joints widened by groundwater erosion are common in roadcuts, as are karst pinnacles, rounded masses of limestone that protrude into the overlying soil. The pinnacles form when groundwater seeps into nearly vertical joints and dissolves the surrounding rock.

Along the southbound lanes of US 65 about 3 miles south of Christian County Route EE (4 miles north of Routes A and BB), a roadcut exposes the Highlandville Fault and the unconformity between Ordovician and Mississippian rocks. Vegetation obscures much of the cut, so you need to be looking for it. At the south end of the roadcut, slightly tilted Cotter Dolomite of Ordovician age is at road level, with flat-lying Compton Limestone of Early Mississippian age on top. The folding of the older rocks occurred prior to the deposition of the younger sediments. Some geologists have identified the shale layer that sits directly atop the dolomite (obscured by vegetation and fallen rock debris) as the Chattanooga Shale of Devonian age. But unlike the outcrop featured in the US 71 road guide, the bed here is but a few inches thick. The Chattanooga Shale occurs in Missouri in isolated patches filling low spots in the underlying dolomite, so its thickness varies.

North of the Highlandville Fault, which is near the middle of the cut, the Mississippian rocks are at highway level. The light bluish gray to green Northview Shale provides a good reference layer. You can trace it across the fault,

At the south end of this roadcut (36.903N 93.241W) along the west side of US 65 in Christian County, inclined beds of the Cotter Dolomite (bottom) of Ordovician age are capped by Mississippian limestone. The thin shale bed between them, covered by vegetation in the center of the photo, may be the Chattanooga Shale of Devonian age.

fault zone

Northview Shale

The Highlandville Fault along US 65 in Christian County (near the red cedar tree at arrow) displaces beds about 60 feet. The Mississippian Compton Limestone is at the top of the roadcut south of the fault (on the left side of the photo) and at road level north of the fault. A bluish gray bed of Northview Shale (arrow at right) is above the Compton.

where it is offset by about 60 feet. Rocks on the south side of the fault were lifted up relative to rocks on the north side.

The roadcut about 0.8 mile south of Christian County Routes A and BB (1.3 miles north of the Taney county line), is purportedly the state's tallest. The beds exposed are the same as those at the previously described roadcut, but much more of the Cotter Dolomite is exposed here, about 180 feet. Look for the bluish gray bed of Northview Shale near the top. The pinnacled limestone at the very top is the Reeds Spring. This cut is at the eroded southern margin of the Springfield Plateau.

Another 0.5 mile to the south (0.8 mile north of the Taney county line), folded and faulted Jefferson City–Cotter Dolomite beds of Ordovician age are exposed in the roadcut along the northbound lanes. Near the south end of the cut, the tilted beds are offset a couple of feet. The fault dips to the north at an angle only slightly greater than the rock layers do. This is an example of a low-angle reverse fault, sometimes called a *thrust fault*, in which rocks were pushed up a sloping fault by compressive tectonic forces.

In Taney County, erosion by the White River and its tributaries has largely removed the limestone of the Springfield Plateau, and most of the rocks along US 65 are Ordovician dolomite. Pinnacled Burlington-Keokuk Limestone remains on the ridge between MO 165 and the Arkansas line.

This roadcut in southern Christian County, at the north city limit of Saddlebrooke (36.833N 94.219W), is supposed to be the tallest in the state, at nearly 200 feet. The beds here—the Cotter Dolomite, Compton Limestone, and Northview Shale—are the same formations as those at the Highlandville Fault about 5 miles to the north.

A small reverse, or thrust, fault (left center) displaces Ordovician dolomite along the northbound lanes of US 65 in southern Christian county, about 0.5 mile north of the Taney county line (36.822N 93.226W).

Branson, located in the valley of the White River just upstream from Lake Taneycomo, is surrounded by bluffs of Jefferson City–Cotter Dolomite. Farther west, the same rocks appear along the shores of Table Rock Lake. Table Rock, named for a flat ledge of dolomite exposed on its flank, was the site originally proposed for the dam. The mountain, in turn, was Geologic conditions at the location were deemed too unstable for dam construction by the Corps of Engineers because of the presence of caves and weathered joints, and the dam site was moved to the west. You can view the dam and river valley from the Table Rock overlook located on MO 165 west of US 65 south of Hollister.

In the hills north of Table Rock Lake is Marvel Cave, a commercially operated cavern in the Silver Dollar City amusement park about 5 miles west of Branson. The cave formed near the regional unconformity between Ordovician and Mississippian rocks; the entrance and the upper cave passages are eroded in the Reeds Spring Limestone of Mississippian age. The lower passages are in the Ordovician Cotter Dolomite.

Marvel Cave, a natural national landmark, is the deepest cave in Missouri and has one of the largest entry rooms of any cave in North America. The Cathedral Room is more than 200 feet high and terminates at the top in the sinkhole opening that was the original entrance. It also contains the Liberty Bell, a massive flowstone deposit created by water seeping from a joint in the cave wall.

US 71
Harrisonville—Arkansas Border
168 MILES

South of Harrisonville, the Osage Plains are in Middle Pennsylvanian sandstone, shale, and coal beds that are much less resistant to weathering and erosion than the limestone beds that cap the hills in the Kansas City area to the north. The topography is much flatter, and streams flow through broad floodplains bordered by low bluffs. Typical of these is the Marais de Cygnes (pronounced *Maray duh Seen*) River just north of Rich Hill. Along the north side of its valley, a tall roadcut along the northbound lanes exposes one of the region's thick shale layers, deposited in a river delta in Pennsylvanian time.

The folding and faulting of Middle Pennsylvanian sandstone beds in western Missouri created structural traps in which oil and natural gas accumulated, at least in small amounts. Oil and gas migrate through the permeable sandstones until an impermeable bed or fault zone is encountered, at which point the fluids collect.

Missouri's primary oil- and gas-producing region is west of US 71 from southern Jackson County to northern Barton County. The first indications of petroleum's presence were tarry blebs in limestone and sandstone beds. Drilling began in the Kansas City area in Jackson County after the Civil War and progressed southward into the mid-twentieth century.

A Middle Pennsylvanian river delta became this thick shale bed in the distance, exposed in a roadcut along the northbound lanes of US 71 just north of Miami Creek in Bates County (38.180N 94.353W). —Ken Stalder photo

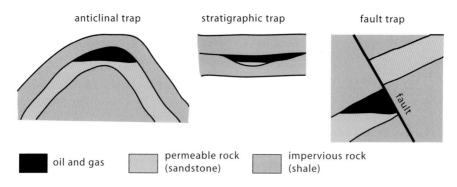

anticlinal trap   stratigraphic trap   fault trap

oil and gas   permeable rock   impervious rock
(sandstone)   (shale)

Oil and natural gas migrate through permeable rocks until they encounter an impervious layer. Three ways that oil can be trapped are shown here. Anticlinal and stratigraphic traps are the most common for Missouri oil fields.

We aren't talking gushers here. The oil is viscous, and the reservoirs small. There are some pumping wells left, pulling out a few barrels of oil a week. Jed Clampett of *The Beverly Hillbillies* notwithstanding, there are no huge oil fields in Missouri. Natural gas was produced in greater quantities, most of it prior to World War II, with peak production of nearly 1.4 billion cubic feet in 1938. In fact, many homes in Jackson County had their own gas wells for domestic use.

The highway crosses Missouri's Southwest Coal Field between Rich Hill and Lamar. This area and the Tebo Coal Field around Clinton were the principal fields in western Missouri. The coal beds mined here are slightly older than those in north-central Missouri near Moberly. Rich Hill was the economic center of local coal mining from around 1895 to 1920. Although the first mines were underground, all of the major mines were strip mines, and most have subsequently been refilled or converted to lakes. The upper reaches of the Harry S. Truman Reservoir flooded part of the Tebo Coal Field.

US 71 crosses the Schell City–Rich Hill Anticline just north of the Marais des Cygnes River. This anticline is one of the broadest in Missouri and is asymmetrical—the beds on the southwest side dip more steeply than those on the northeast side. The folding of Pennsylvanian beds is the surface expression of vertical and horizontal shifting along the Eldorado Springs Fault, known to be present in underlying Mississippian, Ordovician, or older rocks. That fault is traced in the subsurface to the southeast into the Bolivar-Mansfield Fault Zone. Unfortunately, no tilted layers can be seen in roadcuts.

A nice example of a crossbedded sandstone is in roadcuts along both lanes of US 71 on the south bank of the Marmaton River, about 5.5 miles north of the US 54 interchange at Nevada. This rock, the Warner Sandstone of the Cherokee Group, is one of many such beds that are part of Middle Pennsylvanian cyclothems. The sand was deposited by rivers that meandered across delta plains during falls in sea level.

In northern Barton County between the Vernon county line and the junction with Routes C and V, US 71 crosses a fault, although there are no

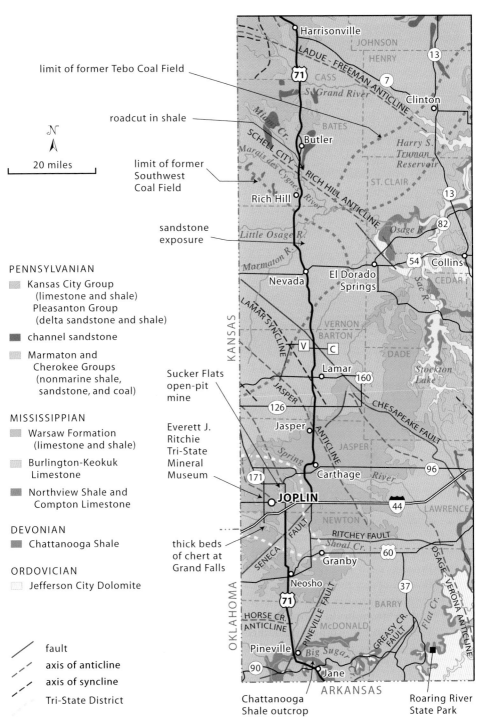

PENNSYLVANIAN

Kansas City Group
(limestone and shale)
Pleasanton Group
(delta sandstone and shale)

channel sandstone

Marmaton and
Cherokee Groups
(nonmarine shale,
sandstone, and coal)

MISSISSIPPIAN

Warsaw Formation
(limestone and shale)

Burlington-Keokuk
Limestone

Northview Shale and
Compton Limestone

DEVONIAN

Chattanooga Shale

ORDOVICIAN

Jefferson City Dolomite

fault

axis of anticline

axis of syncline

Tri-State District

limit of former Tebo Coal Field

roadcut in shale

limit of former
Southwest
Coal Field

sandstone
exposure

Sucker Flats
open-pit
mine

Everett J.
Ritchie
Tri-State
Mineral
Museum

thick beds
of chert at
Grand Falls

N

20 miles

Harrisonville

JOHNSON

HENRY

13

LADUE - FREEMAN ANTICLINE

71

7

CASS

S. Grand River

Clinton

Mid Cr.

BATES

Butler

SCHELL CITY

Marais des Cygnes

Harry S.
Truman
Reservoir

RICH HILL ANTICLINE

ST. CLAIR

Rich Hill

River

13

Little Osage R.

Osage R.

82

Marmaton R.

54

Collins

Nevada

El Dorado
Springs

CEDAR

Sac R.

KANSAS

LAMAR SYNCLINE

VERNON

BARTON

DADE

Stockton
Lake

V   C

Lamar

160

JASPER

126

CHESAPEAKE FAULT

Jasper

ANTICLINE

JASPER

Spring

96

171

Carthage

River

JOPLIN

44

LAWRENCE

FAULT

NEWTON

RITCHEY FAULT

Shoal Cr.

SENECA

60

Granby

OSAGE - VERONA ANTICLINE

Jefferson City Dolomite

Neosho

PINEVILLE FAULT

37

BARRY

71

HORSE CR.
ANTICLINE

McDONALD

GREASY CR.
FAULT

Flat Cr.

OKLAHOMA

Pineville

Big Sugar

90

Jane

ARKANSAS

Chattanooga
Shale outcrop

Roaring River
State Park

Bedrock geology along US 71 between Harrisonville and the Arkansas border.

Large crossbeds (right-center) are present in the Warner Sandstone along both sides of US 71 just south of the Marmaton River in northern Vernon County. Photo is along the northbound lanes (37.919N 94.359W).

outcrops or roadcuts that reveal the offset beds. Its presence was discovered by bed offsets measured in deep drill cores. This fault is the northwestern extension of the Chesapeake Fault, which does affect rocks at the surface southwest of Springfield and is described further in the road guide **I-44: Oklahoma Border—Northview**.

Lamar sits at the north edge of the transition zone between the Osage Plains and Springfield Plateau. US 71 crosses the contact between the outcrop areas of Pennsylvanian and Mississippian bedrock south of Lamar in southern Barton County, approximately halfway between MO 126 and Jasper. From that point south nearly to Arkansas, US 71 crosses Mississippian rocks of the Springfield Plateau. The rocks in the interval between Lamar and Carthage are affected by a series of broad, gently folded synclines and anticlines, the influences of which cannot be discerned in roadcuts. All of the folds trend northwest-southeast. From north to south, they are the Lamar Syncline, the Jasper Anticline, and the Nashville-Carthage Sag.

One layer of particularly pure limestone in the Warsaw Formation has been quarried for building stone near Carthage since the middle 1800s. It is used in the state capitol at Jefferson City. The rock is called Carthage Marble, although the limestone was never metamorphosed. It has a very dense, uniform texture that takes a high polish.

A ledge of limestone was quarried here by the Carthage Marble Company, now part of Carthage Underground.

Sucker Flats Open Pit Mine in Webb City

US 71 passes along the east side of Joplin, which was once the heart of Missouri's part of the Tri-State District. See **Interstate-44: Oklahoma Border—Northview** for a discussion of the district. One of the most accessible former mining pits to visit near Joplin is in Webb City's King Jack Park, an area known as Sucker Flats in the mining days. To reach the park, take the MO 96/MO 171

Webb City's King Jack Park encompasses the Sucker Flats Mine, a former open-pit lead mine.

exit and go west about 8.1 miles. The road becomes East MacArthur Drive west of MO 249. The park entrance is to the south. A drive north from the park on Route D (South Main) toward Oronogo takes you through an area where piles of waste rock remain, and past the Oronogo Circle open pit, which now hosts a commercial diving operation.

From I-44 to Arkansas

New road construction south of Joplin has created many new roadcuts along US 71 between I-44 and Pineville. All expose Mississippian limestone beds, either the Warsaw Formation or the next-older Burlington-Keokuk Limestone. In the 9 miles between Pineville and the Arkansas state line, US 71 follows the valley of Little Sugar Creek, a tributary of the Elk River. Older rocks are exposed in roadcuts in this valley. Most are Ordovician dolomite beds, but north of the MO 90 intersection in Jane, roadcuts reveal the Chattanooga Shale, a black shale of Devonian age. It is much thicker than the Pennsylvanian black shale beds that are exposed around Kansas City. Both have high amounts of organic carbon and metals. Although a similar bed is exposed over large areas from Illinois to Tennessee, in Missouri it remains only in what apparently were low spots on the eroded surface of Ordovician rock.

The Chattanooga Shale of Devonian age is exposed along US 71 north of MO 90 at Jane. Mississippian limestone sits atop it.

Just north of Pineville, new construction for relocation of US 71 has exposed Mississippian limestone beds. This picture is taken looking north from the McDonald County Route EE junction.

Roaring River State Park

A bit out of the way but worth the trip, Roaring River State Park is south of Cassville in Barry County. Roaring River Spring flows at a rate of about 20 million gallons per day and feeds the Roaring River, a tributary of the White River that is famed for its trout fishing. Bluffs of Mississippian and Ordovician rock form steep-walled canyons here, where the White River has cut into the edge of the Springfield Plateau. Roaring River Spring discharges from the Cotter Dolomite, at the base of the bluff. Devil's Kitchen is a rock shelter in the park, eroded in the Mississippian Compton Limestone. The Devonian Chattanooga Shale crops out below the Compton here.

Shaded-relief image of the Ozarks and the St. Francois Mountains.
—Shaded-relief base map from EROS Data Center

THE OZARKS AND THE
ST. FRANCOIS MOUNTAINS

To most Missourians, the Ozarks refers to the hill country in south-central Missouri, from around Lake of the Ozarks southward into Arkansas. To geologists, it means the part of the state in which rocks of Ordovician age are at the surface, forming the Salem Plateau (also called the Ozark Plateau). Although the core of the Ozarks physiographic region is undeniably in Missouri, the extent is less well-defined. Some people also include adjacent parts of Kansas, Oklahoma, and Illinois. The origin of the name Ozarks is also unclear, although it could be a phonetic spelling of either of two French phrases: *Aux Arkansas*, meaning "to the Arkansas" and shortened to *Aux Arks*; or *Aux Arcs*, meaning "with bows," in reference to native tribes.

The St. Francois Mountains (pronounced *Francis*) are at the center of the Ozark Dome, the large geologic uplift that formed during the collision of North America with Africa and South America in Late Pennsylvanian time. Although they are Missouri's only landforms that remotely approach the scale of mountains, they are relatively small ones. The highest peaks are only about 1,700 feet above sea level and around 500 feet higher than the adjacent valleys. Perhaps the most unique thing about the mountains is that the same igneous rocks that form the highest peaks of the modern St. Francois Mountains also formed hills on the landscape more than a half billion years ago. Sedimentary rocks were deposited over the top of them in Paleozoic time, but the mountain core is exposed again today due to erosion of those rock layers. Geologists call this an *exhumed landscape*, meaning one in which an ancient topography reappears due to erosion.

The rock layers that once covered the mountains can still be seen in the Ozarks. Ordovician rocks, primarily dolomite, are exposed all around the center of the Ozark Dome, but the largest outcrop area by far is west of the St. Francois Mountains on the Salem Plateau. Here sedimentary beds dip at a small angle generally in a westward direction away from the center of the dome. On the northern and eastern flanks of the Ozark Dome, sedimentary beds dip at steeper angles than elsewhere around the dome, although the rocks will still look horizontal in most roadcuts. On the northern flank, sedimentary rocks are squeezed between the dome and the Lincoln Fold; on the east side, beds dip off the dome into the Illinois Basin at the steepest angle of any regional dip in the state but still generally less than 10 degrees. The steeper dips here produce a rather interesting pattern on the geologic map, where bands of rock of different ages arc around the east side of the St. Francois Mountains. If you drive

WEST

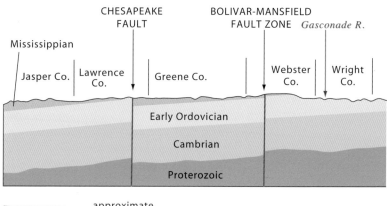

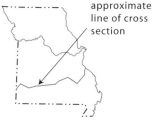

approximate
line of cross
section

across the bands, you can see beds representing large portions of the sequence of Missouri's sedimentary rocks—from Cambrian to Pennsylvanian age—in a reasonably short road trip.

The Gasconade Dolomite, the oldest Ordovician rock exposed on the Salem Plateau, is composed nearly entirely of dolomite, but at its base is the Gunter Sandstone Member, a bed deposited in shallow water as sea level rose. The Roubidoux Formation, the next youngest, is mostly dolomite, but it also typically contains a sandstone bed at or just above its base, and sometimes has two more sandstone beds, one near the middle and one at the top.

Atop the Roubidoux, in order of decreasing age, are the Jefferson City and Cotter Dolomites. These rocks look so similar in outcrops and roadcuts that it is sometimes difficult to distinguish them, even for geologists. They are without question the two most widely outcropping formations in Missouri's Ozarks and are the ones that you will see in many roadcuts on the Salem Plateau, with older beds appearing mainly in roadcuts near stream valleys.

It is probably worthwhile to include here a brief discussion of the last three formations of Early Ordovician time: the Powell Dolomite, Smithville Dolomite, and Everton Formation, the latter a sandy dolomite and sandstone. In northwestern Arkansas, the Powell fills the interval between the Cotter Dolomite and Everton Formation, and in northeast Arkansas, the Smithville fills the gap. But in Missouri neither the Powell nor the Smithville Dolomite is positively identified in outcrops. The Everton Formation was deposited on an eroded surface—either the Cotter or Powell or Smithville—at the end of Early

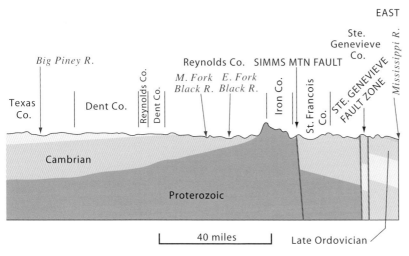

This west to east cross section through southern Missouri shows the structure of the Ozark Dome. The dome is asymmetrical; the beds on the east side dip more steeply than those on the west. Horizontal scale and topography are approximated, and the vertical scale has been exaggerated to illustrate bed dips. —Modified from Anderson, 1979

Ordovician time. The Everton was eroded prior to deposition of the St. Peter Sandstone, and it is not present everywhere in Missouri.

Because the Jefferson City and Cotter are difficult to distinguish in roadcuts and the remaining three formations are either disputed or discontinuous, on the maps in this book I have combined the sequence from the Jefferson City Dolomite through the Everton Formation under the all-encompassing name Jefferson City Dolomite. I have used that convention for most discussions as well, except where individual identification is useful for clarity.

Filled-Sink Structures

The Ordovician dolomite beds on the northern and northwestern flanks of the Ozark Dome are peppered with hundreds of small, circular or elliptical structures in which the rocks inside are younger than those surrounding them. They vary in size from tens to hundreds of feet across. Most are found in the Jefferson City Dolomite, but some are in the Roubidoux Formation. Some structures contain a white quartz sandstone that looks nearly identical to the St. Peter Sandstone, which was deposited just after the prolonged erosion period during Middle Ordovician time. Others contain Pennsylvanian beds of clay, coal, and sandstone.

Many explanations have been proposed for how these structures formed. The earliest hypothesis was that they were stream channels eroded into the surface of the host rock during Late Ordovician time when sea level temporarily fell. That explained the presence of crossbedded sandstone similar to the St.

Peter Sandstone but not the circular shapes or the presence of Pennsylvanian coal or clay beds.

A second explanation was that they were ancient sinkholes formed by collapse into a cavern. This idea accounted for the circular shapes and the different types and ages of sediment filling them. Some of the structures may indeed have been formed in this way. But in many of the structures, the in-filling rocks are not broken as would be expected if collapse had occurred. In fact, the beds inside some of the structures are horizontal.

In 1950, Missouri geologist J. Harlen Bretz proposed another, perhaps more unusual, explanation for how the structures formed, and he named them *filled-sink structures*, sometimes shortened to *filled sinks*. In Bretz's model, the structures were indeed the result of groundwater erosion, but without the formation of caves. Rather, microscopic grains of dolomite were dissolved slowly over time, creating tiny spaces in the rock. The loss of rock allowed the dolomite bed to compact under the weight of overlying beds. As it did so, beds above it sank very slowly into the structure. The amount that younger beds settled varied, depending on the amount of dolomite rock mass removed: the more rock removed, the greater the subsidence. Groundwater erosion of the dolomite grains probably began shortly after the rock lithified and occurred at different rates in different places, depending on variations in rock composition

Filled sinks may have formed over time as microscopic grains of dolomite were dissolved and removed by groundwater. These models are based on those of geologist J. Harlen Bretz (1960).

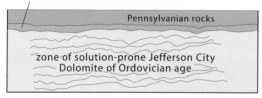

(A) Original sequence of beds
Ordovician, Devonian, and Pennsylvanian rocks are present atop the Jefferson City Dolomite in different places in the Ozarks.

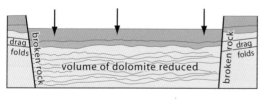

(B) Solution and subsidence
Groundwater dissolved and removed dolomite gradually over time. Overlying beds sank downward as the dolomite below them compressed, creating roughly circular structures in which younger rocks are bounded by faulted and broken rock.

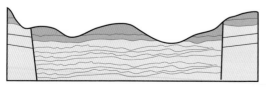

(C) Present appearance
The final appearance of a filled sink depends not only on the type and age of rocks within it, but the extent to which erosion has removed parts of the structure.

and groundwater flow. Once uplift of the Ozark Dome began in earnest in Late Pennsylvanian time, the water table across the Salem Plateau dropped, ending the process.

Bretz's model accounts for the observed characteristics of many of the structures: the circular shape (groundwater dissolution began at intersecting joints and spread radially); the presence of crossbedded sandstone (part of a younger bed that was lowered into the structures); the uniform composition of sandstone in different filled sinks (once part of the same overlying bed); the tilting or faulting of adjacent or overlying dolomite layers (slowly pulled down by subsidence); the lack of rubble piles (no collapse was involved); and the variable age of the in-filling rocks (different amounts of subsidence at different places).

Be that as it may, some circular features found in Ordovician dolomite in the Ozarks are indeed attributed to collapse of deeper caves. These structures, called "circles," are similar in shape to filled sinks but always contain broken, tilted, and shattered beds rather than horizontal strata. However, given the range in appearances of both types of structures, the origins of some of the plateau's circular features remain the subject of discussion.

Many filled sinks contain valuable resources such as iron, lead, barite, fire clay, and coal, which were mined until the mid-twentieth century. See **Interstate 44: Rolla—St. Louis** for a discussion of the filled-sink iron mining district and fire clay district.

Several filled sinks in an area southwest of Jefferson City contain galena and barite. The ore minerals likely were deposited by the same lead-rich water that deposited ores elsewhere in the state during late Paleozoic time. The filled-sink galena deposits are small, and none could be exploited commercially. Barite, which has long been used to increase the thickness of paint and the lubricating

The approximate boundaries of the lead, barite, fire clay, and iron mining districts in central Missouri.

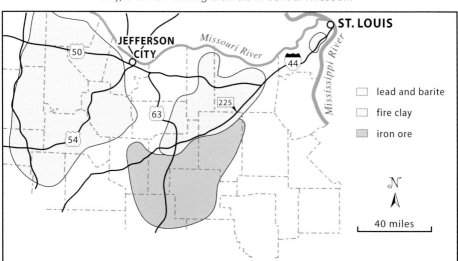

mud used in drilling oil and gas wells, was mined from a few filled sinks in central Missouri.

Meandering Valleys in the Ozarks

Many of the Ozark's streams flow in deep, meandering, almost canyonlike valleys with broad, flat uplands in between. The Osage River, along with its tributaries, drains most of the western Salem Plateau, flowing into the Missouri River near Jefferson City. The Osage and several of its main tributaries have been dammed to create lakes for hydroelectric power generation and recreational uses. Because the river valleys were steep walled, the shorelines of many of these lakes preserve the sinuous patterns of the rivers.

A long-standing puzzle for geologists has been the origin of the deep meandering river valleys in the Ozarks—in particular those of the Osage and Gasconade Rivers. In other parts of the world, for example on the Colorado Plateau, the explanation for a stream flowing in a deep meandering valley or canyon is that the stream that carved the valley was at one time meandering across a very flat floodplain. Tectonic forces then caused slow uplift of this surface over an extended period of time, and the stream managed to keep pace by cutting its channel deeper and deeper while preserving the meandering pattern. Such valleys are called *incised meanders*, or *entrenched meanders*.

The traditional explanation for Ozarkian stream valleys is that they formed much the same way. In this model, which some refer to as the "ancient landscape" model, it all began with the Ozark peneplain (pronounced *PEEN-uh-plain*), a rather flat surface near sea level. (See **Interstate-44: Rolla—St. Louis** in this chapter for more about peneplains.) Streams that were meandering across this low-relief surface began to incise valleys as the Ozark uplift slowly elevated the region beginning in Late Pennsylvanian time. The Pliocene gravels that covered Missouri, the Mounds Gravel and their equivalents, buried the landscape, including the meandering valleys, which were reexposed, or exhumed, by the renewed erosion cycle that started in Late Pliocene or Early Pleistocene time.

Not all geologists accept this idea, though. Some propose a slightly different model for landscape evolution in the Ozarks and question the interpretation that the Ozarks region was ever a peneplain. The fundamental difference lies in just when and how the incised valleys eroded. In the second model, the stream valleys are considered to be very young, possibly Pliocene or later in age.

In this alternative model, the Ozarks region was periodically uplifted and downdropped because of stresses caused by distant plate collisions and mountain building episodes. This model would certainly be consistent with the repeated activation of faults that we see in Missouri's basement rock. The region always had considerable topographic relief and was never a plain near sea level across which sluggish streams meandered. The Ozarks were instead part of the much larger Central Highlands region, a continuous area of elevated topography that extended from Oklahoma to Maine.

The most recent uplift cycle began a few million years ago. Erosion accelerated during Pleistocene time, and ongoing subsidence of the Mississippi Embayment allowed the Mississippi River to breach the Central Highlands drainage divide, separating it into the modern Ozarks, Ouachita, and Appalachian highlands. In this model of landscape development, the deep meandering canyons of the Ozarks formed much more recently than Late Pennsylvanian time, and partly as a result of stream courses following paths controlled by pressurized groundwater emerging from large springs rather than solely from the incision of a low-gradient, meandering channel. While this idea is intriguing, it has yet to gain wide acceptance.

Caldera Eruptions of the St. Francois Mountains

The St. Francois Mountains, at the center of the Ozark Dome, contain Missouri's highest elevations and oldest rocks. The topography is dominated by steep-sided, rounded peaks, locally called "knobs." The highest of these, Taum Sauk Mountain, tops out at 1,772 feet above sea level and is the highest point in Missouri. Many other knobs are in the 1,300- to 1,600-foot elevation range.

The geology the St. Francois Mountains is unique and sheds light upon the earliest years of the formation of the midcontinent. The mountains are composed of igneous rocks that formed about 1.5 billion years ago when magma rose toward the surface, perhaps due to the presence of a mantle hot spot, a plume of hot mantle rocks, similar to what is happening at Yellowstone today. Or there may have been a tectonic subduction zone that created an environment that melted rock. Large, shallow magma chambers fed volcanoes that mostly erupted pyroclastics—volcanic ash, cinders, and pumice—that either fell back to Earth in ashfalls or raced across the surface as pyroclastic flows.

Magma rose to the surface along faults, and the ash—and some lava—erupted from a network of closely spaced circular vents or linear fissures above the fault zones. As eruptions drew down the level of magma in the source chamber, the recently crystallized rocks above slowly sank along bounding faults, creating

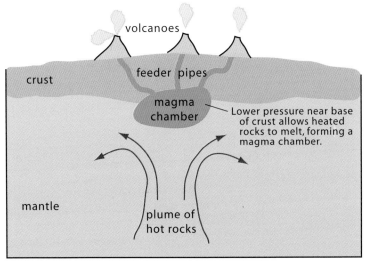

A plume of hot rocks slowly rising through the Earth's mantle may have melted rocks in the lower crust, leading to the volcanism in southeast Missouri 1.5 billion years ago.

6- to 12-mile-wide craters called *calderas*. The magma chambers then refilled, and subsequent eruptions sent more ash flows into the centers of the calderas, where thousands of feet of volcanic rock accumulated, compacted, and crystallized. This cycle happened several times. The eruptions produced only small lava flows but enormous volumes of pyroclastics, and the resulting sequence of volcanic rocks is more than 5,000 feet thick. Eventually, the end of the cycle was marked by a final, cataclysmic eruption as the caldera collapsed.

At least four distinct eruption centers—the Taum Sauk, Lake Killarney, Butler Hill, and Eminence Calderas—have been identified in the St. Francois Mountains, each containing rocks from multiple eruptions. There may have been more calderas, but if so, they remain hidden beneath younger sedimentary rocks. Each eruption created its own unique deposit, and geologists are still unraveling the sequence. To complicate the interpretation, some volcanic rocks were tilted and broken by later eruptions or faulting.

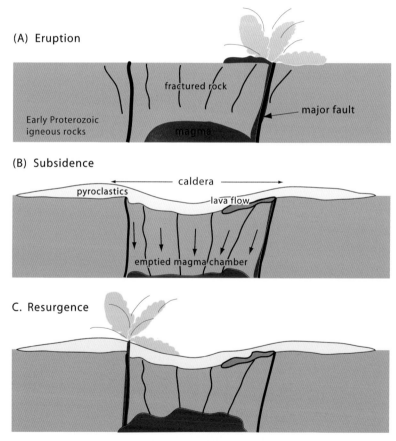

Stages in the caldera eruptions in the St. Francois Mountains. (A) Lava and pyroclastics erupt along a fault zone in Late Proterozoic basement rock. (B) Basement and volcanic rocks subside along faults, above the emptied magma chamber. (C) Magma chamber refills and the eruption occurs along another fault zone.

Once eruptions ended, magma that remained in the chambers beneath the calderas slowly crystallized into large masses of granite called *plutons*. Some magma migrated into the perimeter fracture zones of the calderas and hardened into a set of smaller plutons called *ring intrusions*. Radiometric dating of the largest pyroclastic flows and granite plutons give ages between 1.48 and 1.46 billion years, give or take a few million. The youngest granite in the area is around 1.3 billion years old.

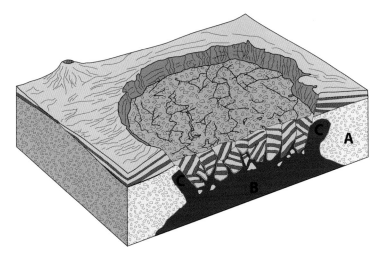

Two types of granite plutons intruded older pyroclastic rocks in southeast Missouri (A), which were fractured during caldera collapse. Large plutons (B) crystallized directly beneath former calderas. Often the uppermost granite in these plutons differs slightly in composition and appearance from the lower rock. Ring intrusion plutons (C) formed where magma moved through fractured rocks around the perimeter of the calderas.

VOLCANIC ROCKS. The oldest rocks in the St. Francios Mountains are volcanic rocks, also called *extrusive igneous rocks* because they solidified from molten rock or pyroclastics erupted on Earth's surface. They have similar chemical composition to the slightly younger granites because they crystallized from the same magma. But they look entirely different because of their microscopic grain size and because they are more resistant to weathering.

There are many terms applied to the volcanic rocks in the St. Francois Mountains. The fine-grain rock that is chemically equivalent to granite is rhyolite, and nearly all the volcanic rocks in the St. Francois Mountains are of rhyolitic composition. Their pyroclastic origin leads them to be called *ash-flow tuffs*. A few compacted while still very hot, which caused their minerals to fuse into a very dense rock called *ignimbrite*.

The manner in which pyroclastics were erupted, deposited, and compacted led to considerable variation in both color and texture of the rocks. At least fifteen distinct volcanic deposits have been found thus far in the St. Francois Mountains, and they exhibit a wide array of physical features. Some are layered, a characteristic called *flow banding*. Others have chunks of older volcanic rocks trapped in them and are called *flow breccias*. Some contain compacted pieces of pumice. Still others formed from ash that fell into lakes in the calderas.

The Taum Sauk Rhyolite and Grassy Mountain Ignimbrite, the two volcanic rocks exposed over the largest areas, are ash-flow tuffs formed during the final eruptions of the Taum Sauk Caldera and Butler Hill Caldera, respectively. The two rocks are very similar in mineral composition, texture, and appearance. In some places these rocks contain angular fragments of slightly older volcanic rocks.

A few of the volcanic rocks in the St. Francois Mountains are rhyolite lava flows or sills. One example is the rock in the Devil's Honeycomb on Hughes Mountain. Columnar jointing, a fracture pattern in which the rock splits apart in multisided pieces, developed in the rock as it cooled and contracted.

Columns in the Devil's Honeycomb, an outcrop of rhyolite on Hughes Mountain, formed as the rock contracted during cooling. In this photo, you can see the polygonal tops of the columns. Access is via a trail from County Route 541 off Washington County Route M (37.802N 90.710W).

GRAIN SIZE IN IGNEOUS ROCKS

The size of individual minerals in an igneous rock depends on how fast the magma or lava cools. The slower the cooling rate, the larger the mineral crystals grow. Slow cooling, which occurs over thousands or millions of years, happens far below the Earth's surface, where overlying rock and soil insulate magma chambers against rapid heat loss. The intrusive rocks contain visible mineral grains that you can see without a magnifying glass. Granite, for example, has visible grains of quartz, feldspar, and mica.

When magma gets close to or erupts onto the surface, the molten rock crystallizes quickly and minerals do not have the time to get very big. You need to use a magnifying glass—and sometimes a microscope—to distinguish different mineral grains. These rocks appear more uniform in color than intrusive rocks and are more resistant to erosion because of the smaller crystals. For this reason, rhyolitic volcanic rocks form the knobs of the St. Francois Mountains, while granite and sedimentary rocks underlie the rolling plains at lower elevations.

Many of the volcanic rocks in Missouri have two different sizes of mineral grains. Visible grains 1 to 2 millimeters across are embedded in a finer-grained rock mass, a texture called *porphyritic.* The larger mineral crystals began to grow slowly, when the magma was still belowground, but when the magma neared or was erupted at the surface, it cooled much faster and the remaining minerals crystallized too fast to grow very big.

GRANITIC ROCKS. The rocks composing the plutons are called *intrusive igneous* because they cooled below ground. All of the plutonic rocks of the St. Francois Mountains are classified as granite because they are rich in silica. The mineral compositions of the ring intrusions differ slightly from those of the large plutons directly below the calderas, and even from each other because the magma composition changed over time as the magma chambers refilled. The most obvious difference between the plutonic rocks is their color, which ranges from dark reddish brown to gray to pink, primarily depending on the kind (and color) of feldspar and other minerals they contain.

Seven granite plutons outcrop in the St. Francois Mountains. The intrusive rock that outcrops over the largest area is the Butler Hill–Breadtray Granite, which crystallized beneath the Butler Hill Caldera. The two names distinguish the rock that crystallized deeper in the magma chamber (the Butler Hill Granite) from the rock that solidified closer to the surface, at the top of the chamber (Breadtray Granite). In some places the granite contains pieces of the older Grassy Mountain Ignimbrite, demonstrating that the granite magma intruded the ignimbrite. The outcrop area of the Butler Hill–Breadtray Granite is the Flatlands, a rolling lowland. Three ring intrusion granites, the Slabtown, Knoblick, and Silvermine, are found around the Butler Hill Caldera.

Two younger granites, the Graniteville and Munger Granites, are also exposed. The Graniteville Granite is exposed in a small area near and in Elephant Rocks State Park. Drill holes encounter it beneath the Cambrian sedimentary rocks in the Belleview Valley, a broad lowland. At about 1.32 billion years old, this rock is considerably younger than the other granites in the area, so it solidified long after the caldera eruptions.

Different granite plutons in the St. Francois Mountains can be distinguished by their colors and textures, which vary due to differing mineral content. Two are shown here: the Slabtown Granite (left) has slightly larger mineral grains and is redder than the Knoblick Granite (right), except when both are weathered.

Pink Graniteville Granite, part of one of the youngest plutons in the St. Francois Mountains, weathers into large boulders at Elephant Rocks State Park. It was quarried at several locations near Graniteville, in northern Iron County.

SKRAINKA DIABASE. The youngest intrusive igneous rock in the region, the Skrainka Diabase, crystallized from iron-rich magma during the final stages of igneous activity. The magma seeped close to the surface and solidified in tabular masses called *sills*. The composition of the rock is diabase, but because the crystals are coarse enough to see, the rock has also been called *gabbro*. Magma seeping away from the main sill chamber found its way into fractures to form the narrow diabase dikes that cut through the granite and volcanic rocks. Only small discontinuous outcrops of the Skrainka Diabase remain.

Fault-Bound Basins and the Great Unconformity

The Proterozoic basement rocks beneath Missouri are broken into large fault-bound blocks that are the largest-scale geologic structures in the state. Where blocks of Proterozoic igneous rocks dropped down along steep faults, structural basins formed and were filled with sediment during Cambrian time. Although the faulting occurred prior to deposition of Paleozoic sediments, the large blocks have moved repeatedly since they first formed. The most pronounced shifting may have been associated with the tectonic episodes that led to the uplift of the Ozark Dome in Pennsylvanian time.

Two structural basins occur in the St. Francois Mountains. The Belleview Valley is located on the northwestern edge of the igneous rock exposures, and the Sabula Basin is on the southwestern edge. Both are named after towns within them. The floors of these valleys are 300 to 600 feet below the peaks of surrounding volcanic knobs, and the Proterozoic bedrock is another several hundred feet below the surface. If the Proterozoic rocks in these two basins were once at the same elevation as the surrounding terrain, almost 1,000 feet of downdropping must have occurred along the faults.

MO 21 between Graniteville and Belleview crosses the Belleview Valley, which is bounded by faults in Proterozoic rocks and filled with Cambrian sedimentary rocks. This view is to the east from a roadside park (37.704N 90.743W).

The Lamotte Sandstone and next-younger Bonneterre Dolomite were both deposited directly atop eroded igneous rocks in Middle Cambrian time. In places, the Lamotte is a conglomerate composed of pebbles of igneous rocks that were rounded by wave action on the shores of igneous rock islands. The unconformity between the eroded igneous rocks of Proterozoic age and the younger sedimentary rocks of Cambrian age is known as the Great Unconformity. You can see it in several places around the St. Francois Mountains, but the rocks involved are not always the same. For example, the Lamotte Sandstone rests on Butler Hill Granite in a roadcut on US 67, and the Davis Formation and Derby–Doe Run Dolomite rest on a knob of Taum Sauk Rhyolite at Taum Sauk Power Plant. The largest area of exposures of Cambrian rock are in the Belleview Valley and Sabula Basin.

⚓ Road Guides in the Ozarks and St. Francois Mountains

Interstate 44
Northview—Rolla
90 MILES

Ordovician rocks are the rule along I-44 between Northview and Rolla. Between Northview and Hazelgreen (mile markers 96 to 145), the Jefferson City Dolomite appears in roadcuts where I-44 crosses stream divides. When the highway dips into river valleys, the Roubidoux Formation and the Gasconade Dolomite appear, particularly between Phillipsburg and Lebanon (mile markers 118 to 129).

The interstate passes over a number of small faults between Marshfield and Lebanon. Because the faults—which likely formed about the same time as the larger faults to the west—all trend northwest-southeast, the highway crosses them at nearly right angles. The displacement on the faults is sometimes slight, and the faults are often obscured by erosion and vegetation. The easiest faults to find along I-44 between mile markers 100 and 140 are as follows:

108.3 Both lanes: Jefferson City Dolomite southwest of fault; Roubidoux Formation (sandstone) northeast of fault.

120.4 Both lanes: Same as above.

129.5 Both lanes: Roubidoux Formation (sandstone) at southwest end of cuts; Jefferson City Dolomite at northeast end. Fault is not visible.

133.6 Both lanes: A fault zone extends from about mile marker 133.5 to 134.1. Younger rocks are at the east end. Broken Jefferson City Dolomite from about mile marker 133.6 to 133.7 may mark the fault.

138.5 Along northwest frontage road: Small fault near west end of roadcut in Jefferson City Dolomite.

138.8 Both sides: Several small faults at west end of a long roadcut.

Most Ordovician dolomite beds contain abundant chert, however one bed in the Jefferson City Dolomite does not. The lack of harder chert nodules gives the rock economic value for use as construction aggregate, for which it is mined. The bed is therefore known as the Quarry Ledge. Geologists use it to estimate the location of the contact between the Jefferson City Dolomite and the Roubidoux Formation, which is almost always 30 to 40 feet below the bottom of the Quarry Ledge. The Quarry Ledge is exposed in many of the roadcuts between mile markers 109 and 160, although at highway speeds it may be difficult to

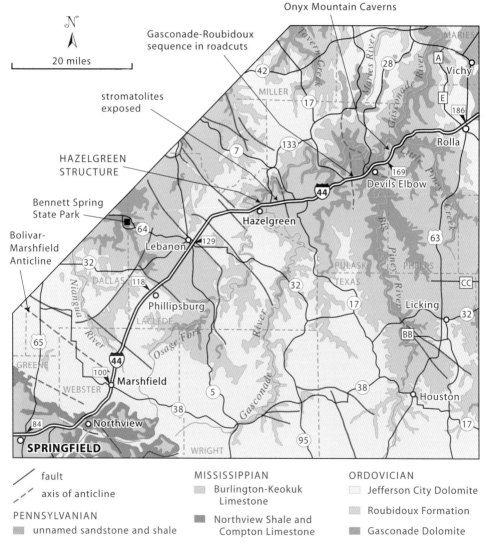

Bedrock geology along I-44 between Northview, at the eastern edge of the Springfield Plateau, and Rolla.

distinguish from the rest of the dolomite. A few places where the Quarry Ledge appears along both sides of the highway are at mile markers 109, 115, and 135.

About 12 miles west-northwest of I-44 on MO 64 (exit 129) is Bennett Spring State Park. The spring is the fourth largest in the state, with a daily flow of about 100 million gallons. It flows from a conduit in the Gasconade Dolomite.

The Gasconade River, crossed at mile marker 143.1, is the biggest free-flowing river in the northern Ozarks—it is not dammed. There were proposals to do so in the 1930s, but the Great Depression and World War II diverted attention from the projects, and none were ever built. The Gasconade is an example of a sinking, or losing, stream because water seeps from its channel into the groundwater in places where permeable dolomite lines the riverbed. One such stretch on the Gasconade is north of Hazelgreen (exit 145). The Gasconade Dolomite, which forms many of the large bluffs along the Gasconade River, is home to many caves and springs.

North of I-44 between the Gasconade River and exit 145 is the Hazelgreen Structure, one of Missouri's smaller cryptoexplosive structures. Drill cores in the structure encounter Cambrian dolomite breccia and a 35-foot-thick layer of volcanic pyroclastic rocks. Geologists have yet to determine the exact mechanism that created this structure.

Stromatolites, mounds of sediment trapped by algae, are the predominant fossil in bioherms present in many roadcuts along I-44. They do not often stand out from the gray dolomite, but between mile markers 143 and 148, the wavy bedding caused by the structures is more obvious than at other places.

Beds of dolomite in the Roubidoux Formation undulate around stromatolite bioherms exposed in a roadcut along the eastbound lanes of I-44 at mile marker 148. This photograph was taken near the east end of the roadcut.

The base of the darker gray bed at the right-center of the photo is slightly concave upward. This sandstone layer in the Roubidoux Formation was deposited into a channel that was eroded into previously deposited carbonate sediments. The roadcut is along the westbound lanes of I-44 at mile marker 167.3.

Between the Gasconade River and Rolla (exit 186), I-44 crosses primarily Roubidoux Formation or Gasconade Dolomite. Roadcuts on the approaches to Roubidoux Creek (mile markers 158 to 160) and Big Piney River (mile markers 167 to 168) expose nearly all of these Late Ordovician rocks.

The town of Devils Elbow is named for a sharp bend—an entrenched meander—in the Big Piney River, a tributary of the Gasconade. The name came from the days of rafting logs down the river and the difficulty encountered in maneuvering around the tight curve. If you want to visit the elbow, it's only a couple of miles off I-44. Take exit 163 and follow Pulaski County Route Z northeast to Teardrop Road and proceed east to the town. By the way, there are more than eighty natural features in Missouri that have "devil" as part of their name.

Onyx Mountain Caverns and Boiling Springs

Onyx Mountain Caverns (exit 169) was a commercial cave located in the bluffs east of the Gasconade River. The 400- by 100-foot entrance was used as a shelter by early peoples of the Woodland Culture. In the 1800s, settlers mined the decorative "cave onyx," layers of calcium carbonate deposited where water seeped across the cave wall. The cave onyx superficially resembles true onyx, a microcrystalline variety of quartz. This type of cave deposit is also called *flowstone*. In 2006 the owner sold the cave to the U.S. Forest Service, which has gated the entrance and manages the cave as a refuge for endangered bat species.

Shaded-relief image showing deep meanders along the Gasconade River and its tributaries. —Shaded-relief base map from EROS Data Center

About 0.9 mile north of the cave is a parking area with a trail that leads to a view of Boiling Spring, the state's ninth largest. Direct access to the spring, which discharges in the bed of the Gasconade River, is on private property, but the upward flow of groundwater produces a boil in the river that you can see near the far bank at the base of the cliff.

Interstate 44
Rolla—St. Louis
90 MILES

Between Rolla and Crawford County Route F (exit 203), I-44 crosses a flat upland. Many of the hilltops in this part of Missouri north of I-44 are flat, close to the same elevation, and capped by Pennsylvanian sandstone and shale that were deposited on top of the Jefferson City Dolomite. This topography is sometimes called the Ozark peneplain. The term *peneplain* was coined in the early study of landform evolution to describe the ultimate erosional landscape—a surface of low relief near sea level that took millions upon millions of years to form. In this model, the passage of time was a primary factor in how the Earth's surface looked. As scientific study progressed, it became clear that time was far less significant in creating landscapes than were the nature and intensity of the erosion processes at work, combined with the resistance of the geologic materials on which they acted. Modern investigators of landform development have abandoned the time-dominant concept of landform development in favor of

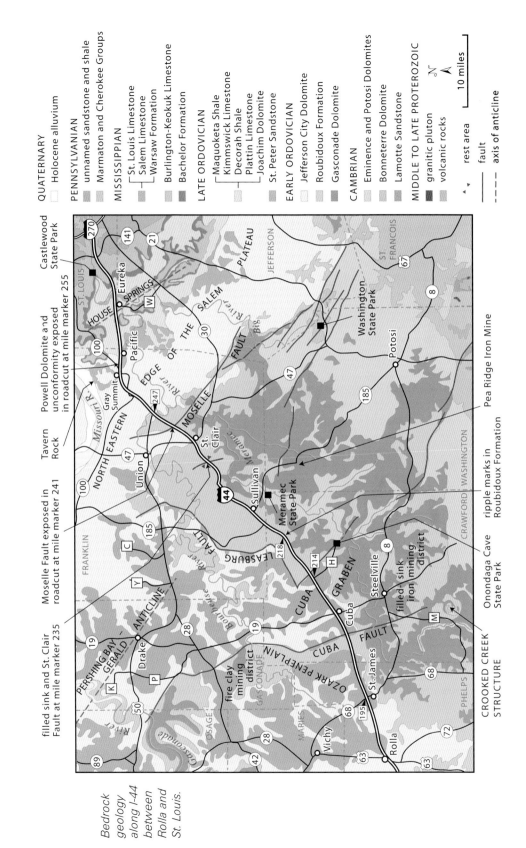

Bedrock geology along I-44 between Rolla and St. Louis.

QUATERNARY
Holocene alluvium

PENNSYLVANIAN
unnamed sandstone and shale
Marmaton and Cherokee Groups

MISSISSIPPIAN
St. Louis Limestone
Salem Limestone
Warsaw Formation
Burlington-Keokuk Limestone
Bachelor Formation

LATE ORDOVICIAN
Maquoketa Shale
Kimmswick Limestone
Decorah Shale
Plattin Limestone
Joachim Dolomite
St. Peter Sandstone

EARLY ORDOVICIAN
Jefferson City Dolomite
Roubidoux Formation
Gasconade Dolomite

CAMBRIAN
Eminence and Potosi Dolomites
Bonneterre Dolomite
Lamotte Sandstone

MIDDLE TO LATE PROTEROZOIC
granitic pluton
volcanic rocks

▲▼ rest area
—— fault
- - - axis of anticline

10 miles

a process-dominant one, and the term *peneplain* no longer carries with it the implication of erosion to sea level. It is not often used today, but lingers from the early days of landform study when areas like this one were thought to have eroded to sea level. There are also a few filled sinks in this interval, but they are impossible to distinguish in roadcuts.

Missouri Fire Clay District

Extending 50 miles north of I-44 roughly between mile markers 190 and 225, is an area in which many filled-sink structures contain clay with unusually high alumina (aluminum oxide) content. This chemical composition makes the clay valuable in the manufacture of bricks used in high-temperature applications, such as the linings of kilns and furnaces. These fire clays are thought to have formed during Pennsylvanian time when groundwater altered and removed minerals from the original clay or shale bed in the sinks, leaving the less soluble aluminum oxide minerals behind. Most of the deposits are small, less than 100 feet across and 10 to 20 feet deep, although some cover several acres and extend up to 100 feet below the surface. The boundary of the filled-sink fire clay district corresponds to the outcrops of Pennsylvanian rocks. Among the more interesting uses of bricks made from Missouri fire clay were as linings of boilers in World War II ships and in launch pads at Cape Canaveral, Florida.

Fire clay is also mined farther north, but in that area the clay is in beds that were not lowered into filled sinks. The deposits likely formed at the same time, through the same leaching process, and perhaps from the same original clay or shale beds.

Cuba Graben

Between mile markers 206 and 214, I-44 crosses the Cuba Graben. The Cuba Fault (crossed at mile marker 205.5) bounds it on the west, and the Leasburg Fault bounds it on the east. Beds are 125 to 150 feet lower in elevation in the graben than to either side, and Pennsylvanian sandstone and shale are at road level. To the east and west of the graben, the Roubidoux Formation outcrops along the interstate.

Steelville and the Filled-Sink Iron Mining District

Iron ore was first mined in Missouri from filled-sink deposits on the northern flank of the Ozark Dome. Not only did European settlers exploit these resources, in at least one case a group of Native Americans mined a deposit to retrieve iron oxides for red pigment. The ore minerals probably formed when water infiltrated from the surface and dissolved iron from Pennsylvanian rocks. When the infiltrating water reached the groundwater, the difference in chemical conditions led to the precipitation of iron sulfide minerals, such as pyrite, in the porous rocks of the filled sinks. When groundwater levels declined during uplift of the Ozark Dome, the iron sulfide minerals reacted with infiltrating surface water to form the iron oxide minerals that make up the ore deposits. Because this second process acted from the surface down, shallow filled sinks contain only iron oxides, while deeper ones still have some iron sulfide minerals in them.

The largest filled-sink iron mine was the Cherry Valley Mine, located approximately 5 miles southeast of Steelville (south of I-44 at exit 208). The mine, which began production in 1878, measured 900 by 500 feet and extended to a depth of over 300 feet. Hematite was the iron ore mineral. The iron sulfide minerals pyrite and marcasite were also extracted for production of sulfuric acid. The Ruepple Mine, which operated from 1917 to 1943, was located south of I-44 near exit 230. This mine was slightly smaller, though just as deep as the Cherry Valley Mine.

Crooked Creek Structure

According to researchers with the Weaubleau Working Group at Missouri State University, the Crooked Creek Structure is one of three of Missouri's Thirty-Eighth Parallel Lineament structures that are impact craters (the other two are the Weaubleau-Osceola and Decaturville Structures). The Crooked Creek Structure is about 4 miles in diameter and is 10 miles south-southwest of Steelville (37.835N 91.395W). The oldest formation affected by the disturbance is Bonneterre Dolomite of Cambrian age and the youngest is Jefferson City Dolomite of Ordovician age. The date of impact has not been precisely determined but was most likely during Mississippian time.

Onondaga Cave State Park

Onondaga Cave State Park is located about 7 miles south of I-44 at Leasburg (exit 214) on Crawford County Route H. The cave is in the Gasconade Dolomite of Early Ordovician age. It contains about 1.5 miles of passages, the largest of which is a room that measures 500 feet long and up to 150 feet wide and 80

Cave deposits in Onondaga Cave include stalactites, stalagmites, flowstone (at right), and lily pads (in the pool in the foreground).
—Missouri Department of Natural Resources photo

feet high. Rich in flowstone, stalactites, and stalagmites, Onondaga Cave also has unusual calcium carbonate deposits called "lily pads" that appear to float in cave pools. It is listed as a national natural landmark and is considered by many cave experts to be one of the most beautiful caves in the United States.

Ripple Marks in the Roubidoux Formation

Outcrops of the Roubidoux Formation are much more visible on the northeast flank of the Ozark Dome, and not only in river valleys. Roubidoux sandstone appears in many of the roadcuts between mile markers 215 and 245. The beds are often crossbedded and in some places contain ripple marks formed by gentle waves that sculpted the sandy bottom of the shallow shelf.

Sandstone beds in the Roubidoux Formation sometimes have ripple marks on their top surfaces. This ledge is in a roadcut along the north frontage road of I-44 at exit 218.

Meramec State Park

About 3 miles south of I-44 at exit 226 (MO 185) is Meramec State Park. Among the more than forty caves within the park boundaries is Fisher Cave, through which park naturalists lead public tours. The visitor center houses exhibits pertaining to local wildlife, as well as examples of rocks collected in the park. Roadcuts through the Gasconade Dolomite are at the turnoff to the park entrance.

Pea Ridge Iron Mine

The biggest and deepest iron mine in Missouri is not a filled-sink deposit. It is the Pea Ridge Iron Mine, near Sullivan (south of I-44 at exit 226 on MO 185). Unlike the filled-sink deposits, the iron ore at the Pea Ridge Iron Mine is in Proterozoic volcanic rocks. It is called a "hard-rock iron mine" because geologists call igneous and metamorphic rocks "hard rocks," to distinguish

A piece of Ordovician dolomite on display at the Meramec State Park visitor center contains large fossil snails.

them from sedimentary rocks, which are softer. The principal ore mineral at this mine is magnetite, a magnetic oxide of iron. Hematite is also present. Mining had reached a depth of 2,700 feet when the mine closed in 2001. Exploratory drilling indicates that the iron ore continues for at least another 300 feet below mined levels. The mine produced more than 50 million tons of iron ore from an ore body that is up to 60 percent magnetite. Another famous hard-rock iron mine in Missouri is at Pilot Knob in the St. Francois Mountains.

St. Clair Area

The rest area near mile marker 235, which serves both directions of the interstate, provides an excellent view of either a filled sink or a fault zone. In roadcuts, horizontal beds of Roubidoux sandstone and dolomite surround jumbled, tilted blocks of Pennsylvanian sandstone and shale. The picnic area west of the restroom building definitely sits atop a filled sink in the Roubidoux Formation that was mined for coal (known as the Anaconda Coal Mine). But the Pennsylvanian beds in the roadcuts might also be part of a downdropped block on the east side of the St. Clair Fault Zone, which crosses the interstate near the west end of the cuts.

The area around St. Clair (exit 240), was the site of the earliest lead mines in Missouri, which produced ore between 1830 and the mid-1890s. At mile marker 241.1, the highway crosses the Moselle Fault, which may have been the epicenter of a small earthquake in 1945. Geologists at the time placed the actual movement of rocks at a depth of about 27 miles. No surface displacement was observed, and in fact the tremor was not felt by many people near the epicenter. Most Missouri earthquakes occur in the southeast corner of the state and are associated with the New Madrid Seismic Zone. However, small earthquakes (almost always too small

Tilted blocks of Pennsylvanian sandstone and shale along the westbound lanes of I-44 north of the rest area at mile marker 235 are part of either a downdropped block of rocks along a fault zone or a filled-sink structure, or perhaps both.

to be felt) do occur elsewhere in the state. Many geologists think they are related to occasional shifting along the faults in basement rocks.

Washington State Park

Washington State Park was the location for ceremonies of the Mississippian Culture. Among the things they left behind are the largest number of petroglyphs yet found in Missouri, which are dated to around AD 1000. The carvings are in Late Cambrian dolomite. The park, which is also on the National Register of Historic Places, is located in Washington County on MO 21, about 27 miles southeast of I-44 on MO 47.

Tavern Rock

Tavern Rock, a large bluff along the Missouri River at St. Albans, north of Gray Summit, served as a landmark for early travelers. Exposed in the cliff are beds from the Ordovician St. Peter Sandstone (at the base) to the Mississippian Burlington-Keokuk Limestone (capping the bluff). Members of the Lewis and Clark expedition visited and described a rock shelter eroded into the St. Peter Sandstone here. The river has been straightened, so it no longer flows along the base of the bluff. The cave is inaccessible, and the surrounding land is privately owned.

Gray Summit to I-270 at St. Louis

Jefferson City Dolomite beds are in roadcuts to about exit 253 at Gray Summit, where I-44 crosses the northeastern edge of the Salem Plateau. Between Gray Summit and St. Louis, rocks are progressively younger to the east, as the interstate crosses the narrow bands of beds exposed on the northeast flank of the Ozark Dome. In the 23 miles between Gray Summit and I-270 (exit 276), the age of rocks exposed along the highway changes from Middle Ordovician to Middle Mississippian.

The St. Peter Sandstone of Middle Ordovician age, which was deposited atop a very irregular erosion surface cut into Early Ordovician rocks, is exposed along I-44 in several roadcuts between mile markers 253 and 257. The St. Peter is valued as a source of pure quartz sand—commercially known as Ottawa Sand—and is mined at several places southwest of the St. Louis metropolitan area, including Pacific (exit 257), Festus, Crystal City, and Pevely. Because it is more than 99 percent silica, it used in glassmaking and as an abrasive. The sand was deposited in layers offshore in shallow water. Because the grains are frosted, geologists surmise that the source may have been coastal sand dunes.

The St. Peter Sandstone was deposited on a wavy, eroded surface of Powell Dolomite. The unconformity, visible in several roadcuts along I-44 between mile markers 254.9 and 255.2, is near highway level in this cut along the westbound lanes at mile marker 255.1.

The rock in the lower half of this roadcut along the westbound lanes of I-44 at mile marker 261 is the Joachim Dolomite, and that in the top half is the Plattin Limestone. Both are of Late Ordovician age. Trace fossils in the Plattin Limestone include those of burrowing organisms, which indicate the depositional environment was probably a carbonate mud bottom in calm water.

EUREKA–HOUSE SPRINGS STRUCTURE ALONG ROUTE W

The Eureka–House Springs Structure, a zone of folded and faulted rocks up to a few miles wide, extends from the Missouri River near St. Albans to the southeast, possibly all the way to the Mississippi River near Imperial. Within the zone, the two largest structures are the House Springs Fault and House Springs Anticline, with a series of smaller faults and folds parallel to them. The House Springs Anticline brings to the surface slightly older rocks (Late Ordovician age) than would otherwise appear here.

Although I-44 crosses the northern end of the structure between mile markers 262.0 and 262.3, it is not exposed along I-44. However, 1.3 miles south of the interstate on Jefferson County Route W (exit 264), you can see one of the small parallel folds and a fault in the roadcut just north of the Meramec River. Beds of Late Ordovician Joachim Dolomite (the oldest formation, exposed at the north end), Plattin Limestone, Decorah Shale, and Kimmswick Limestone are present. The fault is near the north end of the roadcut, with dipping, downdropped younger beds to the south.

The Decorah Shale at road level south of the fault contains beds of bentonite clay formed from volcanic ash. These beds are found over large areas of North America, and the ash that composes them was produced by a string of volcanic islands that existed off the eastern margin of North America in Middle Ordovician

Faulted and folded beds of Ordovician rocks are exposed in the roadcut along the northbound lane of County Route W north of the Meramec River, 1.3 miles south of I-44 (exit 264). The fault zone is in the treeless part of the cut. Joachim Dolomite and Plattin Limestone are north of the fault, and beds of younger Decorah Shale and Kimmswick Limestone are on the south side. These structures lie parallel to and west of the House Springs Fault.

Dipping beds along the eastbound lanes of MO 30 a short distance north of House Springs mark the location of the House Springs Anticline (38.420N 90.574W). —Kevin Ginther photo

time, prior to collision of the island arc with the continent during the Taconic mountain building episode.

The House Springs Anticline can be visited by continuing south on Route W for an additional 7 miles to the junction with MO 30 at House Springs, then traveling northeast on MO 30 another 0.7 mile. Here the Ordovician rocks are tilted even more steeply.

Castlewood State Park, which stretches for about 5 miles along the Meramec River, is the site of former resorts popular with St. Louis residents prior to World War II. Burlington-Keokuk Limestone forms the bluffs along the river. To get to the park, take MO 141 (exit 272) north from I-44 to Big Bend Road, turn west, and go to Ries Road. Turn left and follow Ries Road to the parking area.

The Bushberg Sandstone, the only rock from Devonian time exposed in this part of Missouri, is in the roadcut along the westbound lanes of I-44 at about mile marker 268.8. East of this point to downtown St. Louis, all of the rocks are of Mississippian age.

At the I-270 interchange, the shale in the cuts is the lower part of the Mississippian Warsaw Formation. In western Missouri, the Warsaw Formation contains all limestone and is mined there as Carthage Marble. Here it is mostly shale

The Mississippian Keokuk Limestone, which in other places in Missouri is indistinguishable from the Burlington Limestone beneath it, is exposed in this roadcut along the southeast frontage road at exit 272. The grayer (lower) bed is crossbedded and composed of broken and rounded fossil fragments and some oolith sand. The upward-concave shape of the bottom of the bed and the way that the bed thins to either side suggest that the fossil debris was deposited in a tidal channel.

The younger Salem Limestone is interbedded with shale of the older Warsaw Formation at the top of the roadcuts on all corners of the I-44 and I-270 interchange (exit 276). The cut on the northeast corner is shown here.

with a few thin limestone layers. On the northeast corner of the interchange, the Salem Limestone is interbedded with the shale of the upper Warsaw; both are exposed in the roadcut along the access road. The Salem Limestone and next-younger St. Louis Limestone are in the cut on the southeast corner.

Interstate 55
St. Louis—Cape Girardeau
116 MILES

A detailed discussion of the geology of the St. Louis area is presented in the Glaciated Plains chapter. Bedrock along I-55 between downtown St. Louis and mile marker 187 is all of Mississippian age and predominantly gray or tan, cherty limestone beds of the St. Louis and Salem Limestones. South of mile marker 187, I-55 crosses into the outcrop area of Ordovician sedimentary rocks on the eastern flank of the Ozark Dome. The highway runs west of, and more or less parallel to, the Mississippi River, and the rocks in the numerous highway roadcuts also form the western bluffs of the river valley.

Mastodon State Historic Site

Mastodon State Historic Site, a short distance northwest of the interstate at exit 186 at Imperial, is the former location of a small quarry from which the bones of a wide variety of Pleistocene mammals were excavated. The bones were contained within a clay deposit known as the Kimmswick Bone Bed. The clay was likely deposited in a swampy area associated with mineral springs where animals came to drink. In 1979, a Clovis projectile point was excavated at the site, establishing the coexistence of humans and mastodons in eastern North America at the end of Pleistocene time, about 12,000 years ago.

Paleozoic Rocks between Arnold and Cape Girardeau

With the exception of one roadcut in Devonian rocks and a few in Mississippian, most roadcuts between Arnold and Cape Girardeau are in Ordovician rocks. The highway is located along the contact between Middle and Late Ordovician beds for much of the way. The Middle Ordovician rocks are mainly dolomites belonging to the Powell Dolomite and Everton Formation, which are more or less equivalent to the upper part of the Jefferson City (or Cotter) Dolomite on the Salem Plateau. I have included these two formations as part of the Jefferson City Dolomite on the road guide maps.

In this part of the state, deposition of the St. Peter Sandstone was followed by deposition of the Joachim Dolomite, Plattin Limestone, Decorah Shale, Kimmswick Limestone, Maquoketa Shale, and Girardeau Limestone. I've included photos of some of the more interesting and instructive roadcuts along I-55.

The Bushberg Sandstone of Devonian age is present in a roadcut along the southbound lanes at mile marker 185.8. Unconformities separate this yellowish brown sandstone from both the older Maquoketa Shale beneath and the younger Mississippian Bachelor and Fern Glen Formations above. Sandstone of the Bachelor Formation is the oldest Mississippian rock here.

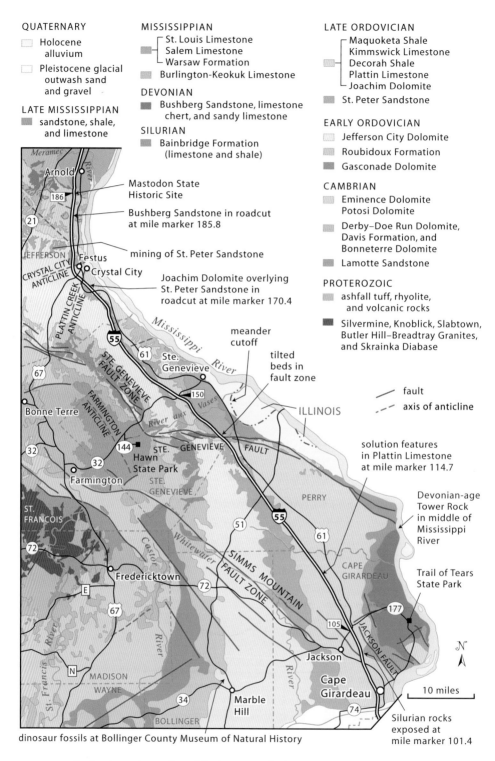

QUATERNARY

- ☐ Holocene alluvium
- ☐ Pleistocene glacial outwash sand and gravel

LATE MISSISSIPPIAN

- ▨ sandstone, shale, and limestone

MISSISSIPPIAN

- ▨ ⎡ St. Louis Limestone
  ⎢ Salem Limestone
  ⎣ Warsaw Formation
- ▨ Burlington-Keokuk Limestone

DEVONIAN

- ▨ Bushberg Sandstone, limestone chert, and sandy limestone

SILURIAN

- ▨ Bainbridge Formation (limestone and shale)

LATE ORDOVICIAN

- ▨ ⎡ Maquoketa Shale
  ⎢ Kimmswick Limestone
  ⎢ Decorah Shale
  ⎢ Plattin Limestone
  ⎣ Joachim Dolomite
- ▨ St. Peter Sandstone

EARLY ORDOVICIAN

- ▨ Jefferson City Dolomite
- ▨ Roubidoux Formation
- ▨ Gasconade Dolomite

CAMBRIAN

- ▨ Eminence Dolomite Potosi Dolomite
- ▨ Derby–Doe Run Dolomite, Davis Formation, and Bonneterre Dolomite
- ▨ Lamotte Sandstone

PROTEROZOIC

- ▨ ashfall tuff, rhyolite, and volcanic rocks
- ▨ Silvermine, Knoblick, Slabtown, Butler Hill–Breadtray Granites, and Skrainka Diabase

Mastodon State Historic Site

Bushberg Sandstone in roadcut at mile marker 185.8

mining of St. Peter Sandstone

Joachim Dolomite overlying St. Peter Sandstone in roadcut at mile marker 170.4

meander cutoff

tilted beds in fault zone

— fault

– – – axis of anticline

solution features in Plattin Limestone at mile marker 114.7

Devonian-age Tower Rock in middle of Mississippi River

Trail of Tears State Park

10 miles

N

Silurian rocks exposed at mile marker 101.4

dinosaur fossils at Bollinger County Museum of Natural History

Bedrock geology along I-55 between St. Louis and Cape Girardeau.

In this roadcut along the southbound lanes of I-55 at mile marker 185.8, the Maquoketa Shale of Ordovician age is at the bottom, the Bushberg Sandstone of Devonian age is the yellowish brown bed in the middle of the cut, and the Bachelor and Fern Glen Formations of Mississippian age are on top. Unconformities separate the rocks of different ages.

Ordovician St. Peter Sandstone (bottom half of cut) and Joachim Dolomite (at the top) are exposed in this roadcut along the southbound lanes of I-55 at mile marker 170.4. This view is to the north from the northbound lanes of the highway. The St. Peter Sandstone is crossbedded, which causes it to weather and fracture on rounded surfaces, imparting an almost flowing appearance to the rock.

Late Ordovician Kimmswick Limestone and Decorah Shale (at highway level) are in roadcuts near mile marker 183.7. This photo was taken at the middle of the cut along the southbound lanes.

The Powell Dolomite of Early Ordovician age is exposed in roadcuts between mile markers 166 and 156. This cut is along the southbound lanes near mile marker 163.3.

The Plattin Limestone is one of the Late Ordovician rocks exposed along I-55. This cut is near Cape Girardeau at mile marker 114.7. Groundwater erosion has widened joints in the rock.

Hawn State Park and Pickle Springs Natural Area

Hawn State Park is a great place to see some of Missouri's oldest rocks. The park is located about 11 miles west of I-55 on MO 32 (at exit 150) and then south on MO 144. Outcrops of Lamotte Sandstone of Cambrian age cap the hills. Proterozoic Butler Hill Granite and Hawn Park Gneiss are in the bed of Pickle Creek, a tributary to the River aux Vases.

The Hawn Park Gneiss is the only metamorphic rock known to outcrop in Missouri, and its origin and identification remain somewhat speculative. Its age—about 1.5 billion years—makes it slightly older than the Butler Hill Granite. It is probably a piece of a much larger mass of basement rock that broke off when magma intruded through it and transported it closer to the surface.

Hawn State Park is within a large outcrop area of Lamotte Sandstone, one of the Cambrian rocks that was deposited directly on the eroded surface of Proterozoic rock. The sandstone is usually tan or brown and is sometimes crossbedded. Its grain size varies. In places the lowermost beds of Lamotte are conglomerate, containing cobbles and pebbles of weathered igneous rocks. Grain size decreases upward to fine sand, and the composition becomes less variable, consisting of mostly quartz grains. The sediment composing the rock washed off adjacent highlands. Most of the sand appears to have come from near its deposition area, but some mineral analyses indicate that at least some of the sediment may have originated as far away as the area around Lake Superior.

You can see erosional features in the sandstone at the Chimney Rocks area in Hawn State Park and even more erosional features, including rock shelters, ledges, and arches, at Pickle Springs Natural Area, which is just west of Hawn State Park. Arches formed in the Lamotte when a narrow ridge of sandstone weathered on both sides and eroded from both directions, most likely due to loosening of sand grains over time by freeze-thaw cycles and seeping groundwater. Eventually, the ridge was breached, leaving a passageway through the remaining rock. To reach the natural area, follow MO 32 west of Hawn State Park to Ste. Genevieve County Route AA. Turn south and, after 1 mile, turn left on Dorlac Road.

Illinois West of the Mississippi River

Four miles east of I-55 on MO 32 (exit 150), you will find Ste. Genevieve, the earliest settlement in Missouri, established by French traders in 1732. About 7 miles south on US 61 is the town of St. Mary, once known as Ste. Maries Landing for its location on the west bank of a broad, sweeping meander of the Mississippi River. In fact, an entrepreneur purchased the town site in 1839 with the idea of making it a major river port.

But if you want to see the river today, bring good eyes or a pair of binoculars. It's 4 miles to the east. What started as a promising business venture in 1839 was literally cut short by the Mississippi River, which altered its course in 1881, breaching the neck of the meander, stranding part of Illinois west of the river, and leaving St. Mary on an oxbow.

Ste. Genevieve Fault Zone

At Ste. Genevieve County Route Z, I-55 crosses the Ste. Genevieve Fault Zone, one of the most complex fault zones in Missouri. The main rupture, called the Ste. Genevieve Fault, is crossed at about the overpass, but the zone contains a set of fault segments that extends for at least 50 miles northwest and 30 miles southeast of I-55. Although the Ste. Genevieve Fault is not exposed along the interstate, its presence is revealed in the juxtaposition of Late Mississippian beds on the north side of the Route Z overpass and St. Peter Sandstone of Late Ordovician age on the south side. Along the southbound lanes of I-55, the Mississippian rocks in the fault zone are tilted and broken.

Mississippian limestone beds in the Ste. Genevieve Fault Zone are tilted and broken in roadcuts north of the fault. This cut is along the ramp from southbound I-55 to Route Z in Ste. Genevieve County. The overpass provides a good view of the rocks on both sides of the fault.

The fault—like others in the state—is likely connected to an older fault system in Proterozoic rocks deep beneath the surface. The way in which the Paleozoic rocks at the surface moved suggests they were squeezed by tectonic forces from the northeast and southwest. The Ordovician rocks south of the fault were pushed to the north on a southward dipping, low-angle thrust fault. There were at least two major episodes of movement along this fault, one during Late Mississippian time and a second in Late Pennsylvanian time. Some geologists think that the fault might have formed as early as Cambrian time. The forces involved in the large displacement along the thrust fault were probably generated by plate collisions associated with assembly of Pangea in Pennsylvanian time.

Tower Rock

Tower Rock, a landmark for early travelers of the Mississippi River, is a mass of Bailey Limestone of Devonian age that protrudes about 90 feet above the water. The rock and adjacent land in Missouri are protected as the Tower Rock Natural Area. From Uniontown on US 61 east of I-55, head east on Perry County Route A. Go 5 miles past Altenburg and look for a sign. The landmark is also called Grand Tower.

Dinosaur Fossils at Marble Hill

Exit 99 or 105 at Jackson takes you to MO 34, which is the shortest route to Marble Hill, where Missouri's dinosaur fossils are on display at the Bollinger County Museum of Natural History. It's out of the way but well worth the trip, especially if you have a young (or old) dinophile in the vehicle. Missouri's first dinosaur bones were found in 1942 in some Cretaceous clay deposits in Bollinger County. The bones belonged to a duck-billed dinosaur called *Hypsibema missouriense*. The site has since yielded fossils of several other dinosaurs, as well as turtles, amphibians, and fish.

Tower Rock, a bedrock island in the channel of the Mississippi River near Altenburg, was used as a landmark by early travelers. It is composed of Bailey Limestone of Devonian age. —Missouri Department of Natural Resources photo

A crowd of geologists peer into the excavation pit at the Chronister site in Bollinger County. Although the site is not open to the public, many of the fossils found there are on display at the Bollinger County Museum of Natural History in Marble Hill.

Trail of Tears State Park

At mile marker 101.4, Silurian shale and limestone beds of the Bainbridge Formation are in the overgrown roadcut along the northbound lanes. These beds are at the southern end of the Simms Mountain Fault Zone and tilt to the south due to movements along the nearby Jackson Fault. You can see more Bainbridge Formation rocks, as well as Devonian limestone beds, on the drive to and in Trail of Tears State Park. MO 177 (exit 105) will take you to the park through the outcrop area. Devonian limestone beds are exposed in bluffs along the river in the park. The park preserves the location where nine of thirteen groups of Cherokee Indians crossed the river during the winter of 1838–1839 during their forced relocation.

US 50
Sedalia—Jefferson City
61 MILES
See map on page 179.

Sedalia is on the eastern edge of the Osage Plains. Mississippian limestone beds are present in the roadcuts between Sedalia and Otterville. Folded beds of Early Mississippian limestone are along both sides of US 50 about 0.5 mile west of the MO 135 (south) junction (38.690N 93.050W). The oldest Mississippian rocks in this part of Missouri are the Compton Limestone, Sedalia Limestone, and Northview Shale, all combined into the Chouteau Group. The Sedalia Limestone resembles the Compton Limestone.

An anticline arches beds of Mississippian Chouteau Group limestone in a roadcut along the westbound lanes of US 50, 0.5 mile west of Cooper County Route A near Otterville.

East of Otterville, US 50 crosses the northern margin of the Salem Plateau, and the bedrock is predominantly Jefferson City Dolomite of Ordovician age. About 1 mile east of the MO 135 (south) junction, roadcuts on both sides of the highway expose the unconformity between the Jefferson City Dolomite and the Cedar Valley Limestone of Devonian age. The cut along the south side of the highway contains some sandstone that is probably in a filled-sink structure. Because the horizontal bed of Devonian limestone caps the structure, we know that subsidence in the filled sink must have stopped prior to Devonian time.

One mile east of the Lamine River in Morgan County, the roadcut along the eastbound lanes exposes what may be the largest filled-sink structure in the state. The structure, which does not extend across the highway into the roadcut along the westbound lanes, is in the Jefferson City Dolomite and is filled with crossbedded quartz sandstone. The origin and age of the sandstone filling this, and many other similar structures in this part of the state, are still debated. It looks very much like the Ordovician St. Peter Sandstone that outcrops in eastern Missouri, but because the beds in the filled sinks are discontinuous and do not contain fossils, they have not been definitely correlated with that formation. A thin layer of shale lines the eastern edge of the structure.

The unconformity between Ordovician Jefferson City Dolomite (white rock at bottom) and Devonian Cedar Valley Limestone (dark rock on top) is exposed in the roadcuts along US 50 about 1 mile east of the MO 135 (south) junction in Morgan County (38.683N 93.018W). This photo was taken along the eastbound lane.

More filled-sink structures, with their accompanying distorted beds and small faults, appear in roadcuts west of Jefferson City at the interchanges for Cole County Routes T/D and MO 179.

Jefferson City is located at a bend where the Missouri River turns from a southeast to easterly direction. The river's valley from just northwest of Jefferson City to St. Louis predates Pleistocene glaciation. The ice sheet did not push across the valley in eastern Missouri and so did not affect the location of the river as it did farther west. That said, the enormous amounts of water that flowed through the valley as the glaciers melted certainly eroded it wider and deeper than it would otherwise have been. In downtown Jefferson City, the plaza north of the capitol building provides a nice view of the Missouri River. Access to the plaza is from Broadway or Jefferson Street.

A roadcut along the westbound lanes of US 50 at Cole County Route D shows the contact between beds of Ordovician Jefferson City Dolomite (left) that were dragged down as a filled-sink structure formed, and the crossbedded sandstone (right) that fills the center of the structure.

View of the Missouri River from the observation plaza north of the capitol building in Jefferson City.

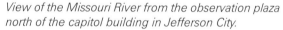

The capitol building in Jefferson City was constructed from Carthage Marble, a pure limestone layer in the Warsaw Formation mined at Carthage, Missouri. Fossil brachiopods, crinoids, gastropods, and blastoids are visible in the rock, both inside and outside. —Hylan Beydler photo, Missouri Department of Natural Resources

US 50
Jefferson City—Interstate 44
82 MILES

Between the US 54 and US 63 junctions (east Jefferson City), the rock exposed in roadcuts along US 50 is Jefferson City Dolomite, except for a sandstone bed that appears at the top of roadcuts along the north side of the highway just west of the Moreau River. Is this another filled-sink structure? Maybe, but although it looks similar, it does not share many physical characteristics with the filled-sink sandstone. For example, there is no clay-filled contact between this bed and the dolomite. The Jefferson City Dolomite shows no signs of compression or drag folding. And the sandstone is uniform in thickness, although it is apparently discontinuous because it is not in the roadcut across the highway. Some geologists have proposed that this sandstone may be an undisturbed layer of the sandstone that occupies filled-sink structures elsewhere, perhaps even the St. Peter Sandstone. Others suggest that it may be a sandy bed in Cedar Valley Limestone of Devonian age.

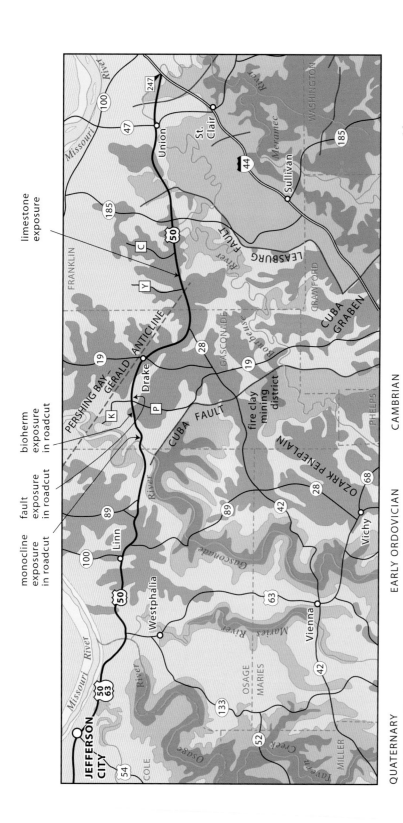

Bedrock geology along US 50 between Jefferson City and the I-44 junction.

QUATERNARY
- Holocene alluvium

PENNSYLVANIAN
- unnamed sandstone, shale and limestone

EARLY ORDOVICIAN
- Jefferson City Dolomite
- Roubidoux Formation
- Gasconade Dolomite

CAMBRIAN
- Eminence and Potosi Dolomites
- fault
- axis of anticline

N

10 miles

Between the Gasconade River and Drake, roadcuts reveal a suite of geologic features in the Jefferson City Dolomite. From west to east they are:

A type of fold called a *monocline* just east of the Gasconade River

A large stromatolite bioherm in the cut about 0.7 mile west of Gasconade County Routes K and P (38.480N 91.562W)

A fault at the west end of the cut just east of Second Creek (about 0.8 mile east of Routes K and P)

In eastern Gasconade County and western Franklin County, roughly the 31 miles between the valley of Schulte Creek and Franklin County Route BB, US 50 follows ridges capped by Pennsylvanian limestone, shale, and sandstone. The younger rocks are in direct contact with underlying Ordovician rocks, so the unconformity spans at least 150 million years. The Pennsylvanian rocks are not dated too precisely, so geologists don't know exactly when they were deposited; the best guess is Middle to Late Pennsylvanian time. Good exposures are east of Drake, especially between the intersections of Routes Y and C in Franklin County. See **Interstate-44: Rolla—St. Louis** for further discussion of these Pennsylvanian sediments.

East of Franklin County Route BB, the Jefferson City Dolomite appears again, and it lines US 50 between Union and the junction with I-44.

The rusty brown sandstone bed at the top of this roadcut along the westbound lanes of US 50 west of the Moreau River may be an undisturbed layer of the sandstone that occupies filled sinks elsewhere, or a sandy bed in the Cedar Valley Limestone of Devonian age (38.541N 92.111W).

monocline

This roadcut in Jefferson City Dolo-mite along the westbound lane of US 50 just east of the Gascon-ade River in Gasconade County exposes a monocline, *a fold in which an otherwise horizontal layer of rock bends in one direction.*

Beds in the Jefferson City Dolomite wrap around a large stromatolite bioherm in the roadcut west of Routes K and P (38.480N 91.562W) in Gasconade County.

These limestone beds are in a roadcut about 2 miles east of Route Y (at Gerald) and 2 miles west of Route C, in Franklin County (38.415N 92.303W). Although they are exposed in the area where Pennsylvanian beds are present on hilltops, their exact age is not established.

Sagging beds of Pennsylvanian sandstone and shale along US 50 about 0.8 mile west of Route C in Franklin County may sit atop a filled sink. Large fragments of loose rock obscure the beds in places.

US 54
Preston—Jefferson City
83 MILES

Preston is near the western edge of the Salem Plateau, and the bedrock is Jefferson City Dolomite to about 5 miles east of the US 65 junction. But between that point and the MO 52 junction near Eldon, erosion has removed the younger Jefferson City Dolomite beds, and downcutting by tributaries of the Osage River has exposed the oldest Ordovician rocks in Missouri: the Roubidoux Formation and Gasconade Dolomite. The latter appears at lower elevations near streams.

About 1.5 miles west of the Niangua Arm of Lake of the Ozarks, near Lake Road 54-81, drag-folded beds of Gasconade Dolomite are exposed in the roadcut along the westbound lane. The Red Arrow Fault, which produced the dipping beds, is one of many northwest-southeast-trending normal faults that produce stair-step offsets of beds on both flanks of the Proctor Anticline, the axis of which crosses the highway near the town of Linn Creek. The anticline, with its flanking faults, is a result of drape folding in overlying rocks caused by vertical movements in blocks of deeper Proterozoic rocks.

Beds of Eminence Dolomite of Cambrian age are in the roadcuts at the bottom of the hill, near the Niangua Arm bridge. These cherty dolomite beds were deposited in very Late Cambrian time, just prior to the withdrawal of the Cambrian sea from the continental platform. They are the only Cambrian

Dipping beds of Gasconade Dolomite mark the Red Arrow Fault near Lake Road 54-81, about 1.5 miles west of the Niangua Arm of Lake of the Ozarks. The layers were tilted by drag folding along the fault.

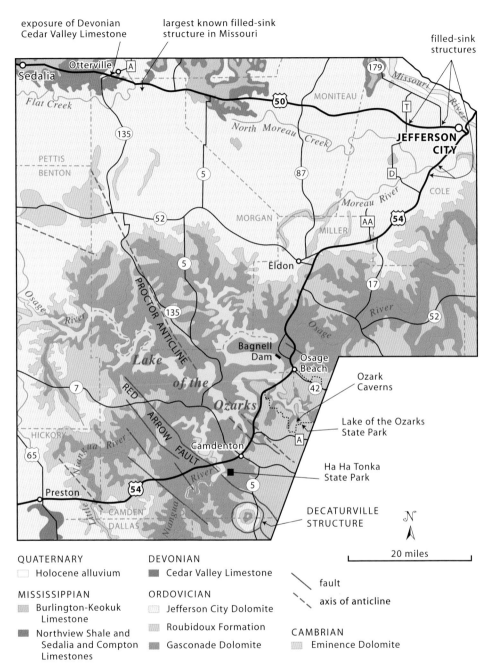

exposure of Devonian
Cedar Valley Limestone

largest known filled-sink
structure in Missouri

filled-sink
structures

Otterville
Sedalia
A
179
Missouri River
MONITEAU
50
JEFFERSON CITY
T
North Moreau Creek
Flat Creek
135
5
87
D
PETTIS
BENTON
COLE
52
MORGAN
AA
54
MILLER
Moreau River
5
Eldon
17
135
River
52
Osage River
Osage
Lake
Bagnell
Dam
Osage Beach
of the
42
Ozark
Caverns
7
Ozarks
Lake of the Ozarks
State Park
PROCTOR ANTICLINE
HICKORY
A
RED ARROW FAULT
Camdenton
65
Ha Ha Tonka
State Park
Niangua River
54
Preston
5
Niangua River
Little
CAMDEN
DALLAS
DECATURVILLE
STRUCTURE

N

20 miles

QUATERNARY
☐ Holocene alluvium

MISSISSIPPIAN
▧ Burlington-Keokuk
   Limestone
■ Northview Shale and
   Sedalia and Compton
   Limestones

DEVONIAN
■ Cedar Valley Limestone

ORDOVICIAN
▧ Jefferson City Dolomite
▧ Roubidoux Formation
■ Gasconade Dolomite

╲ fault
╱ axis of anticline

CAMBRIAN
▧ Eminence Dolomite

*Bedrock geology along US 50 between Sedalia and Jefferson
City and along US 54 between Preston and Jefferson City.*

rocks along US 54 and the oldest outcropping in the western Ozarks. The rock layers seen here also are exposed in two nearby state parks that feature karst topography.

Ha Ha Tonka State Park

Ha Ha Tonka State Park is located along the east side of the Niangua Arm south of Camdenton. The park features sinkholes, a natural bridge, caves, and the state's twelfth largest spring. Take Route D south off US 54 (the turn is at the top of the hill east of the Niangua Arm) and go about 1.4 miles, following signs, to the park visitor center.

Eminence Dolomite of Cambrian age is in the roadcuts along both lanes of US 54 where the highway crosses the Niangua Arm of the Lake of the Ozarks. This photo was taken looking west from the bridge (at Lake Road 54-80).

Ha Ha Tonka Spring is Missouri's twelfth largest in terms of flow volume. Groundwater reaches the surface through solution-enlarged tunnels in the Eminence Dolomite of Cambrian age. The hollow into which the spring discharges is a collapsed cave passage.

Natural Bridge at Ha Ha Tonka State Park is the remaining part of the roof of a collapsed cave. The former cave is in Eminence Dolomite of Cambrian age, and the top of the bridge is Gasconade Dolomite of Ordovician age.

The bluffs along the Niangua Arm of Lake of the Ozarks in Ha Ha Tonka State Park reveal Ordovician and Cambrian rocks. Gasconade Dolomite of Ordovician age caps the bluff. The Gunter Sandstone Member, found at the base of the Gasconade, is the light-colored bed. Eminence Dolomite of Cambrian age is beneath the Gunter, to the waterline.

Decaturville Structure

Another of Missouri's likely impact structures, the Decaturville Structure, is about 5 miles southeast of its Camdenton on MO 5. At only 5 miles in diameter, this structure is considerably smaller than the Weaubleau-Osceola Structure to the west. It is not well expressed topographically, but it has similar features, and the ring shape of its rock outcrops show up on geologic maps, suggesting a meteorite impact origin. Steeply dipping beds of rock on the east flank of the structure are exposed in roadcuts along MO 5 just south of Decaturville. Outside the structure, Gasconade Dolomite and Roubidoux Formation of Early Ordovician age are undisturbed, and the depth to Proterozoic rocks is about 1,400 feet. At the center are broken beds of Late Ordovician Plattin and Kimmswick Limestones. Bonneterre Dolomite of Cambrian age is also found there.

As with each of the six cryptoexplosive structures in Missouri, the Decaturville seems to present unique geology. Drilling and outcrops at the center of this one reveal a block of very coarse-grained Proterozoic granite, called *pegmatite*, about 300 feet thick sitting on top of Eminence Dolomite. This rock is too old to have solidified from molten material formed at impact. Most likely the rebound caused by the force of the meteorite impact sent a piece of deeply buried pegmatite up from below. The age of the event has not been determined but is definitely post-Mississippian and perhaps as recent as Permian time.

Be aware that local landowners are notoriously vigilant for trespassers, so please keep viewing to the roadside.

Lake of the Ozarks State Park

Lake of the Ozarks State Park, at nearly 17,500 acres, is the largest in Missouri's park system. The park was established by the national park system in the mid-1930s, shortly after the completion of Bagnell Dam, and turned over to the state in 1946. The park is in an area known as the Osage River Hills and straddles the Grand Glaize Arm.

Bagnell Dam, a hydroelectric dam, impounds the Lake of the Ozarks. The concrete arch dam, which was completed in 1931, spans the Osage River. It is 0.5 mile wide and 148 feet tall and required over 500,000 cubic yards of concrete. Twenty thousand men, most of whom were part of the Civilian Conservation Corps, working twenty-four hours a day, seven days a week, completed the dam in under two years. Eight hydroelectric generators within the dam produce 215 megawatts of electric power.

The Lake of the Ozarks, which is the largest lake in Missouri and the largest non-flood-control reservoir in the United States, has nearly 90 square miles of surface area. It has approximately 1,200 miles of shoreline (estimates vary from 1,150 to 1,300) and inundates 92 linear miles of the Osage River valley. The valleys of three tributary streams to the Osage River—the Niangua River, Grand Glaize Creek, and Gravois Creek—are now arms of the lake.

Ozark Caverns is at the south end of Lake of the Ozarks State Park. Formed in the Gasconade Dolomite, the cave is famous for its stalagmites and stalactites and the Angel Showers, a place where groundwater continuously rains down from the cave ceiling. Footprints and claw marks left behind by animals in Pleistocene time remain on the cave walls. To reach the cave, take Camden County Route A (at the town of Linn Creek) east from US 54 for about 6.5 miles to McCubbins Drive/A33. Go north (left) on McCubbins another 0.7 mile to Ozark Caverns Drive to the east (right). Follow that road down the hill to the visitor center. The cave is open from mid-April to mid-October, when it closes for the bat hibernation season.

Eldon to Jefferson City

Between Eldon and Jefferson City, the only place where rocks are not the Jefferson City Dolomite is on the narrow ridge between the junctions of Miller County Route AA and MO 17, where weathered ledges that just barely jut from the soil are Mississippian limestone.

Between MO 17 and the Moreau River valley south of Jefferson City, several roadcuts expose filled sinks in the Jefferson City Dolomite. The best one is along the northbound lanes of US 54 about 3 miles north of Cole County Route D (0.75 mile south of the Moreau River). The dolomite beds at the north end of the roadcut dip to the south toward the structure, which is filled with Pennsylvanian sandstone. Another good example of a filled sink is in the roadcut west of the highway about 0.5 mile north of the Moreau River.

Beds in the Jefferson City Dolomite dip into a filled sink along the northbound lanes of US 54 about 0.75 mile south of the Moreau River in Cole County. The sandstone filling the structure is at the right side of the photo, which was taken looking to the south.

US 60
Poplar Bluff—Springfield
183 MILES

Between Poplar Bluff and Van Buren, roadcuts reveal sandstone and dolomite beds of the Roubidoux Formation. As the iron in the beds weathers, it stains them reddish orange. The soil that forms from this rock has the same color and contains abundant amounts of chert gravel. Recent highway construction has created many fresh roadcuts in this interval, but many of them are graded slopes lacking nice ledges of rock (rats!). Rock is graded when it is too unstable to stand in vertical cuts or where buying more right-of-way to accommodate wider benches is too costly.

West of the junction with MO 21 North and MO 34, the topography becomes a bit hillier through the rest of northern Carter County due to erosion by the

Between its junctions with MO 21 North and South, US 60 has several roadcuts that consist only of graded slopes and lack the rock ledges typical of most Missouri roadcuts.

Fortunately, the Missouri Highway Department didn't grade all of the roadcuts along US 60. Dolomite and sandstone in the Roubidoux Formation are exposed in this cut along the westbound lanes of US 60 east of Van Buren (37.039N 90.946W).

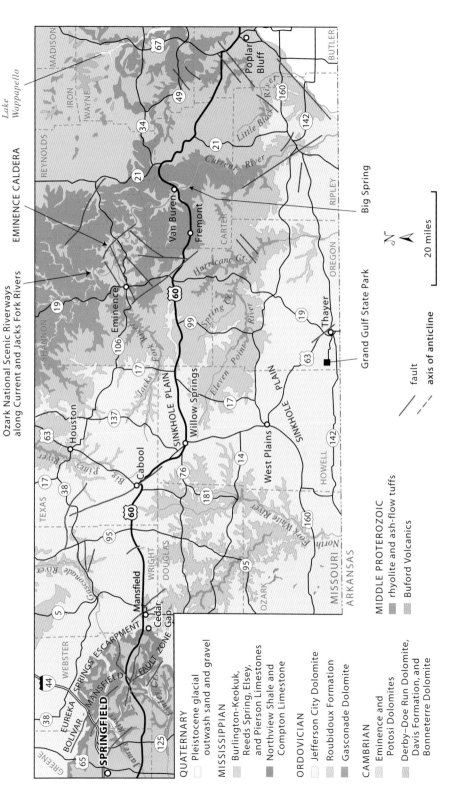

Bedrock geology along US 60 between Poplar Bluff and Springfield.

Ozark National Scenic Riverways
along Current and Jacks Fork Rivers

EMINENCE CALDERA

Big Spring

Grand Gulf State Park

QUATERNARY
Pleistocene glacial
outwash sand and gravel

MISSISSIPPIAN
Burlington-Keokuk,
Reeds Spring, Elsey,
and Pierson Limestones
Northview Shale and
Compton Limestone

ORDOVICIAN
Jefferson City Dolomite
Roubidoux Formation
Gasconade Dolomite

CAMBRIAN
Eminence and
Potosi Dolomites
Derby–Doe Run Dolomite,
Davis Formation, and
Bonneterre Dolomite

MIDDLE PROTEROZOIC
rhyolite and ash-flow tuffs
Buford Volcanics

fault
axis of anticline

20 miles

N

MISSOURI
ARKANSAS

Lake
Wappapello

MADISON
IRON
WAYNE
REYNOLDS
SHANNON
TEXAS
WEBSTER
GREENE
WRIGHT
DOUGLAS
OZARK
HOWELL
OREGON
RIPLEY
CARTER
BUTLER

Poplar
Bluff

Van Buren
Fremont

Eminence

Houston
Caboool
Willow Springs
West Plains
Thayer

Mansfield
Cedar Gap

SPRINGFIELD

SINKHOLE PLAIN
SINKHOLE PLAIN

BOLIVAR – MANSFIELD
FAULT ZONE

EUREKA SPRINGS ESCARPMENT

MANSFIELD

Current River
Little Black River
Jacks Fork
Hurricane Cr.
Spring Creek
Eleven Point River
North Fork White River
Big Piney River
Gasconade River
James River

67
49
34
21
21
19
106
60
99
17
137
76
181
14
95
63
38
17
5
44
38
65
125
160
142
160
19
63
142
95

Current River and its tributaries. The scenic rivers in this part of Missouri are popular for canoeing. They flow to the south and southeast in deeply incised valleys on the southern flank of the Ozark Dome.

Ozark National Scenic Riverways

Ozark National Scenic Riverways is a federal preserve protecting two pristine rivers: the Current and its main tributary, the Jacks Fork. The preserve extends from the headwaters of the Current River at Montauk State Park to south of Van Buren. Cambrian dolomite—the Potosi and Eminence—are exposed in the valleys of these two rivers. They appear at river level along the Current River from near Cedar Grove (just downstream from Montauk State Park) to about 5 miles south of Van Buren. South of that point, Ordovician dolomite lines the river. The new highway bridge at Van Buren takes you over the Cambrian rocks. The Ordovician Gasconade Dolomite caps the bluffs at Van Buren. The upstream reaches of the Jacks Fork River cut through Ordovician rocks, but Cambrian rocks appear downstream of the town of Eminence to the confluence with the Current River.

Located on a tributary to the Current River, Big Spring (36.952N 90.884W) is Missouri's largest. Average daily flow exceeds 270 million gallons. Studies of the recharge area have shown that water comes from as far away as 50 miles, giving it one of the longest recharge flow paths known in the United States. To

Gasconade Dolomite of Ordovician age lines US 60 at the bridge over the Current River at Van Buren. Cambrian dolomite is below the bridge, at river level but not visible in this photo.

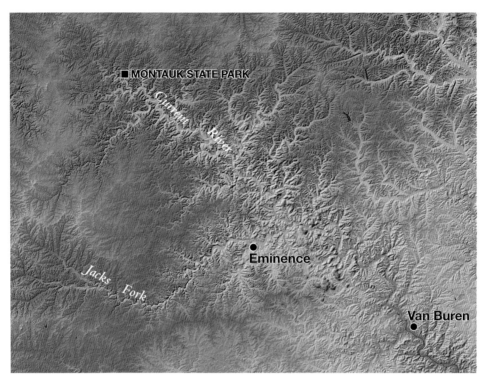

Shaded-relief image of the Ozark National Scenic Riverways area. Note the knobs of rhyolite east of Eminence. —Shaded-relief base map from EROS Data Center

reach the Big Spring area of the Ozark National Scenic Riverways, take MO 103 south from US 60 for about 4 miles and follow the signs to the parking lot and trailhead.

Proterozoic volcanic rocks form knobs, including Coot Mountain, near the confluence of the Current and Jacks Fork Rivers. As in the St. Francois Mountains, the silica-rich rhyolitic rock is more resistant to erosion than the surrounding sedimentary rock. These knobs are the southernmost igneous rock outcrops in Missouri and are part of the Eminence Caldera, one of the Proterozoic volcanic eruption centers. The movement of magma to the surface here seems to be associated with the faults that bound the Missouri Gravity Low. To reach the area, take MO 19 north from US 60 at Winona. At Eminence, turn east on MO 106.

Van Buren to Springfield

Gasconade Dolomite continues along the highway between Van Buren and Fremont (Carter County Route J). Across most of Shannon County, bedrock is Roubidoux Formation. Jefferson City Dolomite caps ridges east of Birch Tree and near the Shannon-Howell county line. Between Mountain View and Cedar Gap, the highway crosses the rolling plains of the southern Salem Plateau, with Jefferson City Dolomite at the surface. This part of the plateau has many sinkholes scattered across it, though they are not generally visible from the highway.

There are few roadcuts east of Cabool, but between Cabool and Cedar Gap are cuts revealing the Jefferson City Dolomite. The junction with MO 5 North is at the south end of the Bolivar-Mansfield Fault Zone, one of the large faults in the Paleozoic rocks.

You encounter the Eureka Springs Escarpment just east of Cedar Gap (about 0.75 mile east of Wright County Route O), where the highway traverses a moderate slope as it crosses the boundary between the Salem Plateau and the slightly

Rolling plains typify the topography on the southern Salem Plateau, as here on US 60 west of Montier in western Shannon County.

The Eureka Springs Escarpment rises in the distance. View looking west, 3 miles west of MO 5 South and 1.4 miles east of Wright County Route O (37.101N 92.651W). The rock in the right foreground is Jefferson City Dolomite, while the rocks at the top of the escarpment are of Mississippian age.

The oldest Mississippian beds in southwestern Missouri are the Compton Limestone (right) and the Northview Shale (left). This roadcut is along the westbound lanes of US 60 at the Eureka Springs Escarpment, about 0.7 mile east of Wright County Route O (37.112N 92.663W).

higher Springfield Plateau. Shale and limestone beds at the top of the hill are Early Mississippian in age. As the tilted beds of the Ozark Dome erode, the erosional edge of the top layers forms a drop-off called an *escarpment*. Beds that are resistant to erosion tend to form clifflike escarpments. If beds are softer or if sediment collects at an escarpment's base, it may have a more gradual slope.

There are few roadcuts through the Springfield Plateau of Webster County. Reddish orange soil with white chert gravel forms from weathering of iron-rich limestone, which appears in roadcuts between MO 125 and US 65 in Greene County.

US 63
Jefferson City—Cabool
120 MILES

In the 13 miles between downtown Jefferson City and the Osage River crossing, US 63 shares the road with US 50. See **US 50: Jefferson City—Interstate-44** for a description of the geology along this segment. At the Osage River, US 63 turns south across the heart of the Salem Plateau. Between US 50 and I-44 at Rolla, the best roadcuts are in the valley of the Maries River near Westphalia and in the valley of the Gasconade River between Vienna and Vichy. In both valleys, the Roubidoux Formation is exposed, and the Gasconade Dolomite is in the cuts closest to the Gasconade River. The Jefferson City Dolomite is exposed on the uplands in this interval. On a few hilltops and ridges, Pennsylvanian shale, sandstone, or limestone cap the dolomite, but these younger rocks are not very

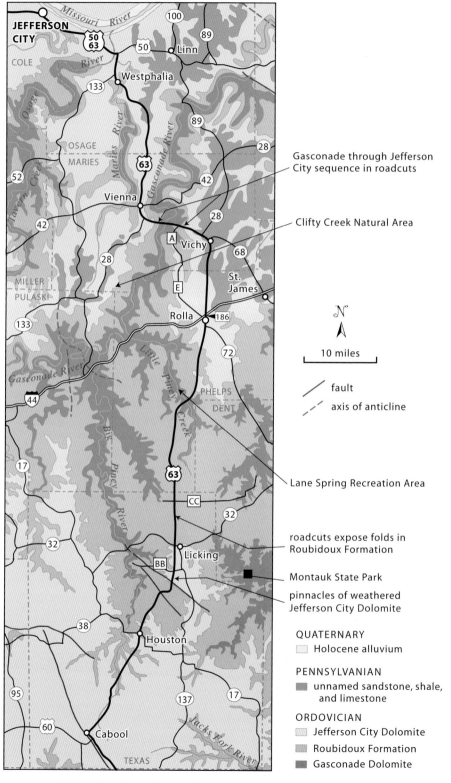

Bedrock geology along US 63 between Jefferson City and Cabool.

The Roubidoux Formation is at road level, and the Jefferson City Dolomite is above the step in the middle of this roadcut along the southbound lanes of US 63 south of the Maries River.

In these beds in the Roubidoux Formation in roadcuts along US 63 south of the Maries River, stromatolitic bioherms have been replaced by chert, which forms almost spherical masses. The silica of the chert replaced the original carbonate mineral that composed the shells.

well exposed in roadcuts. The best glimpses of them are in cuts between Osage County Routes E and JJ, and just north of Vichy.

A sequence of four roadcuts between the MO 28 South junction and the Gasconade River crossing reveals all of the Ordovician dolomite formations of the Salem Plateau: the Jefferson City Dolomite, Roubidoux Formation, and Gasconade Dolomite (from west to east, youngest to oldest, and higher to lower elevations). The Jefferson City Dolomite in the westernmost outcrop contains a suite of interesting structures, including a series of small faults, some solution cavities, and either a fault zone or filled sink.

The Jefferson City Dolomite beds that cap the roadcuts along US 63 about 0.75 mile west of the Gasconade River contain rows of small cavities eroded along bedding planes. The voids might be where chert nodules weathered out of the rocks, or they may be examples of differential weathering, in which more soluble parts of the dolomite were eroded by groundwater. This photo was taken at the roadcut farthest west of the Gasconade River.

fault

A set of small faults offset beds of Jefferson City Dolomite in the second of four roadcuts along US 63 east of the MO 28 South junction. The fault shown here is at the south end of the cut along the northbound lanes about 0.75 mile west of the Gasconade River bridge.

The origin of this zone of jumbled beds in the Jefferson City Dolomite is not clear. It is either a filled sink, collapse structure, or a fault zone. This roadcut is the third cut east of the MO 28 South junction, about 0.4 mile west of the Gasconade River.

The Gasconade Dolomite is in the roadcut in the foreground, and the Jefferson City Dolomite is in the roadcut on the hilltop in the background. The Roubidoux Formation is in the interval without roadcuts in between. Due to movement along a fault, which also crosses in the interval, the upper beds of the Roubidoux and lower beds of the Jefferson City are missing here. This photo is looking west from the Gasconade River bridge on US 63.

This composite photo-graph shows a filled sink in Jefferson City Dolomite along the northbound lane of US 63 halfway between Maries County Route A and MO 28 North (38.133N 91.825W). The sink is filled with jumbled chunks of sandstone and shale.

An unusually large bioherm is visible in the roadcut in Jefferson City Dolomite along the southbound lane of US 63 between Maries County Route A and MO 28 North (38.133N 91.825W). Bioherms vary in size depending on to the amount of fossilized organisms and sediment present.

Beds of Roubidoux sandstone and dolomite are in roadcuts east of the Gasconade River, near the junction with Maries County Route A. About halfway between Route A and the intersection with MO 28 North, a series of roadcuts reveals a filled sink, a bioherm, and folds in the Jefferson City Dolomite. At the east end of this sequence is a roadside park from which you can get a panoramic view of the Gasconade River valley and Salem Plateau. Across from the entrance to this park is a slope that exposes Pennsylvanian shale.

A syncline-anticline pair in Jefferson City Dolomite is exposed in this roadcut along US 63 about 2.8 miles south of Maries County Route A and 1.2 miles north of MO 28 North (38.123N 91.813W).

Clifty Creek Natural Area

Clifty Creek Natural Area, the first designated natural area in Missouri (1971), includes a natural bridge that formed when a tributary of Clifty Creek eroded through a narrow drainage divide in Gasconade Dolomite (38.035N 91.981W). To reach the area, take MO 28 south from US 63 (north of Rolla) about 11 miles to Maries County Route W. Turn east and follow the road, which becomes gravel, to the parking area. A 2.5-mile trail provides scenic views.

Rolla to Cabool

Between Rolla and Cabool, US 63 passes through the upper part of the Gasconade River's drainage basin, crossing or following the valleys of several small tributaries. Rolla is built on Jefferson City Dolomite, and outcrops of those beds continue south to the valley of Beaver Creek. Between there and Licking, the Roubidoux Formation appears on hills and the Gasconade Dolomite in river valleys.

Just south of Rolla, and not far off US 63, Lane Spring Recreation Area along Little Piney Creek provides some geologic scenery in addition to trout fishing. Lane Spring discharges into the bed of Little Piney Creek. The upward water pressure from the spring discharge lifts and churns the sand in the creek bed, creating sand boils and quicksand conditions. A short hike down Blossom Rock Trail takes you to a mound of weathered sandstone, the shape of which conjured up to someone the image of a flower. The sand likely collected in a cave in Gasconade Dolomite. Silica deposited by groundwater cemented the sand, making it more resistant to erosion than the surrounding carbonate rock, which was removed by dissolution.

To reach the campground, go south on US 63 about 4.4 miles from the Phelps County Route W intersection at Vida. Turn west on the forest service road at the big sign. The spring is near the picnic area. To get to Blossom Rock trailhead, turn left at the picnic area and go another 1.3 miles down the road.

In northern Texas County, folded beds in the Roubidoux Formation appear in several roadcuts between Texas County Route CC and the MO 32/MO 137 intersection. These folds might have been caused by tectonic forces, but another possible explanation is that the beds deformed when the underlying dolomite was dissolved and removed by groundwater and the overlying rock sank.

Montauk State Park encompasses the headwaters of the Current River. The discharge from several springs combine with Pigeon Creek to form the river. The park is primarily known for trout fishing. To get to the park, take MO 32 east from US 63 at Licking for about 11 miles. Turn south on MO 119 and go another 10 miles to the park.

Between Licking and Houston, US 63 encounters mostly Roubidoux beds, but some patches of Jefferson City Dolomite are present on ridges. Most of the Jefferson City is poorly exposed, but on the ridge just south of the Texas County

Anticlines and synclines in thin beds of Roubidoux Formation are exposed along the southbound lane of US 63 just south of Route CC in northern Texas County (37.577N 92.863W).

Routes P and BB junction, you can easily see beds along the highway. They are present here because they are on the downdropped side of a fault that US 63 crosses between this hill and Dixon Road (37.429N 91.870W). Roubidoux beds are on the next hill to the south. Another fault crosses the highway in the valley of Arthur Creek, where the Gasconade Dolomite is exposed.

South of Houston, Roubidoux beds are in the valleys of Big Piney River and tributary streams, but elsewhere along this segment roadcuts expose mostly Jefferson City Dolomite.

Jefferson City Dolomite is weathered along joints to form large pinnacles of rock in this roadcut along the southbound lane of US 63, just north of a fault zone that crosses the highway between Licking and Houston (37.445N 91.866W).

Grand Gulf State Park

South of Cabool, US 63 runs atop the Salem Plateau and Jefferson City Dolomite. This part of the plateau contains many sinkholes and caverns, and water infiltrates readily into the groundwater system. Once belowground, it moves south to discharge at Mammoth Spring, which is just (and I do mean *just*) south of the state line, in Arkansas.

Grand Gulf State Park, near the Arkansas border west of Thayer, showcases the region's karst topography, including the largest collapsed cave and natural bridge in the Ozarks. Grand Gulf, the 130-foot-deep chasm, formed around 10,000 years ago when a cave passage collapsed. The small stream at the bottom of the valley still flows through remaining parts of the cave system, carrying water to Mammoth Spring, located about 9 miles to the south. To get to Grand Gulf State Park from US 63 at Thayer, go south on MO 19 (just north of town), then turn right (west) on Oregon County Route W. Drive 6 miles to the parking area. Trails, including one that is wheelchair accessible, lead you to overlooks with interpretive kiosks.

Grand Gulf is a sinkhole valley, also called a polje (pronounced pohl-yeh), that formed when the roof of a cave in the Jefferson City Dolomite collapsed.

US 65
Sedalia—Springfield
120 MILES

Between Sedalia and Preston, at US 54, US 65 is located within the transition between the Salem Plateau and the Osage Plains. Mississippian rocks, in effect a northern extension of the Springfield Plateau, also outcrop here. While the highway runs pretty straight, the contact between Ordovician dolomite and Mississippian limestone winds back and forth across the route. Jefferson City Dolomite outcrops at lower elevations in and near stream valleys, while beds of Mississippian limestone, ranging from Compton to Burlington-Keokuk, cap the hills. Just north of the Pettis-Benton county line, there is even some Pennsylvanian sandstone and shale of the Cherokee Group.

There are few roadcuts between Sedalia and Lincoln, and they generally expose only reddish brown soil containing white chert gravel. Lincoln is known as the home of mozarkite, Missouri's state rock. This colorful variety of chert, which is cut and polished to make jewelry, is found primarily in this part of west-central Missouri in the Ordovician Cotter Dolomite. Near Lincoln, the topography is a bit hillier because US 65 cuts across the valleys of a couple of tributaries of the Osage River rather than following the ridges between them.

Chert gravel from the Cotter Dolomite around Lincoln has been the main source of specimens of Mozarkite. This roadcut is 3 miles north of Lincoln on US 65. —Ken Stalder photo

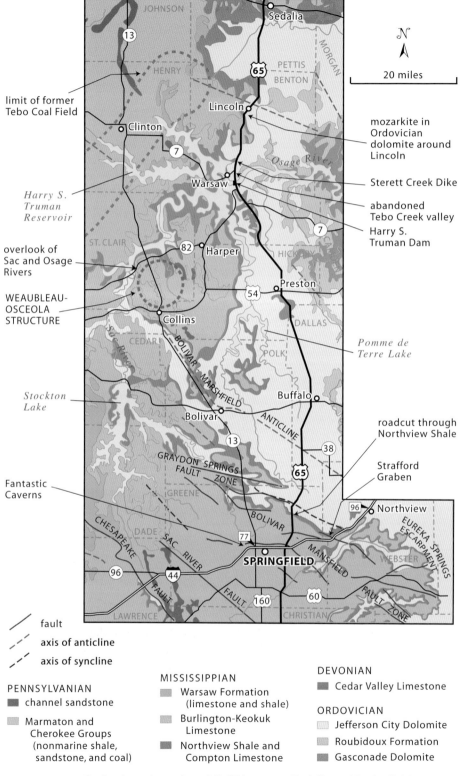

limit of former
Tebo Coal Field

*Harry S.
Truman
Reservoir*

overlook of
Sac and Osage
Rivers

WEAUBLEAU-
OSCEOLA
STRUCTURE

*Stockton
Lake*

Fantastic
Caverns

mozarkite in
Ordovician
dolomite around
Lincoln

Sterett Creek Dike

abandoned
Tebo Creek valley

Harry S.
Truman Dam

*Pomme de
Terre Lake*

roadcut through
Northview Shale

Strafford
Graben

Sedalia

Clinton

Lincoln

Warsaw

Harper

Preston

Collins

Bolivar

Buffalo

Northview

SPRINGFIELD

N

20 miles

JOHNSON

HENRY

PETTIS

BENTON

MORGAN

Osage River

ST. CLAIR

HICKORY

DALLAS

POLK

CEDAR

Sac River

BOLIVAR-MARSHFIELD ANTICLINE

GRAYDON SPRINGS FAULT ZONE

GREENE

DADE

CHESAPEAKE FAULT

SAC RIVER FAULT

LAWRENCE

CHRISTIAN

WEBSTER

EUREKA SPRINGS ESCARPMENT

MANSFIELD FAULT ZONE

fault

axis of anticline

axis of syncline

PENNSYLVANIAN

channel sandstone

Marmaton and
Cherokee Groups
(nonmarine shale,
sandstone, and coal)

MISSISSIPPIAN

Warsaw Formation
(limestone and shale)

Burlington-Keokuk
Limestone

Northview Shale and
Compton Limestone

DEVONIAN

Cedar Valley Limestone

ORDOVICIAN

Jefferson City Dolomite

Roubidoux Formation

Gasconade Dolomite

Bedrock geology along US 65 between Sedalia and Springfield.

Mozarkite, the Missouri state rock, is a type of chert with rust, red, pink, or purple bands, making it a popular stone for use in jewelry.
—Mark Sherwood photo; specimen from the collection of Bruce Stinemetz

Osage River and Harry S. Truman Reservoir

Harry S. Truman Reservoir, the largest flood control reservoir in Missouri, fills the valley of the Osage River and those of three of its major tributaries: the Sac, Pomme de Terre, and Grand Rivers. The dam is over 1 mile long and 126 feet tall. Although under normal conditions the lake is slightly smaller than the Lake of the Ozarks to the east, which has a surface area of about 90 square miles, the reservoir is capable of expanding to more than 300 square miles during heavy rains to help protect the lower Osage and Missouri River valleys against flooding. In addition to its recreational uses, the lake provides hydroelectric power to central Missouri through the six turbine generators in the dam, which are capable of producing 160 megawatts of electricity.

To reach the Harry S. Truman Regional Visitor Center, turn west onto the clearly marked Truman Dam Access Road about 2 miles north of the Osage River. The entrance is about 1.25 miles up this road. The center has several exhibits about hydroelectric power generation and the Pleistocene fossils found in the Osage River valley. Mississippian rocks cap nearby Kaysinger Bluff but are at lake level at the west end of the reservoir. Jefferson City Dolomite is at lake level along the eastern shore. Continuing west on the access road will take you across the dam to the Bledsoe Ferry powerhouse exhibit area.

Long roadcuts in the Jefferson City Dolomite are on both sides of the highway on either side of the Osage River at Warsaw. Tebo Creek, a tributary of the Osage River, once flowed in a valley parallel to and north of the Osage and

Truman Dam (at right) is built below the Harry S. Truman Regional Visitor Center (middle distance), which sits atop Mississippian limestone on Kaysinger Bluff. Rocks at water level and along US 65 north and south of the Osage River are Ordovician dolomite. The Mississippian rocks were deposited directly on the dolomite—there are no Silurian or Devonian rocks separating them. —Ken Stalder photo

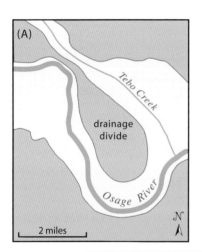

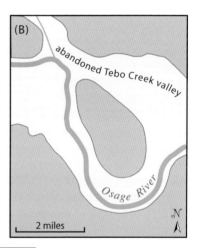

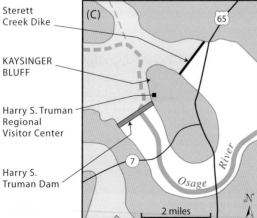

(A) Tebo Creek once flowed parallel to the Osage River, north of the present location of Truman Dam. (B) A meander of the Osage River eroded through the divide separating the rivers, shifting the junction of the two to a location upstream of the original confluence. (C) The abandoned lower Tebo Creek valley remains north of the Osage River. The Sterett Creek Dike blocks the valley west of US 65.

joined it just east of the present US 65 bridge. At some time in the past, the two meandering rivers eroded through the divide separating their valleys at a location about 3.5 miles upstream from their former confluence. The flow in Tebo Creek diverted through this breach, abandoning its valley farther east. This process, called *stream piracy*, is common in the Ozarks, where many rivers have incised deep, meandering valleys.

The confluence of the rivers is now upstream of the dam. But the abandoned Tebo Creek valley remains as the lowland along the east side of the highway north of the Osage River. The Sterett Creek Dike, which parallels the west side of US 65, prevents the lake from draining out through this valley.

In southern Benton County south of MO 7, US 65 crosses uplands east of the Pomme de Terre River that are capped with Mississippian limestone. All that is visible is cherty red soil. Through Hickory and Dallas Counties, the highway is positioned farther east onto the Salem Plateau, and the rocks are Jefferson City Dolomite. At the MO 38 junction, the highway crosses the axis of the Bolivar-Marshfield Anticline, visible in beds of the Jefferson City Dolomite. The fold is located on the east edge of the Bolivar-Mansfield Fault Zone.

The Sterett Creek Dike, which blocks off the former valley of Tebo Creek, runs parallel to US 65 on the west side of the highway north of the Osage River.

US 65 crosses the axis of the Bolivar-Marshfield Anticline just south of the MO 38 junction in Dallas County. Folded beds are in the Jefferson City Dolomite.

US 67
Festus—Poplar Bluff
121 MILES

US 67 skirts the eastern edge of the center of the Ozark Dome, encountering older rocks than those along I-55 to the east. Most of US 67 crosses Ordovician and Cambrian sedimentary rocks, but a short segment clips the easternmost exposures of Missouri's Proterozoic igneous rocks. The regional dip of sedimentary rocks is to the east, but because the highway runs nearly at right angles to the dip, the beds appear horizontal in most roadcuts.

Dolomite and shale beds in the Jefferson City Dolomite appear along both sides of the highway for its entire route through Jefferson County. At the southeast corner of the junction of US 67 with Jefferson County Route V, beds of Jefferson City Dolomite dip south due to movement of rocks on the Ste. Genevieve Fault, which crosses US 67 between here and the St. Francois county line. Through most of St. Francois County, roadcuts reveal Cambrian rocks. North of the St. Francis River, these beds are mostly dolomite deposited in Late Cambrian time.

The Derby–Doe Run Dolomite of Late Cambrian age is exposed along the northbound lanes of US 67 about 1 mile north of Big River (37.997N 90.543W).

Bonne Terre Mine and the Old Lead Belt

Early mining of galena began southwest of St. Louis near St. Clair, where the ore was found in fractures in the Bonneterre Dolomite of Cambrian age. By the mid-1700s, mining shifted south and east to richer deposits in what came to be called the Old Lead Belt, near the towns of Bonne Terre, Mine La Motte, and Potosi. These lead and zinc ores are also in the Bonneterre Dolomite. The mines soon delved belowground as miners followed mineralized fractures. The Bonne Terre Mine was a room-and-pillar mine that operated from 1864 to 1961 and reached a depth of nearly 450 feet. Once the groundwater pumps were turned off, the water table rose almost 300 feet. The Bonne Terre Mine is now a Scuba diving operation, open to the public; walking and boat tours are also available.

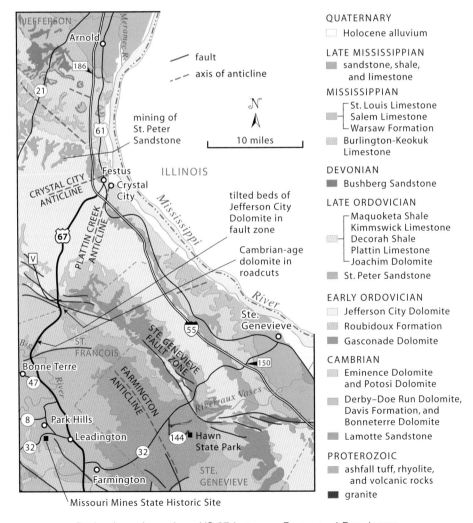

Bedrock geology along US 67 between Festus and Farmington.

Missouri Mines State Historic Site at Park Hills preserves old buildings on the former site of one of Missouri's Old Lead Belt mines.

The mine is west of US 67 off MO 47 in Bonne Terre. Lead production from the Old Lead Belt mines declined through the first half of the twentieth century, and Missouri's production shifted to the Tri-State District in western Missouri.

Missouri Mines State Historic Site

Missouri Mines State Historic Site is in Park Hills, a short drive west of US 67 on MO 32 (at Leadington). It preserves facilities and artifacts of the largest mining and milling facility in the Old Lead Belt. A museum contains examples of machinery used in mining, information on the history of the mining district, and mineral specimens from the local mines and other places in Missouri. St. Joe State Park, named for the company that owned the mine, comprises land donated to the state after mining operations ceased. About 25 percent of the park lies above mined-out rock.

Farmington to Fredericktown

Between Farmington and Fredericktown, US 67 crosses the St. Francis River at two places, about 4 miles apart. The oldest sedimentary rock in the state, the Cambrian Lamotte Sandstone, appears in several roadcuts between the southern St. Francis River bridge and St. Francois County Route DD. The rock is tan-colored, crossbedded, and composed of sand grains weathered from the granite beneath it. Some roadcuts also expose the Great Unconformity, the contact between the 520-million-year-old Lamotte Sandstone and the 1.4-billion-year-old Butler Hill Granite of Proterozoic age.

The Knoblick Granite, one of the ring intrusions of the Butler Hill Caldera, is exposed at the intersection of US 67 with Knob Lick Tower Road. This mass of hard granitic rock forms Knob Lick Mountain to the west of US 67 at this intersection. South of this point, yet another ring intrusion granite—the Slab-town Granite—appears in roadcuts. About 1 mile north of Madison County Route H, diabase dikes are exposed at the north end of the roadcuts on both sides of the road. The dikes intruded along fractures in the Slabtown Granite during Late Proterozoic time. They dip at a high angle to the south, are a few

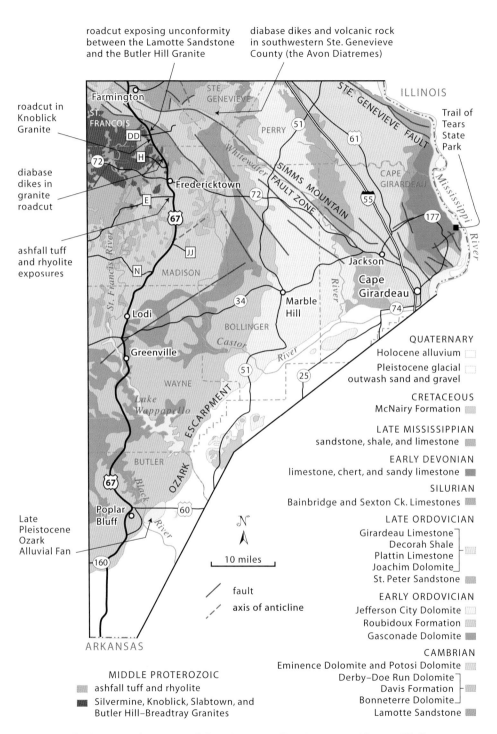

Bedrock geology along US 67 between Farmington and Poplar Bluff.

roadcut exposing unconformity
between the Lamotte Sandstone
and the Butler Hill Granite

diabase dikes and volcanic rock
in southwestern Ste. Genevieve
County (the Avon Diatremes)

roadcut in
Knoblick
Granite

diabase
dikes in
granite
roadcut

ashfall tuff
and rhyolite
exposures

Late
Pleistocene
Ozark
Alluvial Fan

ILLINOIS

Farmington

ST.
FRANCOIS

DD

H

72

Fredericktown

E

67

JJ

N

MADISON

Lodi

Greenville

Lake
Wappapello

WAYNE

BUTLER

67

Poplar
Bluff

160

60

ARKANSAS

STE.
GENEVIEVE

PERRY

51

Whitewater River

SIMMS MOUNTAIN

Whitewater FAULT ZONE

72

34

Marble
Hill

BOLLINGER

Castor River

51

ESCARPMENT

OZARK

Black River

River

STE. GENEVIEVE FAULT

61

CAPE
GIRARDEAU

55

Jackson

Cape
Girardeau

74

25

177

Mississippi River

Trail of
Tears
State
Park

QUATERNARY
Holocene alluvium
Pleistocene glacial
outwash sand and gravel

CRETACEOUS
McNairy Formation

LATE MISSISSIPPIAN
sandstone, shale, and limestone

EARLY DEVONIAN
limestone, chert, and sandy limestone

SILURIAN
Bainbridge and Sexton Ck. Limestones

LATE ORDOVICIAN
Girardeau Limestone
Decorah Shale
Plattin Limestone
Joachim Dolomite
St. Peter Sandstone

EARLY ORDOVICIAN
Jefferson City Dolomite
Roubidoux Formation
Gasconade Dolomite

CAMBRIAN
Eminence Dolomite and Potosi Dolomite
Derby–Doe Run Dolomite
Davis Formation
Bonneterre Dolomite
Lamotte Sandstone

N°

10 miles

fault
axis of anticline

MIDDLE PROTEROZOIC
ashfall tuff and rhyolite
Silvermine, Knoblick, Slabtown, and
Butler Hill–Breadtray Granites

This roadcut along the southbound lanes of US 67 just south of the southern St. Francis River bridge is the best roadcut at which to view Missouri's Great Unconformity, which represents nearly 1 billion years of missing rock record. The 520-million-year-old Lamotte Sandstone rests on the 1.4-billion-year-old Butler Hill Granite. The upper foot or two of the granite is composed of loose grains called grus, which was the weathered surface in Proterozoic time (37.704N 90.399W).

inches wide at most, and are somewhat difficult to distinguish from the granite because the latter rock has weathered to a similar color. Geologists think this dike swarm was created by magma that seeped away from the Skrainka Diabase, a thick sill exposed about 1.5 miles southwest of this cut. The sill has a similar mineral composition to the dikes, but it has larger crystals because it cooled slightly slower, allowing the crystals to grow.

Avon Diatremes

A diatreme is a volcanic vent that explosively intruded sedimentary rock layers. The Avon Diatremes are part of the Avon Volcanic District, an area in Ste. Genevieve County about 10 miles southwest of the Ste. Genevieve Fault Zone near Farmington. More than eighty volcanic vents, pipes, and dikes are found here. They were formed sometime around 396 million years ago in Devonian time based on radiometric dating of biotite mica grains in the rocks. Blocks of overlying sedimentary rocks appear to have dropped into the vent structures, which are now entirely filled with breccia composed of both igneous and sedimentary rocks. This area is one of Missouri's cryptoexplosive structures, and

Diabase dikes (dark bands) cut through the slightly older, lighter-colored Slabtown Granite in a roadcut along the west side of US 67 (southbound lanes), 1.2 miles north of the junction with Madison County Route H. Geologists drilled the small holes in the rock to obtain samples for analysis. The hammer is about 12 inches long. —Missouri Department of Natural Resources

the only one that is indisputably volcanic in origin. The composition of the magma suggests it came from a mantle source. Why magma moved to the surface during Devonian time is debated, but it may have been caused by stretching of the crust due to settling in the Illinois Basin to the east. The nearby Ste. Genevieve Fault was reactivated at the same time, when rocks south of the fault dropped down.

Fredericktown to Poplar Bluff

Between Fredericktown (MO 72) and about Greenville (in Wayne County), Cambrian dolomite and shale are exposed along US 67 except at the Madison County Route E interchange, where Proterozoic ashfall tuff is in roadcuts. The Bonneterre Dolomite, Davis Formation, and Derby–Doe Run Dolomite outcrop in the valley of Twelvemile Creek north of Madison County Route JJ. Elsewhere between Fredericktown and Greenville the Eminence and Potosi Dolomites outcrop. South of Greenville, rocks are Ordovician beds of Gasconade Dolomite in the valleys and Roubidoux Formation on the hills. There are few roadcuts, but orange, cherty soil attests to the weathering of iron in the dolomite.

Ashfall tuff, a cemented volcanic ash, is in roadcuts along the ramps at Madison County Route E. This cut is along the northbound ramp to US 67.

Ozarks topography greets the US 67 traveler through southern Madison and northern Wayne Counties, where streams have incised valleys through Cambrian dolomite on the southern flank of the Ozark Dome. View to the north about halfway between Routes JJ and N in southern Madison County.

Poplar Bluff is located near the edge of the Ozark Escarpment, the transition between the Salem Plateau and the alluvial plain of the Mississippi Embayment. The escarpment is south of the US 160 West intersection. Between there and the Arkansas border, the highway crosses the northern margin of the Southeast Lowlands.

View looking north along US 67 (36.645N 90.520W) at the Ozark Escarpment rising in the distance. The escarpment is about 1.3 miles south of the US 160 West junction.

Arcadia Valley Loop through the St. Francois Mountains
60 MILES

You can drive a loop through the scenic center of the St. Francois Mountains, an area known as the Arcadia Valley. The start and end point is the junction of MO 72 and US 67 near Fredericktown. Drive MO 72 from Fredericktown to Ironton. Then, head north on MO 21, turn southwest on County N, then east on MO 49, and retrace your path to Fredericktown on MO 72. If you spend any amount of time at the sites described here, this side trip will take a full day. The geology of the St. Francois Mountains, the center of the Ozark Dome, is discussed in detail at the beginning of this chapter.

Fredericktown to Ironton

Some of the best roadcuts showing the features of the igneous and sedimentary rocks of the St. Francois Mountains are along MO 72 between US 67 and the St. Francis River in northern Madison County. At the highway junction and for another 1.5 miles west, the Bonneterre Dolomite of Cambrian age is exposed in several cuts.

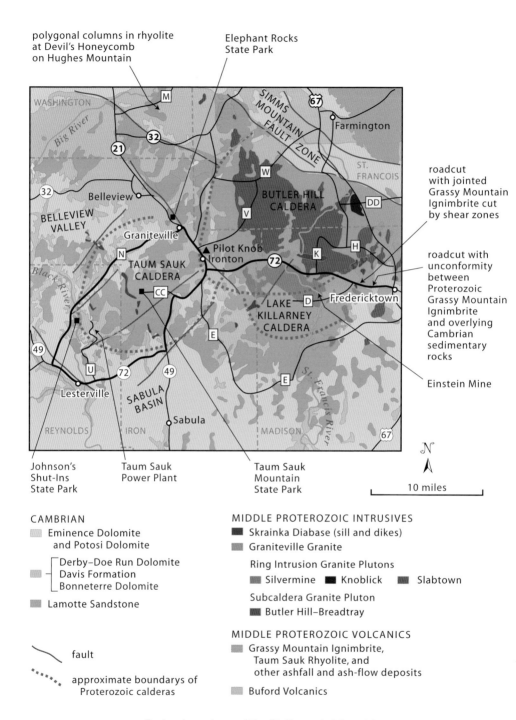

polygonal columns in rhyolite at Devil's Honeycomb on Hughes Mountain

Elephant Rocks State Park

WASHINGTON

Big River

SIMMS MOUNTAIN FAULT ZONE

67

Farmington

ST. FRANCOIS

M

32

21

32

Belleview

BELLEVIEW VALLEY

Graniteville

N

TAUM SAUK CALDERA

Black River

CC

U

72

49

Lesterville

SABULA BASIN

Sabula

REYNOLDS

IRON

W

V

BUTLER HILL CALDERA

DD

Pilot Knob
Ironton

72

K

H

D

Fredericktown

LAKE KILLARNEY CALDERA

E

E

St. Francis River

MADISON

67

roadcut with jointed Grassy Mountain Ignimbrite cut by shear zones

roadcut with unconformity between Proterozoic Grassy Mountain Ignimbrite and overlying Cambrian sedimentary rocks

Einstein Mine

49

N

10 miles

Johnson's Shut-Ins State Park

Taum Sauk Power Plant

Taum Sauk Mountain State Park

CAMBRIAN

Eminence Dolomite and Potosi Dolomite

Derby–Doe Run Dolomite
Davis Formation
Bonneterre Dolomite

Lamotte Sandstone

fault

approximate boundarys of Proterozoic calderas

MIDDLE PROTEROZOIC INTRUSIVES

Skrainka Diabase (sill and dikes)

Graniteville Granite

Ring Intrusion Granite Plutons

Silvermine   Knoblick   Slabtown

Subcaldera Granite Pluton

Butler Hill–Breadtray

MIDDLE PROTEROZOIC VOLCANICS

Grassy Mountain Ignimbrite, Taum Sauk Rhyolite, and other ashfall and ash-flow deposits

Buford Volcanics

Bedrock geology of the St. Francois Mountains.

Bonneterre Dolomite of Cambrian age is present in roadcuts along MO 72 west of US 67. This cut is about 1.3 miles west of the interchange (37.568N 90.343W).

At the next large cut, about 1.6 miles west of US 67, the erosion surface on top of the Grassy Mountain Ignimbrite is clearly visible. The base of the Lamotte Sandstone, deposited on top of the eroded surface, is a layer of conglomerate containing rounded cobbles of the volcanic rock. The sandy Bonneterre Dolomite lies above the Lamotte. At the west end of the roadcut, a diabase dike intrudes the ignimbrite. On the north side of MO 72, the dike is somewhat narrower, and the eroded surface is covered with overlying soil. But in the south roadcut, the dike is several feet wide, more weathered, and terminates at the conglomerate bed. Geologists use such crosscutting relationships to establish the relative age of rocks. In this case, the dike cuts through the ignimbrite but then the conglomerate was deposited on top of both, which tells us that the dike is younger than the ignimbrite but older than the conglomerate.

About 3.2 miles west of US 67, jointed Grassy Mountain Ignimbrite is in the roadcut along the north side of MO 72. The joints are only a few inches apart, which causes the rock to break into rectangular blocks. Also visible in the roadcut are two shear zones along which some very slight thrust faulting has occurred. This area of fractured rock lies within the Annapolis Lineament, a 1- to 2-mile-wide, 75-mile-long structure in Proterozoic rocks that trends northeast-southwest from near Eminence to east of Farmington. Within this structure, basement rocks are highly fractured, as exhibited at this roadcut. The Avon Diatremes are also within the Annapolis Lineament.

A bit farther west, on either side of the St. Francis River, are rounded boulders and ledges of weathered Butler Hill–Breadtray Granite. Close inspection of the rock will reveal the clearly visible grains of quartz and feldspar that distinguish granite from its fine-grained chemical cousin, rhyolite.

You can see the Great Unconformity between the Proterozoic Grassy Mountain Ignimbrite and the Cambrian Lamotte Sandstone in a roadcut along the eastbound lane of MO 72, about 1.6 miles west of US 67 (37.566N 90.347W). A diabase dike intruded the Grassy Mountain Ignimbrite before both were eroded and then covered by a conglomerate bed at the base of the Lamotte Sandstone. This photo is of the south side of the road near the west end of the roadcut. The diabase, like other iron-rich igneous rocks, is more susceptible to weathering than the silica-rich ignimbrite, so it has eroded back into the cut.

Vertical joints and two shear zones (the diagonal fractures running from lower right to upper left, at arrows) in the Grassy Mountain Ignimbrite appear in the cut along the westbound lane of MO 72 about 3.2 miles west of US 67 (37.569N 90.376W).

Silvermine Granite outcrops on the far bank near the remains of a dam constructed across the St. Francis River just upstream of the Einstein Mine (37.558N 90.442W).

Einstein Silver Mine

About 3 miles south of MO 72 on Madison County Route D is the Silver Mines Recreation Area in Mark Twain National Forest. Continue on Route D to the St. Francis River and turn north onto Riverside Camp Road west of the river. Where this road crosses the river, a hiking trail leads north to the Einstein Mine. Mining began in this area in the 1870s and continued intermittently to 1946. The Einstein Mine was one of the earliest mines and produced most of the silver during the early mining period (1877–1894). The silver-bearing minerals occur in quartz veins in the Silvermine Granite, which is present along and in the channel of the St. Francis River for about 0.5 mile upstream of the bridge.

Fort Davidson State Historic Site and Pilot Knob

To reach Fort Davidson State Historic Site, go north at Ironton on MO 21 for about 2 miles to the town of Pilot Knob and follow the signs. The mountain east of the park, called Pilot Knob, is composed of rhyolite breccia in which rock fragments are cemented by the iron oxide minerals hematite and magnetite. Surface mining and smelting operations, which produced iron pellets primarily, began in 1835, and the old mine cut is still visible on the peak. The mountain is now part of Pilot Knob National Wildlife Refuge. Shafts of the old iron mines are home to two endangered species of bats.

During the Civil War, the importance of iron to the war effort led the Union to maintain a garrison at Fort Davidson. Confederate forces laid siege to the

Pilot Knob rises east of Fort Davidson State Historic Site. The bare rock in the former cut of the iron mine on the peak is visible above the tree line. The knob is at the northeastern margin of the Taum Sauk Caldera.

fort, but Union forces escaped, blowing up their gunpowder storage facility on the way out of town. The crater remains.

Elephant Rocks State Park

Elephant Rocks State Park is about 6 miles north of Ironton on MO 21. Large boulders of reddish pink Graniteville Granite litter the hillsides and give the park its name. The largest boulder is 27 feet tall. These rocks are examples of a process called *spheroidal weathering*. It starts when the rock begins to weather along joint surfaces belowground. Groundwater circulating through the joints weathers the surfaces of the granite blocks, with corners weathering faster than flat faces. Erosion eventually removes the weathered material, exposing rounded blocks. The weathering process continues aboveground. Water seeps into tiny fractures parallel to the exposed surfaces of the rock and then freezes and expands, causing bits to flake off over time. The sediment washes away, leaving behind the smooth, clean boulders and ledges.

The Graniteville Granite is known commercially as Missouri Red Granite. In the past, this reddish stone was used for paving stones, or pavers, particularly in St. Louis, where by 1900 most of the streets in the downtown business district and riverfront, and most of the levee, were paved with Graniteville pavers. The foundation supports for the Eads Bridge just north of the Jefferson National Expansion Memorial were faced, up to the high water line, with Missouri Red

Elephant Rocks State Park is the best place see the Graniteville Granite, which weathers to large boulders.

Granite. The governor's mansion in Jefferson City has pillars of the granite. At 1.3 billion years old, this is the youngest granite in the St. Francois Mountains. It is still quarried as of this writing and is used primarily for monument stones. So check out your local cemetery; there might be some Missouri Red there.

Johnson's Shut-Ins State Park

To reach Johnson's Shut-Ins State Park from Graniteville, go south about 13 miles on Iron County Route N. Shut-ins are places where streams flow through narrow defiles eroded into jointed bedrock. Nearly 2,000 feet of volcanic rocks are exposed in the shut-ins, the oldest of which is the Taum Sauk Rhyolite. Younger rocks consist of alternating layers of ashfall pyroclastics and ash that was reworked by water, probably in a lake, before being deposited. Interpretive information about the geology is available for the trails through the park.

In December 2005, a debris flow buried much of Johnson's Shut-Ins State Park when the upper reservoir failed at Taum Sauk Power Plant, a pump-back hydroelectric plant constructed at the base of Proffit Mountain. The plant's primary function is to provide additional electricity for peak-usage times in the St. Louis area. The facility consists of two storage reservoirs with hydroelectric turbines between them. Water pumped into the reservoir on top of the mountain during the night is released to spin the turbines when extra electrical power is needed on the grid, usually during the afternoon. The economic benefit comes from the fact that the electricity used to pump water up at night costs less to produce than the price for which the daytime, peak-demand electricity is sold.

The East Fork Black River courses through eroded joints in rhyolite in Johnson's Shut-Ins State Park.

In December 2005, much of Johnson's Shut-Ins State Park (center) was buried beneath a debris flow generated by floodwaters from the failed Taum Sauk Power Plant upper reservoir at the head of the scar (back left). —Missouri Department of Natural Resources photo

The force of running water scoured the side of Proffit Mountain, a rhyolite knob, below the breach in the Taum Sauk Power Plant upper reservoir, exposing Proterozoic Taum Sauk Rhyolite and Munger Granite, as well as the Cambrian Lamotte Sandstone and dolomite. Sediment was deposited at a change of slope near the base of the hillside. —Missouri Department of Natural Resources photo

At about 5:00 a.m. on December 14, 2005, the concrete wall that contained the upper reservoir failed when the reservoir overfilled and the retaining wall was overtopped and collapsed. The reservoir drained in about 12 minutes, sending an estimated 1.3 billion gallons of water down a small tributary valley of the East Fork Black River and through Johnson's Shut-Ins State Park. The park was buried under flood debris, and the park supervisor and his family barely escaped with their lives. The park was reopened to the public in the summer of 2008.

Missouri's Great Unconformity is exposed in the rock cut at the base of Proffit Mountain where water is discharged from the hydroelectric turbines at Taum Sauk Power Plant (37.521N 90.834W). Beds of Cambrian shale and dolomite—the Davis Formation (lower left) and Derby–Doe Run Dolomite (top left)—are in contact with a knob of Proterozoic Taum Sauk Rhyolite (the massive pinkish rock the power plant is built into).

Great Unconformity at Taum Sauk Power Plant

Missouri's Great Unconformity, the eroded surface of Proterozoic rock upon which sedimentary rock was deposited in Cambrian time, is exposed where water is discharged from the hydroelectric turbines at Taum Sauk Power Plant. The power plant was built into a knob of Proterozoic rhyolite. The facility is reached by taking Reynolds County Route U north off MO 21/MO 49/MO 72 east of Lesterville, then a series of county roads to the turbine discharge cut and the upper reservoir.

Taum Sauk Mountain State Park

Taum Sauk Mountain State Park features a couple of Missouri points of interest. Taum Sauk Mountain, the highest point in Missouri at 1,772 feet elevation, is a rhyolite knob composed of several formations. The lookout tower at the top sits on Taum Sauk Rhyolite, an ash-flow tuff produced during the final collapse stage of the Taum Sauk Caldera. The Taum Sauk Rhyolite is the youngest of the volcanic rocks that outcrop here. Mina Sauk Falls, Missouri's highest waterfall at 132 feet, is a 1.5-mile hike from the lookout tower. The falls flows over porphyritic Taum Sauk Rhyolite.

To reach this area, take Iron County Route CC off MO 21/MO 72 (the intersection is between Arcadia and Hogan). On the drive to the lookout tower, you will pass through the outcrop areas of seven different rhyolite formations. There are some boulders and outcrops along the way, and several of the formations are better seen along Taum Sauk Trail north of Route CC. Most were deposited as ash flows during caldera eruptions, but the Royal Gorge Rhyolite is a lava flow and the Bell Mountain Rhyolite is an ashfall tuff, deposited by ash falling back to the land surface from a nearby eruption. Each formation has a slightly different composition and structure. Some are banded due to flow of the ash or lava. For those interested in knowing more, I recommend the detailed logs in *Guidebook to the Geology and Ore Deposits of the St. Francois Mountains, Missouri* by Eva Kisvarsanyi and others (1981).

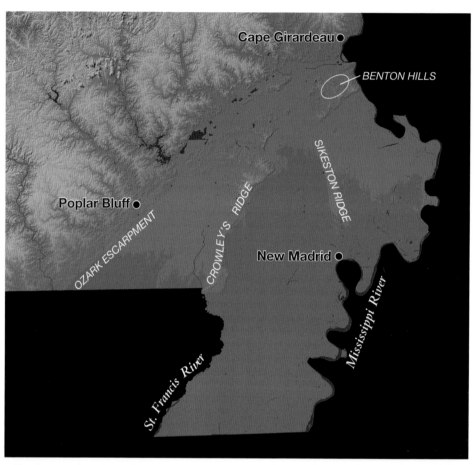

Shaded-relief image of the Southeast Lowlands.—Shaded-relief base map from EROS Data Center

THE SOUTHEAST LOWLANDS

With the exceptions of Crowley's Ridge and the Benton Hills—a line of hills arcing from southwest to northeast across the northern portion—the entire Southeast Lowlands of Missouri is a flat alluvial floodplain created by the combined work of the Mississippi and Ohio Rivers. The average elevation in the lowlands is around 300 feet above sea level. Missouri's lowest elevation, at 230 feet above sea level, is along the St. Francis River at the Arkansas border in the southwest corner of the Bootheel, the oddly shaped southward projection of Missouri into what by all rights should be northeast Arkansas. And just why, you may ask, does Missouri dangle thus?

In the original petition for statehood, Missouri's southern boundary was placed along the 36º 30′ parallel of latitude, which is the southern boundary of the rest of the state. But an influential rancher owned land that would have ended up in Arkansas under this plan. For whatever reasons, he much preferred that his property be part of Missouri. So he lobbied Congress to shift the proposed state boundary to encompass his lands. Congress eventually agreed, and when Missouri became a state in 1820, it came with the Bootheel.

The lowlands occupy the apex of the Mississippi Embayment, an extension of the Gulf Coastal Plain, which stretches from the Gulf of Mexico to Missouri and Illinois. The sediment in the embayment, including Ordovician limestone and more than 10,000 feet of marine and river sediment deposited since Late Cretaceous time, fills a low spot in the Earth's crust that formed when the continent began to rift apart in Late Proterozoic time (sometime after 750 million years ago), during the breakup of the supercontinent Rodinia. The rift did not completely split the continent here, but large blocks of Proterozoic bedrock slipped down along faults, forming a broad rift valley. A similar rift is forming today in east Africa. At the north end of the Mississippi Embayment, a set of two parallel faults crossing the Southeast Lowlands from southwest to northeast delineate a structure called the Reelfoot Rift. Within this downdropped block of Proterozoic rocks are other faults that formed as the continent split. These faults make up the New Madrid Seismic Zone, and some of the biggest earthquakes ever to strike North America happened here in 1811 and 1812.

Sea level rises inundated the Mississippi Embayment repeatedly through Paleozoic time, and as sediment collected the embayment continued to subside. By Pennsylvanian time the rift valley was buried. The northern end of the embayment remained underwater through much of Cretaceous time, although the types of sediment deposited there indicate there were likely two cycles of sea level rise and fall. As a result, the beds deposited are a mix of marine and delta deposits. Patches of Cretaceous and Tertiary rocks, though many are not entirely lithified, outcrop on Crowley's Ridge and the Benton Hills. They dip into the embayment, where they are buried beneath Quaternary alluvium.

The oldest Cretaceous-age rocks in Missouri's Southeast Lowlands belong to the McNairy Formation and are composed mostly of sandstone and shale deposited in a delta that built southward from the north end of the embayment. Deposition of alternating beds of predominantly marine and delta sediments continued into Tertiary time, forming the Midway Group (Paleocene) and Wilcox Group (Eocene). In Pliocene time, stream gravel was deposited, once called the Lafayette Gravel but now known as Mounds Gravel. It is the same age as gravel found across much of southern Missouri in isolated outcrops on hilltops.

It is tempting to think that the weight of all this rock and sediment bearing down on the buried faults of the New Madrid Seismic Zone causes the local earthquakes, but geologists don't think so. Recent studies suggest the cause is more likely the continuing, slow action of compressional forces in the crust.

Subsidence of rocks and alluvium in the embayment combined with uplift of the Ozark Dome caused Paleozoic rock layers, now exposed along the southeastern margin of the Salem Plateau, to dip to the southeast into the embayment. Drill holes encounter them beneath thousands of feet of younger rocks and alluvium. Middle to Late Ordovician dolomite, limestone, and sandstone beds are exposed on the northern margin of the Benton Hills. Cretaceous and Paleogene sandstone, shale, and gravel were deposited on the eroded surface of those rocks—an unconformity representing about 400 million years. To the south on Crowley's Ridge, only Paleogene beds are exposed. Although the sand and clay in these layers are not cemented together very strongly, they nevertheless have enough resistance to erosion to remain topographically higher than the surrounding floodplains. The Paleogene deposits mark the last incursion of the sea into the northernmost part of the Mississippi Embayment.

By the end of Pliocene time, the Ancestral Mississippi and Ohio Rivers had deposited so much alluvium in the northern part of the embayment that the bedrock in the Benton Hills and Crowley's Ridge were nearly buried. The two large, sluggish, meandering streams had created a flat swampland. The Ancestral Mississippi River flowed southwest in a valley between the Ozark Escarpment and Crowley's Ridge and the Benton Hills. The modern St. Francis River today occupies the southern part of that valley. The Ancestral Ohio River flowed parallel to the Ancestral Mississippi but on the southeast side of the low line of hills.

In Pleistocene time, the behavior of both rivers changed from deposition to erosion and back to deposition. Initially, lowering of sea level hundreds of feet by ice sheet development in the northern hemisphere energized the rivers with steeper gradients. Previously deposited alluvium was flushed out of the valleys, and erosion deepened them by as much as 200 feet, exhuming the bedrock ridge that separated the two rivers.

The erosion episode came to an end when surges of sediment flowed down both rivers as the ice sheets melted during interglacials—periodic warm-ups during Pleistocene time. So much sediment entered the rivers that they could

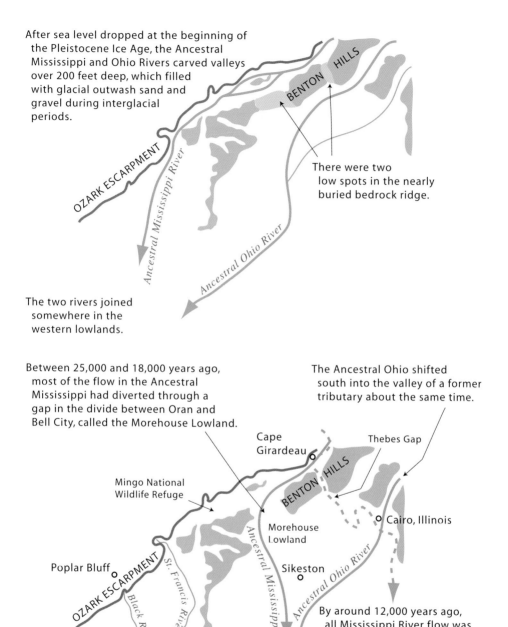

After sea level dropped at the beginning of the Pleistocene Ice Age, the Ancestral Mississippi and Ohio Rivers carved valleys over 200 feet deep, which filled with glacial outwash sand and gravel during interglacial periods.

BENTON HILLS

There were two low spots in the nearly buried bedrock ridge.

OZARK ESCARPMENT

Ancestral Mississippi River

Ancestral Ohio River

The two rivers joined somewhere in the western lowlands.

Between 25,000 and 18,000 years ago, most of the flow in the Ancestral Mississippi had diverted through a gap in the divide between Oran and Bell City, called the Morehouse Lowland.

The Ancestral Ohio shifted south into the valley of a former tributary about the same time.

Cape Girardeau

Thebes Gap

Mingo National Wildlife Refuge

BENTON HILLS

Cairo, Illinois

Morehouse Lowland

Poplar Bluff

OZARK ESCARPMENT

St. Francis River

Black River

Ancestral Mississippi River

Sikeston

Ancestral Ohio River

By around 12,000 years ago, all Mississippi River flow was diverted through Thebes Gap to its present location, intercepting the Ohio River near Cairo, Illinois.

Between 18,000 and 12,000 years ago, the two rivers converged south of Sikeston.

Changes in channel locations of the Mississippi and Ohio Rivers, 50,000 years ago to present. —Adapted from Thacker and Satterfield, 1977; original work in Fisk, 1944

not carry it all. Their channels became wide and braided, and their valleys once more filled with sand and gravel.

By Late Pleistocene time, the two rivers had nearly filled their valleys again, once more nearly burying the bedrock ridge. Then, beginning sometime prior to about 25,000 years ago, toward the end of the Wisconsinan glacial stage, a surge of water that accompanied the melting of the ice sheets flooded down both rivers. Their channels were overwhelmed and they shifted courses.

The first major diversion happened through a low spot in the Benton Hills between Oran and Bell City where the Ancestral Mississippi River breached the ridge and turned to the south, flowing across the lowlands west of Sikeston. Its valley along the western margin of the lowlands was abandoned. At about the same time, the Ancestral Ohio River cut through a divide near Cairo, Illinois, and occupied another west-flowing course south of its former position, joining the Mississippi somewhere south of Sikeston. Later, probably very near the end of Pleistocene time or perhaps early in Holocene time, glacial meltwater flooding down the Mississippi River caused a breach of a low drainage divide near Thebes, Illinois. At that time the channel west of Sikeston was abandoned and the river assumed more or less its present course, intercepting the Ohio River near Cairo.

When the Mississippi changed course, it cut down through the outwash alluvium previously deposited by the Ohio River. Just a few remnants of the older sediment are preserved as stream terraces, broad surfaces that stand 10 to 20 feet above the surrounding floodplain. The largest of these is Sikeston Ridge.

New Madrid Earthquakes of 1811–1812

When the first European settlers arrived in the Southeast Lowlands sometime in the late eighteenth century, the region was a mosquito-infested swamp. Beginning in the mid-1800s, drainage canals were constructed to dewater the lowlands and create the productive farmland that dominates the region today. But the farm fields are not uniformly productive. Patches of ground, ranging in size from a few feet to hundreds of feet across, contained mostly sand rather than fertile floodplain mud. There are literally tens of thousands of these features scattered across the lowlands, most of them south of Sikeston. And while the local farmers cope with them, geologists flock to study them because the sandy areas were formed by earthquakes—really big earthquakes.

In December 1811, the two thousand or so residents of the Southeast Lowlands were enjoying an unusually warm beginning of winter. On the evening of December 15, they went to sleep with no inkling of what was to befall them over the next two months. Thousands of feet below their beds, Proterozoic bedrock was stressed by tectonic forces building up in the crust over time. At about 2:30 a.m. on December 16, 1811, the breaking point was reached.

The epicenter of the first earthquake was west of Blytheville, in northeastern Arkansas. Local residents were thrown from their beds, as was, it is claimed, President James Madison, 800 miles away in the White House. This tremor is estimated to have had a Richter scale magnitude close to 8.0. Geologists estimate that rocks shifted a total of 30 feet along about 90 miles of the Blytheville Fault.

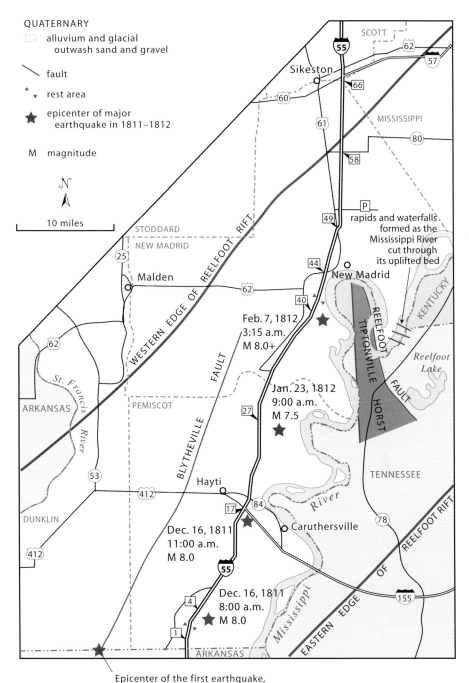

Major geologic structures in the New Madrid Seismic Zone and earthquake features along I-55.

The first big shock was followed by a series of more than fifty aftershocks exceeding magnitude 5.0, but they were dwarfed by two more major aftershocks that came at 8:00 a.m. and 11:00 a.m., both of which were nearly as strong as the first. The latter quakes probably originated along an additional 40 miles of the Blytheville Fault north of the first slippage.

The two largest aftershocks created quicksand conditions across the lowlands as water was squeezed out of the saturated sediment. Farm fields, trees, fences, at least one person, and two towns—Big Prairie (now Helena), Arkansas, and Little Prairie (now Caruthersville), Missouri—disappeared, sinking into the vibrating, liquefied floodplain sediments. In other places, areas of the floodplain dropped, forming troughs that filled with groundwater, creating earthquake lakes. The amount of water expelled from the alluvium was so great that it temporarily increased the flow of the Mississippi River downstream of Little Prairie.

The arrival of the New Year brought nearly daily aftershocks. At about 9:00 a.m. on January 23, 1812, the region was rocked again by another big earthquake. The epicenter was about 10 miles north of the second large aftershock of December 16, and its magnitude was between 7.5 and 8.0. Once again it was slippage on the Blytheville Fault that caused this temblor, an additional 25 feet of slippage at the northern end. This event was followed by at least thirty aftershocks greater than magnitude 5.0.

Reports of the time indicate that the January 23 earthquake was felt from Canada to Mexico and from the Rockies to the Atlantic Coast. Purportedly, the vibrations were strong enough to ring church bells in Boston and caused the North Carolina legislature to adjourn in response to what they thought was a local event. The vibrations broke an ice jam on the Ohio River north of Cairo, Illinois, which allowed boats to once again journey downriver.

On February 5, the nature of the seismic activity was reported to change. In addition to the now-common daily aftershocks, accounts describe the ground as shuddering almost constantly. Many of those boats cut loose on the Ohio River had reached New Madrid and tied up for the night by February 6. They would have been safer if they had floated a bit farther south.

At around 3:15 on the morning of February 7, 1812, one of the largest earthquakes ever recorded in North America shook the region. Estimated to be greater than magnitude 8.0, its epicenter was near Marston, just south of New Madrid. Geologists think that this quake was the result of movement on the Reelfoot Fault, which branches off the Blytheville Fault near New Madrid. The way the rocks shifted along the fault rupture was also different. Much of the movement was vertical rather than sideways.

A 20-square-mile portion of the floodplain southeast of New Madrid pushed upward as much as 30 feet, temporarily reversing the flow of the Mississippi River. The uplift area is called the Tiptonville Horst. The Reelfoot Fault ruptures the surface along the east edge of this feature.

As the river reestablished its course by eroding through the faulted alluvium, a series of rapids and waterfalls, two of which were 6 feet high, formed in the channel and lasted for a couple of days. Across the Mississippi from New

Madrid, the vertical uplift of the floodplain dammed Reelfoot Creek, leading to the formation of Reelfoot Lake. The town of New Madrid did not survive this catastrophe. Whatever remained of the settlement following the initial earthquakes was inundated by the shifting Mississippi River channel.

By the end of February 1812, earthquake activity had ceased. Over a period of eight weeks, the region had been rattled by more than two hundred earthquakes with magnitudes greater than 5.0. The 1811–1812 earthquake sequence is unique in the history of seismology because it included five major events estimated at Richter scale magnitudes greater than 7.0, one of which was an aftershock that was larger than the initial event.

Estimating the size of historical earthquakes is a bit an art, as well as a science. There were no seismographs in 1811 and 1812, so magnitudes have to be approximated based on contemporary descriptions of the severity of shocks, how the ground moved, what damage was done, and so on. The largest New Madrid shocks have been estimated at everywhere from magnitude 7.0 to almost 9.0.

SAND BOILS, SAND BLOWS, AND SAND FISSURES. The formation of quicksand conditions during earthquakes is a process called *liquefaction*. When seismic waves vibrate saturated sand, water pressure in the small openings between sand grains increases and pushes the grains apart. Once the grains are no longer in contact with each other, the sand loses its ability to support weight because the grains are free to move past each other. When this happens below the surface where the sand is covered by an impermeable layer of clay, water pressure can build up so high that the overlying clay layer is abruptly breached, allowing sandy slurry to erupt to the surface through the cracks.

Sand blows are best identified by their influence on crops. Water drains through sand faster than through alluvium with silt or clay, so plants fail to thrive. This sand blow is just south of the Missouri border near I-55. —Louis Odom photo

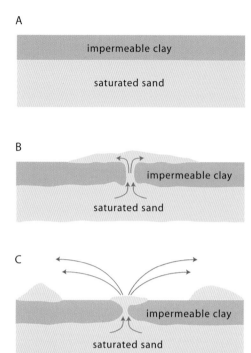

A

impermeable clay

saturated sand

B

impermeable clay

saturated sand

C

impermeable clay

saturated sand

Sand boils form where saturated sand is capped by a clay layer that fractures due to vibration-induced water pressure in the sand. (A) Undisturbed alluvium. (B) Sand boils and fissures form when a sand slurry is forced through cracks in the clay. (C) Where the sand erupts explosively under pressure, it forms a crater ringed by sand, a feature called a sand blow.

The erupted areas of sand are sand boils, blows, or fissures, depending on their size and shape. Sand boils and blows tend to be roughly circular, while fissures are longer than they are wide. The floodplain of the Southeast Lowlands is covered with sand blows and fissures, many of which are among the largest known in the world. For farmers, these interesting earthquake features are simply troublesome, unfertile areas.

Liquefaction also can cause the ground surface to sink. These low areas are referred to as sunken ground or sunken land.

COULD IT HAPPEN AGAIN? Since 1812 there has been no major earthquake in this region. But thousands of small earthquakes (less than magnitude 3.0) occur here every year. The question of greatest concern to the region today is, could a big one happen again?

Because there are no historic accounts of earthquakes prior to 1811, geologists have to rely on geologic studies. Liquefaction features have provided some of the best clues to the seismic history of the New Madrid Seismic Zone. By trenching into floodplain sediments, geologists have exposed ancient sand blows buried beneath modern floodplain sediments. Because the mud that buried older blows was deposited on the floodplain surface, it often contains charcoal fragments that can be dated using carbon-14 or some other method of radiometric dating. The age of a buried sand blow is bracketed by the ages of charcoal-bearing layers above and below it. These studies have led geologists to be reasonably confident that at least three other major earthquake events

The Southeast Lowlands   231

occurred in the region, in about AD 300, 900, and 1400, and that these events may also have included multiple large shocks.

Based on these studies, it is tempting to see a pattern in which very large earthquakes seem to happen every 500 years or so. But caution is warranted, and not only because three data points are inadequate to describe a pattern. Geologists simply do not know enough about the mechanism of the faulting that produced these big earthquakes to be able to make any kind of useful predictions. Some recent studies suggest that activity in the New Madrid Seismic Zone might actually be declining.

Questions remain about why large earthquakes happen here at all. Very large earthquakes typically occur where tectonic plates collide. But there is no such collision occurring in the middle of North America today. On the other hand, the abundance of faults in the rift zone make this part of the Earth's crust weak and perhaps more prone to moving. Nowhere else in the world has a sequence of earthquakes even remotely like those of 1811–1812 been recorded, and it happened here more than once. Geologists are far from understanding the tectonics of the area, but none would be surprised if another major earthquake happened. They just can't say when. That's probably just an eighteen-wheeler rumbling by . . .

Road Guides in the Southeast Lowlands

Interstate 55
Cape Girardeau—Arkansas Border
93 MILES

The I-55 interchange with MO 74 south of Cape Girardeau approximately marks the edge of the Ozark Escarpment—the boundary between Paleozoic bedrock and younger rocks and sediment. To the south, I-55 crosses the 3-mile-wide valley eroded by the Ancestral Mississippi River. At the north edge of the Benton Hills, near mile marker 88, the interstate crosses the unconformity between Ordovician and Cretaceous rocks. Depending on the amount of plant cover, bedrock might be barely visible along both sides of the highway. Otherwise, the soft Cretaceous and Paleogene deposits in the Benton Hills make for very poor roadcut exposures. With any luck you may get a glimpse of gravel in some cuts. South of the hills, the interstate crosses another low spot, this one marking the former channel of the Ancestral Ohio River.

The greatest concentration of the earthquake features known as sand boils and fissures on this route is between exit 66 (US 60/I-57) and exit 40 (New Madrid County Route EE). Although difficult to spot, look for either wet or barren ground, depending on the season. At about mile marker 60, south of the County Route 820 overpass, a series of three sand boils lies very close to the highway. Two along the northbound lanes are about 80 to 100 feet in diameter. The one along the southbound lanes is bigger and easier to locate—not because

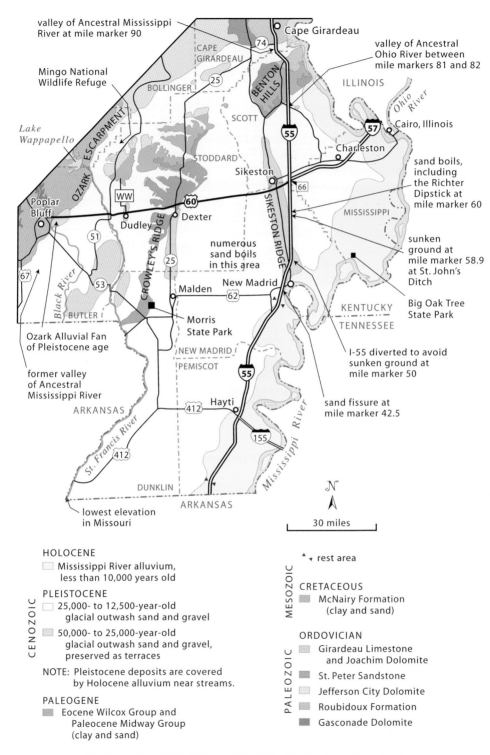

valley of Ancestral Mississippi
River at mile marker 90

Mingo National
Wildlife Refuge

Lake
Wappapello

Poplar
Bluff

Dudley

Ozark Alluvial Fan
of Pleistocene age

former valley
of Ancestral
Mississippi River

CAPE
GIRARDEAU

BOLLINGER

OZARK ESCARPMENT

WW

CROWLEY'S RIDGE

Black River

St. Francis River

Cape Girardeau

74

25

BENTON HILLS

SCOTT

STODDARD

Sikeston

60

Dexter

numerous
sand boils
in this area

25

53

Malden

New Madrid

62

Morris
State Park

NEW MADRID

PEMISCOT

Hayti

412

155

412

DUNKLIN

lowest elevation
in Missouri

ARKANSAS

BUTLER

51

67

55

66

SIKESTON RIDGE

55

valley of Ancestral
Ohio River between
mile markers 81 and 82

ILLINOIS

Ohio River

57

Cairo, Illinois

Charleston

sand boils,
including
the Richter
Dipstick at
mile marker 60

MISSISSIPPI

sunken
ground at
mile marker 58.9
at St. John's
Ditch

Big Oak Tree
State Park

KENTUCKY

TENNESSEE

I-55 diverted to avoid
sunken ground at
mile marker 50

sand fissure at
mile marker 42.5

Mississippi River

N

30 miles

HOLOCENE
☐ Mississippi River alluvium,
less than 10,000 years old

PLEISTOCENE
☐ 25,000- to 12,500-year-old
glacial outwash sand and gravel

▨ 50,000- to 25,000-year-old
glacial outwash sand and gravel,
preserved as terraces

NOTE: Pleistocene deposits are covered
by Holocene alluvium near streams.

PALEOGENE
▨ Eocene Wilcox Group and
Paleocene Midway Group
(clay and sand)

CENOZOIC

▲▾ rest area

MESOZOIC

CRETACEOUS
▨ McNairy Formation
(clay and sand)

ORDOVICIAN
▨ Girardeau Limestone
and Joachim Dolomite

▨ St. Peter Sandstone

▨ Jefferson City Dolomite

▨ Roubidoux Formation

▨ Gasconade Dolomite

PALEOZOIC

Geology along I-55, I-57, and US 60 in the Southeast Lowlands.

View from the Benton Hills, looking north across the ancestral valley of the Mississippi River near mile marker 90 (36.219N 89.549W). The Ozark Escarpment is in the far distance.

The Ancestral Ohio River flowed west through this lowland just south of the Benton Hills. View is to the north toward the Benton Hills from mile marker 81.8.

it is more visible from the ground (in fact, it is a 3-foot-deep depression), but because a company chose to erect a 700-foot-tall transmission tower right in the middle of it. The tower rests on a concrete pad, 2 feet thick and 14 feet square, and weighs about 15 tons.

Why the site was chosen is not known, but perhaps it was because the unfertile sandy ground has little value as farmland. It certainly does not provide much stability. In their book *The Earthquake That Never Went Away*, David Stewart and Ray Knox call the tower their "Richter Dipstick," under the presumption that in the next big earthquake, liquefaction of the ground will cause it to sink up to one of the conveniently marked levels of red and white paint. That's if it doesn't fall over.

Sunken ground, areas where the floodplain dropped during the big earthquakes of 1811–1812, are marked by low spots that are typically filled with

Sand boils may be hard to see from ground level, but sometimes people provide a little help in marking them. This transmission tower, known as the "Richter Dipstick," was built in the middle of one west of I-55 near mile marker 60.

trees and swampy most of the time. They are hard to distinguish from irrigated farmland, including some rice fields and many irrigation canals, all of which may also be tree lined or look swampy. Near mile marker 58.9, the interstate crosses a canal called St. John's Ditch. The low ground to the north and east of the canal is sunken land.

The interstate crosses the northern edge of the Reelfoot Rift at just about mile marker 58. This fault in the Proterozoic bedrock is thousands of feet below the alluvial plain, and it likely dips steeply to the southeast.

A sand fissure with sunken ground lies along the east side of the interstate near mile marker 50, just south of where the road makes a bend. The highway was angled to the west here to avoid being built atop the length of the feature, which runs north-south. The highway crosses a 200-foot-wide fissure between mile markers 43 and 42 (36.559N 89.584W).

Between exit 58 (MO 80) and exit 44 (US 61/I-55 Loop), the surface on which the interstate is built is about 15 to 20 feet higher than that of the surrounding lowlands. This feature, called Sikeston Ridge, is a stream terrace composed of outwash sand and gravel deposited by the Ancestral Ohio River. Recent studies of this and other terraces in the lowlands lead some geologists to propose that there are faults bordering the edges of the terraces, along which movement occurring in Holocene time (the last 11,000 years) helped elevate them above the adjacent floodplain.

Big Oak Tree State Park

Big Oak Tree State Park preserves the appearance of the Missouri Bootheel prior to deforestation in the late 1800s. The park contains the state's only cypress swamp. This type of vegetation became established at the end of Pleistocene time. The tree for which the park was named was 400 years old when it succumbed to disease and was cut down in 1952. To reach the park, take MO 80 east off I-55 (exit 58). Just east of the town of East Prairie, turn south on Missouri 102 and go about 10 miles to the park entrance.

New Madrid to Arkansas

From either exit 49 or exit 44, you can take Business US 61/I-55 Loop to New Madrid. On Main Street, just north of the Mississippi River levee, is the New Madrid Historical Museum, a treasure trove of information about the 1811–1812 earthquakes, and also the repository of an extraordinary collection of Revolutionary War, Civil War, and other historical artifacts.

An observation deck on the bank of the Mississippi River in New Madrid overlooks the former site of the town before it was destroyed by the river in the February 1812 earthquake. The town site is about halfway across the river in the middle of the channel. Just north of here was where the lower of two waterfalls formed in the February 1812 earthquake.

The rest stop between exit 44 to New Madrid and exit 40 to Marston is a great place to get out of your vehicle, stretch your legs, and think about the fact that the epicenter of one of the largest earthquakes ever to strike North America is nearby. In fact, if you stayed at the rest stop for a whole day, there's about a 33 percent chance that you would experience an earthquake, although probably too small to be felt.

Interstate 55 more or less traces the epicenters of the 1811–1812 earthquakes between the rest area and the Arkansas border. The epicenter of the final large earthquake (February 1812) was a mile or so to the east of I-55 near mile marker 40. The epicenter of the January 23, 1812, earthquake was a short distance east of I-55 near exit 27, and the epicenter of the large aftershock on December 16, 1811, was east of the I-155/US 412 interchange at exit 17. The rest stop located between exit 4 and exit 1 is near the epicenter of the first large aftershock on December 16, 1811. The epicenter of the initial earthquake in 1811 was in Arkansas, 5 to 10 miles west-southwest of where the interstate crosses the state line.

US 60 and Interstate 57
Illinois Border—Poplar Bluff
73 MILES
See map on page 232.

Interstate 57 crosses the Mississippi River a few miles upstream of the mouth of the Ohio River. Between the Mississippi River and Charleston, the floodplain is largely the result of meandering and deposition of the modern stream—the river that has existed since the end of Pleistocene time. Although not easy to see from ground level, the surface has somewhat of a washboard nature due to the presence of *meander scars*, ridges of sand left behind when the channel shifts position. Abandoned meanders are also common, often marked by tree-filled low spots called *bayous*. Look for one along the eastbound lanes near mile marker 17.

Between Charleston, where US 60 merges with I-55, and Dexter, the highway crosses the plains over which both the Ancestral Ohio and Ancestral Mississippi Rivers flowed during Pleistocene time. US 60 crosses Sikeston Ridge, a terrace of glacial outwash deposited by the Ancestral Ohio River, in the 2 miles centered on the US 61/US 62 interchange. Between Sikeston Ridge and Dexter, US 60 traverses alluvium deposited when the Ancestral Mississippi River shifted its channel and flowed south through the Benton Hills.

The high ground at the MO 25 junction is Crowley's Ridge, which here rises about 150 feet above the flat landscape. Cretaceous sediments are exposed along the ramps to and from US 60. Loess deposits cap the ridge but are not exposed along the highway. You can also see Crowley's Ridge up close at Morris State Park, which is located between Malden and Campbell. Head south on MO 25, take Business 25 at Malden, then turn west on Dunklin County Route J for about 5 miles, and then left (south) on County Route WW. The park entrance is about 1.5 miles south, on the left. Sediment of the Wilcox Group, the Mounds Gravel, and up to 50 feet of loess are exposed in the park.

The Sikeston Power Plant sits on Sikeston Ridge, a stream terrace created when the Ancestral Mississippi River shifted its channel and eroded alluvium previously deposited by the Ancestral Ohio River.

View to the east from the MO 25 overpass atop Crowley's Ridge near Dexter (36.817N 89.941W). The floodplain east of the ridge is about 50 feet lower than the plain to the west due to erosion by the Ancestral Mississippi River.

Paleogene sand and clay are exposed along the ramps to and from US 60 at MO 25 on Crowley's Ridge.

At Dudley, US 60 encounters another stream terrace. The Stoddard County Route WW overpass is built on top of it, 15 or 20 feet above the surrounding plain. Like Sikeston Ridge to the east, it is composed of glacial outwash sand and gravel. But it is older than Sikeston Ridge and probably formed about 50,000 years ago when the Ancestral Mississippi River briefly eroded into its floodplain. Sand and gravel are exposed along the ramps to and from Route WW.

Between Dudley and the Black River, US 60 crosses the Pleistocene valley of the Ancestral Mississippi River. The valley, now filled with alluvium, was carved into Ordovician bedrock. The buried valley is deepest (about 200 feet) along its eastern edge. Most of the alluvium was deposited sometime between 80,000 and 55,000 years ago. The St. Francis River now flows here. Mingo National Wildlife Refuge, located about 13.5 miles north of US 60 on MO 51, is a wetland that occupies part of the abandoned valley.

The contact between the southeast-dipping beds of Ordovician dolomite and the Pleistocene alluvium is about 1 mile east of the Black River. The transition between the lowlands and the Salem Plateau is gradual—a couple hundred feet of elevation difference over a distance of about 4 miles, roughly from the Black River to the junction with US 67. Sediment eroded off the edge of the Salem Plateau, here made of sandstone of the Roubidoux Formation, was deposited at the base of the escarpment in a gently sloping wedge called the Ozark Alluvial Fan.

Stoddard County Route WW at Dudley is built atop a Pleistocene stream terrace. This view is to the east from the top of the terrace (36.798N 90.334W). Crowley's Ridge rises in the distance.

The US 60 Business exit (middle distance) northeast of Poplar Bluff is at the edge of the Ozark Escarpment. The Ozark Alluvial Fan rises gradually in the foreground. View looking west from the Butler County Routes T and AA overpass.

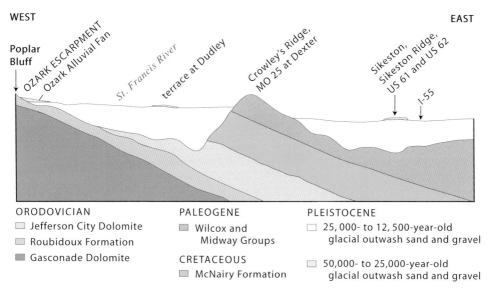

ORODOVICIAN
- Jefferson City Dolomite
- Roubidoux Formation
- Gasconade Dolomite

PALEOGENE
- Wilcox and
  Midway Groups

CRETACEOUS
- McNairy Formation

PLEISTOCENE
- 25,000- to 12,500-year-old
  glacial outwash sand and gravel
- 50,000- to 25,000-year-old
  glacial outwash sand and gravel

Sedimentary rocks dip to the east into the Mississippi Embayment. This cross section along US 60 between Poplar Bluff and Sikeston illustrates the relationship between eroded bedrock and Pleistocene deposits. The vertical scale and dip of beds is exaggerated for the purpose of illustration. The actual angle of bed dip is only a few degrees. —Modified from Santi and others, 2002

GLOSSARY

alluvial fan. A relatively flat to gently dipping, fan-shaped wedge of loose rock material deposited by a stream, especially in semiarid regions, where they flow out of narrow valleys onto broad valleys or plains.

alluvium. Stream-deposited sediment. Also called **alluvial deposits**.

anticline. In layered rocks, a folded arch with the oldest rocks in the center.

ash, volcanic. Small shreds of lava that escape in the air during a volcanic eruption and solidify into glassy fragments. Ash deposits consolidate into ash-flow tuff or ashfall tuff.

barite. A mineral composed of barium sulfate. Found as bladed crystals in filled-sink and collapse structures in Missouri's central mining district and in mineralized stromatolite structures in Washington County.

basalt. A black or very dark gray volcanic rock that consists mainly of microscopic crystals of plagioclase feldspar, pyroxene, and perhaps olivine.

basement. The original igneous or metamorphic rocks of the continental crust. They are usually covered with younger sedimentary rocks.

basin. An elliptical or circular downward flexure in sedimentary rock layers with the youngest rocks in the center.

batholith. A large pluton of coarse-grained igneous rock, generally granite.

bed/bedding. A layer in a sedimentary rock deposited over a more or less continuous time span, and distinguishable from adjacent layers.

bedding plane. The surface between two beds. It often represents a change in deposition.

bedrock. Solid rock exposed in place or that underlies soil, alluvium, or other sediments.

bioherm. A mounded, reeflike mass of carbonate rock separated from surrounding rock by distinct bedding planes, and composed nearly entirely of the fossils or fossil debris of marine organisms. Common in Ordovician dolomite beds in Missouri, often containing stromatolites.

biotite. Dark mica, a platy mineral. It is a minor but common mineral in igneous and metamorphic rocks.

breccia. A rock containing angular fragments that are held together by mineral cement or a finer-grained matrix. The term can be applied to both sedimentary and volcanic rocks.

calcite. A mineral composed of calcium carbonate. It is the principal mineral in limestone and is also found with the ores of lead and zinc.

calcium carbonate. A chemical compound containing a combination of one calcium atom and one carbonate (CO_3) molecule. The mineral calcite. Marine organisms use this mineral to form shells.

carbonate rock. A sedimentary rock composed of carbonate minerals such as calcite and dolomite.

chert. A sedimentary rock composed of microscopic crystals of quartz. It occurs as nodules or thin beds in limestone and dolomite.

clay. A sedimentary material composed of weathered minerals with grain sizes less than $\frac{1}{256}$ millimeter in diameter. The term is also used for a group of hydrous silicate minerals that have layered crystal structures. **Bentonite** is an example.

coarse-grained. A relative term used to describe the size of constituents in a rock. Said of igneous rocks with minerals larger than 0.2 inch in diameter. Said of sedimentary rocks with particles larger than 0.08 inch in diameter.

coastal plain. A low, gently sloping region on the margin of an ocean.

conglomerate. A coarse-grained sedimentary rock composed of pebbles, cobbles, or boulders set in a fine-grained matrix of silt or sand.

continent. A large landmass that is, or was, comparable in size to a modern continent. Laurentia, a Precambrian continent, evolved into the larger North American continent.

continental platform. See **platform.**

continental shelf. The gently dipping part of the continental landmass between the shoreline and the more steeply dipping continental slope.

crossbed/crossbedding. A sedimentary bed, usually in sand or silt, that is at an angle to the main bedding.

crust. The upper surface of the lithosphere. **Continental crust** consists mainly of granite, gneiss, and schist; **oceanic crust** consists of basalt.

cryptoexplosive. A term coined by geologists to describe the origin of a string of circular structures that extend across Missouri within the Thirty-Eighth Parallel Lineament. They contain broken and displaced sedimentary beds and/or igneous rock, some interpreted as forming due to eruption of gases from deep magma pockets.

crystalline. Said of a rock formed of interlocking mineral crystals, usually igneous or metamorphic.

cyclothem. A set of sedimentary beds deposited during one cycle of sea level rise and fall during Pennsylvanian time.

delta. A nearly flat accumulation of clay, sand, and gravel deposited in a lake or ocean at the mouth of a river.

depositional environment. The physical environment in which sediment is deposited, for example, stream channel, delta, beach, continental shelf, and so on.

diabase. An igneous rock with the composition of basalt but which cooled slowly enough to have visible crystals.

diatreme. A volcanic vent, usually found in sedimentary rocks, that formed due to an explosive eruption. Rocks in diatremes are often volcanic breccias, containing both pyroclastics and fragments of the rocks through which the eruption occurred.

dike. A sheet of igneous rock that formed when molten magma filled a fracture in a solid rock. The magma in a **feeder dike** rose to the surface of the Earth.

dip. The sloping angle of a planar surface in rocks, such as a sedimentary bed or metamorphic foliation.

dolomite. A sedimentary rock composed of calcium magnesium carbonate, or the mineral of the same composition.

dome. A circular or elliptical uplift of sedimentary rock layers, with the older beds in the center.

drape fold. A broadly folded structure, typically having very slight angles of dip on its flanks, that formed in sedimentary beds in response to vertical movement of deeper bedrock along faults.

entrenched meander (also incised meander). A deeply eroded, sinuous valley commonly attributed to downcutting by a meandering stream rejuvenated by slow uplift of the surface on which it flowed.

erosion. The process of removing weathered rock, sediment, or soil by streams, wind, glaciers, and other agents.

erratic, glacial. A cobble, boulder, or block of rock transported by glacial ice and deposited at a distance from the bedrock outcrop from which it was derived.

extrusive igneous rocks. Rocks that solidify from magma on the surface of the Earth.

fault. A fracture or zone of fractures in the Earth's crust along which blocks of rock on either side have shifted. A **normal fault** forms under extensional forces, and one side drops relative to the other side. A **reverse fault** forms under compressional forces, and one side is pushed up and over the other side. In a **strike-slip fault**, rocks on one side move sideways relative to rocks on the other side.

feldspar. The most abundant rock-forming mineral group, making up 60 percent of the Earth's crust and including calcium, sodium, or potassium with aluminum silicate.

filled sink. A circular structure in which younger beds have dropped down due to either collapse of a cavernous opening, or from gradual dissolution of dolomite rock.

fine-grained. A relative term used to describe the size of constituents in a rock. Said of igneous rocks with minerals too small to see with the unaided eye. Said of sedimentary rocks with silt-size or smaller particles.

fire clay. A clay suitable for use in high-temperature applications such as the brick lining of kilns.

flank. In structural geology, a term used to describe one side of a fold.

flowstone. A mass of calcium carbonate deposited on the wall of a cave by water seeping from a fracture and flowing down the cave wall.

fold. A bend in a rock layer.

formation. A body of sedimentary, igneous, or metamorphic rock that can be recognized over a large area. It is the basic stratigraphic unit in geologic mapping. A formation may be part of a larger **group** and may be broken into **members**.

gabbro. A dark igneous rock consisting mainly of plagioclase and pyroxene in crystals large enough to see with a simple magnifier. Gabbro has the same composition as basalt but contains much larger mineral grains.

galena. Lead sulfide. The Missouri state mineral.

gneiss. A coarse-grained metamorphic rock with a streaky foliation due to parallel alignment of minerals, usually in bands of light- and dark-colored minerals.

graben. A structure, usually longer than it is wide, bounded by faults, in which rocks have dropped in elevation relative to their position on either side.

granite. An igneous rock composed mostly of the minerals orthoclase feldspar and quartz in grains large enough to see without using a magnifier. Most granites also contain mica or amphibole.

grus. Sediment produced by weathering of granite, typically consisting of fragments of quartz and feldspar.

ice sheet. A thick glacier covering a large region.

igneous rock. Rock that solidified from the cooling of magma or lava.

Illinoian. The second-to-last major glaciation during Pleistocene time.

intrusive igneous rocks. Rocks that cool from magma beneath the surface of the Earth. The body of rock is called an **intrusion**.

island arc. See **volcanic island arc**

joint. A planar fracture or crack in a rock.

Kansan. Term used for the second of four of the traditional glacial stages in Pleistocene time. It is now considered part of **pre-Illinoian** glaciation.

knob. A round-top hill composed of volcanic rocks in the St. Francois Mountains.

lava. Molten rock erupted on the surface of the Earth.

limestone. A sedimentary rock composed of calcium carbonate.

lobe. The rounded, terminal edge of a continental glacier.

loess. Windblown deposit of silt, generally with small amounts of clay and fine sand.

magma. Molten rock within the Earth.

magnetite. A strongly magnetic iron oxide mineral.

mantle. The part of the Earth between the interior core and the outer crust.

marble. Metamorphosed limestone. **Carthage Marble** is a trade name used for unmetamorphosed limestone mined from the Warsaw Formation near Carthage, Missouri.

meander. A curve in a stream channel.

metamorphic rock. Rock derived from preexisting rock that changes mineralogically and texturally in response to changes in temperature and/or pressure, usually deep within the Earth.

mica. A family of silicate minerals, including biotite and muscovite, that crystallize into thin flakes. Micas are common in many kinds of igneous and metamorphic rocks, and occur as grains in sedimentary rocks.

micaceous. Containing micas, such as muscovite and biotite.

mountain building event. An event in which rocks are folded, thrust faulted, metamorphosed, and/or uplifted. Intrusive and extrusive igneous activity often accompanies it.

mudstone. A sedimentary rock composed of mud (silt and clay).

Nebraskan. Term used for the oldest of the four traditional glacial stages in Pleistocene time. It is now considered part of **pre-Illinoian** glaciation.

normal fault. A fault in which rocks on one side move down relative to rocks on the other side in response to extensional forces.

oolith. A sand-sized, spherical grain containing concentric layers. Usually composed of calcite.

outcrop. A natural exposure of bedrock at the Earth's surface.

outwash. Sand and gravel deposited by meltwater from a receding glacier.

Pangea. A supercontinent that assembled about 300 million years ago. It broke into the modern continents beginning about 200 million years ago.

peneplain. Term formerly applied to a land surface eroded over a long period of time to a relatively flat or undulating plain near sea level, or to such a region later uplifted; for example the **Ozark peneplain** in south-central Missouri. The time-dependent nature of such landforms is generally no longer implied.

plateau. An elevated area of relatively flat land.

platform. Term describing the broad, relatively flat erosional surface that formed atop the igneous and metamorphic basement rocks of midcontinent North America. Paleozoic sediments were deposited on the platform.

pluton. An large intrusion of igneous rock.

porphyritic. An igneous texture in which larger crystals exist in a fine-grained but completely crystalline matrix due to two rates of cooling.

pyroclast/pyroclastic. Literally, a "fire-formed fragment." Examples are volcanic ash and cinders. A rock composed of this type of volcanic debris is referred to as **pyroclastic**. A **pyroclastic flow** is a hot mixture of erupted ash and gases that move at great speed along the ground.

quartz. A mineral form of silica. Quartz is one of the most abundant and widely distributed minerals in rocks. It comes in a wide variety of forms, including clear crystals, sand grains, and chert.

quartzite. A metamorphic rock composed of mainly quartz and formed by the metamorphism of sandstone.

radiometric dating. Measure of the age of rocks using radioactive elements in minerals. Also called **isometric dating**. Radiocarbon dating measures age using the decay of carbon-14 in plant material.

rhyolite. A felsic volcanic rock, the extrusive equivalent of granite. It contains quartz and feldspar in a very fine-grained matrix.

rift. A long, narrow rupture in the Earth's crust. A **rift basin** or **rift valley** is the trough formed by the rift.

roadcut. An excavation for road construction that exposes soil, sediment or bedrock.

Rodinia. An early supercontinent consisting of a cluster of all major landmasses that existed by about 750 million years ago.

sand. Weathered minerals grains, most commonly quartz, between $\frac{1}{16}$ millimeter and 2 millimeters in diameter.

sandstone. A sedimentary rock made primarily of sand.

sedimentary rock. A rock formed from the consolidation of loose sediment.

shale. A deposit of clay, silt, or mud solidified into more or less solid rock.

shear zone. The zone in which deformation occurs when two bodies of rock slide past each other. Also called a **shear plane** when not very wide.

sill. An igneous intrusion that parallels the planar structure of the surrounding rock.

silt. Weathered minerals grains larger than clay but smaller than sand (between $\frac{1}{256}$ and $\frac{1}{16}$ millimeter in diameter).

stalactite/stalagmite. Cylindrical or conical cave deposits of calcium carbonate formed by dripping water. Stalactites are suspended from the cave ceiling. Stalagamites build up from the cave floor.

stromatolite. A fossil composed of thin layers of calcite, often mounded in shape, formed from sediment trapped by algae.

subduction zone. A long, narrow zone where an oceanic plate descends into the mantle below another plate at a collision boundary.

supercontinent. A clustering of all of the Earth's continental masses into one major landmass; this has occurred at least three times in geologic history.

syncline. In layered rocks, a folded, downward-sagging trough with the youngest rocks in the center.

tectonics. A branch of geology dealing with the structure and forces within the outer part of the Earth, including continental plate movements.

thrust fault. A low-angle reverse fault.

till. Unsorted and unstratified sediment deposited directly from glacial ice. It is likely to contain rock fragments of all sizes.

tuff. Volcanic ash consolidated into solid rock.

unconformity. A break or gap in the geologic record where one rock unit is overlain by another that is not next in the stratigraphic succession. Often represents a period of erosion. An **angular unconformity** exists when the bedding of the underlying, older rock dips at a different angle, usually steeper, than the bedding of the overlying, younger rock.

volcanic island arc. A curving chain of volcanoes that form in the ocean or offshore of a continent above a plate subduction zone.

weather. To soften, crumble, or discolor because of exposure to atmospheric agents such as rain.

Wisconsinan. The last stage of glaciation in Pleistocene time. It began about 80,000 years ago and ended about 10,000 years ago.

REFERENCES

Many of the resources from governmental agencies and organizations are available online. Because the Internet and URLs are always in flux, most URLs are not included here. Generally, the easiest way to determine their online availability is to enter the title in an Internet search engine. To narrow down the results, you might also include the author's last name or other resource details in your search.

Aber, J. S. 2005. Glacial Geology of the Kansas City Vicinity. In *Lewis and Clark Bicentennial Space-Age Atlas.* www.geospectra.net.

Ambrose, S. 2001. Great Flood. *National Geographic News, Expedition Journal,* May 1, 2001.

Anderson, K. H. 1979. *Geologic Map of Missouri, 1979.* Missouri Department of Natural Resources, Division of Geology and Land Survey, Missouri State Geologic Maps SGM-1979. Scale 1:500,000.

Aughenbaugh, N., T. Beveridge, P. D. Proctor, and A. C. Spreng (eds.). 1972. *Guidebook of the Karst Features and Stratigraphy of the Rolla Area.* 19th Annual Meeting, Association of Missouri Geologists, September 29–30, 1972, Rolla.

Aylor, R. B. 1956. *Highway Geology of Central Missouri.* 3rd Annual Meeting, Association of Missouri Geologists, September 28–29, 1956, Jefferson City.

Barbour, J. R. 2008. *The Origin and Significance of Sinuosity along Incising Bedrock Rivers.* Doctoral thesis, Columbia University.

Beveridge, T. R., and W. C. Hayes. 1960. *Guidebook to the Geology of the Rolla Area Emphasizing Solution Phenomenon.* 5th Annual Midwest Groundwater Conference Field Trip, Missouri Geological Survey and Water Resources.

Beveridge, T. R., and J. D. Vineyard. 1990. *Geologic Wonders and Curiosities of Missouri.* Second edition. Missouri Department of Natural Resources, Division of Geology and Land Survey.

Bostic, J. L., L. M. Nuelle, and K. L. Deason. 1991. *Economic Geology of the Pennsylvanian System in Southwest Missouri, Field Trip Guidebook.* 38th Annual Meeting, Association of Missouri Geologists, September 27–28, 1991, Nevada.

Bretz, J. H. 1960. Origin of the filled sink-structures and circle deposits of Missouri. *Bulletin of the Geological Society of America* 61:789–834.

Brill, K. G., G. E. Wallace, and A. J. Frank (eds.). 1960. *Middle Mississippian and Pennsylvanian Stratigraphy of St. Louis and St. Louis County, Missouri.* 7th Annual Meeting, Association of Missouri Geologists, October 7–8, 1960, St. Louis, Missouri.

Burchett, R. R. 1970. *Guidebook to the Geology along the Missouri River Bluffs of Southeastern Nebraska and Adjacent Areas.* Nebraska Geological Survey.

Callicoat, J. S., C. Hamer, and C. A. Chesner. 2008. Pelletal lapilli in ultramafic diatremes, Avon volcanic district, Missouri. *Geological Society of America North-Central Section, Abstracts with Program.* 42nd Annual Meeting, April 24–25, 2008.

Cargo, D. (ed.). 1982. *Petroleum Geology of Western Missouri, Guidebook.* 29th Annual Meeting, Association of Missouri Geologists, September 24–25, 1982, Grandview.

Childers, A. (ed.). 1993. *The Viburnum Trend, a Second Look, Guidebook.* 40th Annual Meeting, Association of Missouri Geologists, September 24–25, 1993, Salem.

Chung, J. W., and J. Rodgers. 2010. GIS-based virtual geotechnical database for the St. Louis Metro area. *Environmental and Engineering Geoscience* 16(2):143–62.

Committee on Missouri River Ecosystem Science, National Research Council. 2002. Missouri River History, Management, and Legal Setting. In *The Missouri River Ecosystem: Exploring the Prospects for Recovery.* Washington, D. C.: National Academies Press.

Condra, G. E. 1935. *Geologic Cross-Section, Forest City, Missouri, to DuBois, Nebraska.* Paper No. 8, Nebraska Geologic Survey.

Csontos, R., R. Van Arsdale, R. Cox, and B. Waldron. 2008. Reelfoot rift and its impact on Quaternary deformation in the central Mississippi River valley. *Geosphere* 4(1):145–58.

Davis, G. H. (ed.). 1997. *Engineering Geology, Filled-Sink Structures, and Stratigraphy of the Jefferson City Area, Guidebook.* 44th Annual Meeting, Association of Missouri Geologists, Jefferson City.

Dom, J. E., and C. M. Wicks. 2003. Morphology of the Caves of Missouri. *Journal of Cave and Karst Studies* 63(3):155–59.

Elfrink, N. M. 2010. Dynamic topography, pressurized sandstones and hypogene speleogenesis in the Ozarks. *Geological Society of America Abstracts with Programs* 42(2):98.

Elfrink, N. M., and M. A. Siemens. 1998. *Part II: Quaternary Drainage Shifts in Missouri, Guidebook.* 45th Annual Meeting, Association of Missouri Geologists, September 25–26, 1998, Farmington.

Emerson, J. W. In press. *The Quaternary History of Missouri.* Missouri Department of Natural Resources, Division of Geology and Land Survey.

Emerson, J., J. Cocke, and N. Cocke (eds.). 1975. *Pennsylvanian–Pleistocene Channel Fill and Quaternary Geomorphology near Warrensburg, Missouri, Guidebook.* 22nd Annual Meeting, Association of Missouri Geologists, September 27, 1975, Warrensburg.

Evans, K. R., and J. S. Aber (eds.). 2010. *From Precambrian Rift Volcanoes to Mississippian Shelf Margin: Geological Field Excursions in the Ozark Mountains.* Geological Society of America, Field Guide 17.

Evans, K. R., K. L. Mickus, C. W. Rovey II, G. H. Davis. 2003. The Weaubleau-Osceola structure—Evidence of a Mississippian meteorite impact in southwestern Missouri. In *Report of Investigations No. 75 (Guidebook No. 26)*, ed. T. G. Plymate. Missouri Geological Survey and Resource Assessment Division.

Federal Energy Regulatory Commission. 2007. *Final Environmental Assessment: Rebuilding the Taum Sauk Pumped Storage Project Upper Reservoir.* Taum Sauk Pumped Storage Project, FERC No. 2277.

Fisk, H. N. 1944. *Geological Investigation of the Alluvial Valley of the Mississippi River.* Mississippi River Commission, Corps of Engineers, Vicksburg, Mississippi.

Freeman, T. (ed.). 1967. *Middle Devonian of Central Missouri, Guidebook.* 14th Annual Meeting, Missouri Association of Geologists, September 29–30, 1967, Columbia.

Frye, J. C., and A. B. Leonard. 1952. *Pleistocene Geology of Kansas.* Kansas Geological Survey Bulletin 99, online version, 2005.

Fuller, M. Undated web site. *Cliff Cave Park.* St. Louis Community College. http://users.stlcc.edu/mfuller/CliffCave.html.

Gentile, R. J. 1994. *Geology and Utilization of Underground Space in Metropolitan Kansas City, Missouri, Guidebook.* 41st Annual Meeting, Association of Missouri Geologists, September 23–24, 1994, Kansas City.

Gentile, R. J. Undated. *Geology of the Greater Kansas City Area, Part II: The Rock Section.* Unpublished field course guidebook.

Gentile, R. J., and T. L. Thompson. 2004. *Paleozoic Succession in Missouri Part 5: Pennsylvanian Subsystem of Carboniferous System.* Missouri Department of Natural Resources, Geological Survey and Resource Assessment Division, Report of Investigations No. 70.

Golson, G. S. (ed.). 1983. *Geology of Northwestern Randolph County, Missouri, with Emphasis on the Coal Industry, Guidebook.* 30th Annual Meeting, Association of Missouri Geologists, September 23–24, 1983, Moberly.

Gosnell, A. S. 2002. *Site Characterization and Analysis Penetrometer (SCAPS) Demonstration and Geology of Western Cass County, Missouri, Guidebook.* 49th Annual Meeting, Association of Missouri Geologists, September 27–28, 2002, Kansas City.

Hagni, R. D. (ed.). 1986. *Geology and Environmental Concerns in the Tri-State Lead-Zinc District, Missouri, Kansas, Oklahoma, Guidebook.* 33rd Annual Meeting, Association of Missouri Geologists, September 26–27, 1986, Joplin.

Hartley, A. J., G. S Weissmann, G. J. Nichols, and G. L. Warwick. 2010. Large distributive fluvial systems: Characteristics, distribution, and controls on development. *Journal of Sedimentary Research* 80(2):167–83.

Hayes, W. C. (ed.). 1961. *Guidebook to the Geology of the St. Francois Mountain Area, Missouri.* Geological Survey and Water Resources, Report of Investigations No. 26.

Hayes, W. C., and K. C. Thomson. 1973. *Engineering and Environmental Geology of the Springfield Urban Area, Guidebook.* 20th Annual Meeting, Association of Missouri Geologists, September 21–22, 1973, Branson.

Hebrank, A. W. 1997. *The Geologic Story of the St. Louis Riverfront (a Walking Tour).* Missouri Division of Geology and Land Survey, Special Publication No. 6.

Hildebrand, T. G., A. Griscom, W. R. Van Schmus, and W. D. Stuart. 1996. Quantitative investigations of the Missouri gravity low: A possible expression of a large, late Precambrian batholith intersecting the New Madrid Seismic zone. *Journal of Geophysical Research* 101(B10):21921–42.

Hoffman, D., B. L. Stinchcomb, and J. R. Palmer (eds.). 2006. *Chronister Mesozoic Vertebrate Fossil Site, Bollinger County, Missouri, and Earthquake and Mississippi Embayment Geology of Southeast Missouri, Guidebook.* 53rd Annual Meeting, Association of Missouri Geologist, October 6–7, 2006, Sikeston.

Howe, W. B. (ed.). 1968. *Pleistocene and Pennsylvanian Formations in the St. Joseph Area, Missouri, Guidebook.* 15th Annual Meeting, Missouri Association of Geologists, October 4–5, 1968, St. Joseph.

Johnson, C. L. (ed.). 1963. *Guidebook to the Geology in the Vicinity of Joplin, Missouri, including Westside-Webber Mine, Oklahoma.* 10th Annual Meeting of the Association of Missouri Geologists, September 27–28, 1963, Joplin.

Johnston, A. C., and E. S. Schweig. 1996. The enigma of the New Madrid earthquakes of 1811–1812. *Annual Review of Earth and Planetary Sciences* 24:339–84.

Keller, W. D., W. H. Johns, W. H. Allen, J. A. Martin, and H. M. Wharton (eds.). 1974. *Geology of East Central Missouri with Emphasis on Pennsylvanian Fire Clay and Pleistocene Deposition, Guidebook.* 21st Annual Meeting, Missouri Association of Geologists, October 5, 1974, Mexico.

King, N. R. Undated web site. *The I-170 Pennsylvanian Exposure in St. Louis, Missouri.* www.lakeneosho.org.

Kisvarsanyi, E. B. (ed.). 1976. *Studies in Precambrian Geology with a Guide to Selected Parts of the St. Francois Mountains, Missouri.* Missouri Geological Survey, Report of Investigations No. 61.

Kisvarsanyi, E. B., A. W. Hebrank, and R. F. Ryan. 1981. *Guidebook to the Geology and Ore Deposits of the St. Francois Mountains, Missouri.* Missouri Division of Geology and Land Survey, Report of Investigations No. 67.

Klimchouk, A. 2005. Conceptualization of speleogenesis in multi-story artesian systems: A model of transverse speleogenesis. *International Journal of Speleology* 34(1-2):45–64.

Knox, R., A. Childers, L. Unfer, and M. Klosterman (eds.). 1988. *The Lone Star Cement Plant, and the Southeast Missouri Port, Cape Girardeau County, Missouri, Guidebook*. 35th Annual Meeting, Association of Missouri Geologists, September 23–24, 1988, Cape Girardeau.

Koenig, J. W., J. A. Martin, and C. W. Collinson. 1961. *Guidebook, Twenty-Sixth Regional Field Conference of the Kansas Geological Society: Northeast Missouri and West-Central Illinois*. Missouri Geological Survey and Water Resources, Report of Investigations No. 27.

Kramer, K., R. Thom, G. Iffrig, K. McCarty, and D. Moore. 1996. *Directory of Missouri Natural Areas*. Missouri Natural Areas Committee, Missouri Department of Conservation.

Laux, R. J. 1995. *Mining and Mine Reclamation in North Central Missouri, Guidebook*. 42nd Annual Meeting, Association of Missouri Geologists, September 29–30, 1995, Moberly.

Lowell, G. R. 2000. Eruptive style of Mesoproterozoic A-type calderas in southeastern Missouri, USA. *Revista Brasileria de Geosciencias* 30(4):745–48.

Lowell, G. R. 1998. Emplacement of a vitrophyric lava dome in the St. Francois terrane of Missouri: Constraints imposed by amphibole. In *Field Guide and Proceedings Volume, International Geological Correlation Project,* eds. W. R. Van Schmus, B. A. Brown, and M. G. Mudrey Jr. 1998 International Field Conference, September 13–19, 1998.

Lowell, G. R., and R. W. Harrison. 2001. The Eminence-VanBuren volcanic series: A rift-related caldera. *Geological Society of America Programs with Abstracts* 33(4). North-Central Section Meeting, Normal, Illinois.

Lowell, G. R., R. W. Harrison, and D. M. Unruh. 2005. Contrasting rift-margin volcanism in the St. Francois terrane of Missouri at 1.47 Ga. *15th Annual Goldschmidt Conference Program with Abstracts,* May 20–25, 2005, Moscow, Idaho.

Lowell, G. R., and G. J. Young. 1999. Interaction between coeval mafic and felsic melts in the St. Francois terrane of Missouri, USA. *Precambrian Research* 95:69–88.

Martin, J. (ed.). 1977. *Geology in the Area of the Eureka–House Springs Anticline with Emphasis on Stratigraphy, Structure, and Economics, Guidebook*. 24th Annual Meeting, Association of Missouri Geologists, September 30–October 1, 1977, St. Louis.

Martin, J., and W. M. Dressel. 1978. *Energy, Environment, Geology in Bates County, Guidebook*. 25th Annual Meeting, Association of Missouri Geologists, September 29–30, 1978, Kansas City.

McCracken, M. H. 1995. *Major Structural Features of Missouri*. Missouri Division of Geology and Land Survey, Fact Sheet FS-06.

McCracken, M. H. 1971. *Structural Features of Missouri.* Missouri Geological Survey and Water Resources, Report of Investigations No. 49.

Mehl, M. G., and R. B. Aylor (eds.). 1959. *Devonian–Mississippian Stratigraphy of the Columbia, Missouri, Area, Field Trip Guidebook.* 6th Annual Meeting of the Association of Missouri Geologists, October 2–3, 1959, Columbia.

Missouri Department of Natural Resources, Division of Geology and Land Survey. 2008. *Missouri Ozarks.* Fact Sheet FS-20. Rolla, Missouri.

Missouri Department of Natural Resources, Division of Geology and Land Survey. 2008. *Missouri—The Cave State.* Fact Sheet FS-15. Rolla, Missouri.

Missouri Department of Natural Resources, Division of Geology and Land Survey. 2008. *Mozarkite.* Fact Sheet FS-23. Rolla, Missouri.

Missouri Department of Natural Resources, Division of Geology and Land Survey. 2008. *Two Rivers—The Mississippi and Missouri.* Fact Sheet FS-21. Rolla, Missouri.

Missouri Department of Natural Resources, Division of Geology and Land Survey. 2007. *Geologic Map of Missouri, Missouri Environmental Geology Atlas (MEGA).* Version 2.1 (CD with GIS maps). Rolla, Missouri. All bedrock geology maps in the book are modified from this map.

Missouri Department of Natural Resources, Division of Geology and Land Survey. 2002. *Galena.* Fact Sheet FS-22. Rolla, Missouri.

Missouri Department of Natural Resources, Division of Geology and Land Survey. 2002. *Generalized Geologic Map of Missouri, 2002.* Fact Sheet FS-01. Rolla, Missouri.

Missouri Department of Natural Resources, Division of Geology and Land Survey. 2002. *Geologic Time Scale.* Fact Sheet FS-12. Rolla, Missouri.

Missouri Department of Natural Resources, Division of Geology and Land Survey. 2002. *Missouri Groundwater.* Fact Sheet FS-04. Rolla, Missouri.

Missouri Department of Natural Resources, Division of Geology and Land Survey. 2002. *Missouri Lead.* Fact Sheet FS-23. Rolla, Missouri.

Missouri Department of Natural Resources, Division of Geology and Land Survey. 2002. *Missouri Springs.* Fact Sheet FS-18. Rolla, Missouri.

Missouri Department of Natural Resources, Division of Geology and Land Survey. 2002. *Oil and Gas in Missouri.* Fact Sheet FS-19. Rolla, Missouri.

Missouri Department of Natural Resources, Division of Geology and Land Survey. 2002. *Physiographic Regions of Missouri.* Fact Sheet FS-02. Rolla, Missouri.

Missouri Department of Natural Resources, Division of Geology and Land Survey. 2002. *Surface Elevation Map of Missouri.* Fact Sheet FS-07. Rolla, Missouri.

Missouri Department of Natural Resources, Division of Geology and Land Survey. 2002. *Surficial Materials Map of Missouri.* Fact Sheet FS-16. Rolla, Missouri.

Missouri Department of Natural Resources, Division of Geology and Land Survey. 2002. *Topographic Relief Map of Missouri.* Fact Sheet FS-05. Rolla, Missouri.

Missouri Department of Transportation. 2007. *Missouri State Highway Map.* Jefferson City.

Missouri Geological Survey and Water Resources. 1967. *Mineral and Water Resources of Missouri.* Vol. XLIII, Second Series. U.S. Congress, 90th, 1st Session, Senate Document 19.

Missouri State Archives. Undated web site. *Missouri History: How Did the State Boundary of Missouri Come to Include the "Bootheel"?*

Missouri State Archives. Undated web site. *Missouri History: What Is the Origin of "Missouri"?*

Missouri State Archives. Undated web site. *Missouri History: Why Is Missouri Called the "Show-Me State.*

Missouri University of Science and Technology. Undated web site. *Assessment of Seismic Readiness of U.S. 60 in Southeast Missouri.* http://web.mst.edu.

Mitchill, S. L. 1814. A Detailed Narrative of the Earthquakes which occurred on the 16th day of December, 1811, as read before the Literary and Philosophical Society of New York, May 1814. *Transactions of the Literary and Philosophical Society of New York* 1:281–307. Web page transcription by Susan E. Hough, U.S. Geological Survey, Pasadena, California, May 2000.

Mulvany, P. S. 2004. *Field Trip II: Geology of the Crooked Creek Ring Structure, Crawford County, Missouri, Guidebook to Field Trips.* 51st Annual Meeting, Association of Missouri Geologists, October 1–2, 2004, Rolla.

Myers, H. E. (ed.). 1969. *Stratigraphy of the "Lead Belt"; Underground Tour of No. 8 Mine, Guidebook.* 16th Annual Meeting, Missouri Association of Geologists, October 3–4, 1969, Bonne Terre.

Nold, J. L., and C. Priesendorf (eds.). 2005. *Geology of the Valley Anticline beneath the Warrensburg Sandstone, Warrensburg, Missouri; and Devonian and Mississippian Stratigraphy of the Sedalia-Otterville Area, Missouri.* Field Trip Guidebook, 52nd Annual Meeting, Association of Missouri Geologists, October 7–8, 2005, Sedalia.

Ojakangas, R. W. 1963. Petrology and sedimentation of the upper Cambrian Lamotte sandstone in Missouri. *Journal of Sedimentary Research* 33(4):860–73.

Paarlberg, N. (ed.). 1979. *The Viburnum Trend, Guidebook.* 26th Annual Meeting, Association of Missouri Geologists, September 28–29, 1979, Salem.

Palmer, J. R., D. Hoffman, J. D. Vaughn, and R. Harrison (eds.). 1996. *Late Quaternary Faulting and Earthquake Liquefaction Features in Southeast Missouri: the Identification of New Earthquake Hazards, Guidebook.* 43rd Annual Meeting, Association of Missouri Geologists, September 20–21, 1996, Cape Girardeau.

Pederson, D. T. 2001. Stream piracy revisited: A groundwater-sapping solution. *Geology* 11(9):4–11.

Plymate, T. G., K. R. Evans, K. C. Thomson, J. F. Miller, C. W. Rovey II, G. H. Davis, and J. Cutler. 2003. Field Trip III: Ordovician and Mississippian stratigraphy and structural geology of the Springfield-Branson area, southwestern Missouri. In *Report of Investigations No. 75 (Guidebook No. 26)*, ed. T. G. Plymate, Missouri Geological Survey and Resource Assessment Division.

Ragan, V. M. 1999. *Economic Geology, Utilization, and Waste Recycling in Northeast Missouri; Central Stone Co. Quarry #1; Continental Cement Co. and MFR, Inc.; Scheffler's Geode Mine, Guidebook.* 46th Annual Meeting, Missouri Association of Geologists, September 24–25, 1999, Hannibal.

Rohs, C. R., and W. R. Van Schmus. 2007. Isotopic connections between basement rocks exposed in the St. Francois Mountains and Arbuckle Mountains, southern mid-continent, North America. *International Journal of Earth Science* 96:599–611.

Rueff, A. W. 2001. *Mineral Resources in Missouri.* Missouri Division of Geology and Land Survey, Fact Sheet FS-03.

Rueff, A. W., T. L. Thompson, A. C. Spreng, D. Hoffman, and P. Price (eds.). 1987. *Guidebook to the Weldon Spring Area, St. Charles County, and Geology and Utilization of Industrial Minerals in St. Louis County, Missouri.* 34th Annual Meeting, Association of Missouri Geologists, September 25–26, 1987, St. Charles.

Santi, P. M., E. J. Neuner, and N. L. Anderson. 2002. Preliminary Evaluation of Seismic Hazards for Emergency Rescue Route, U.S. 60, Missouri. *Environmental and Engineering Geoscience* 8(4):261–77.

Searight, W. V. 1959. *Pennsylvanian (Desmoinesian) of Missouri.* Missouri Geological Survey and Water Resources, Report of Investigations No. 25.

Seeger, C. M., and J. R. Palmer. 1998. *Part 1: Syndepositional Tectonics during the Late Upper Cambrian, Guidebook.* 45th Annual Meeting, Association of Missouri Geologists, September 25–26, 1998, Farmington.

Sloss, L. L. 1964. Tectonic cycles of the North American craton. In *Symposium on Cyclic Sedimentation*, ed. D. F. Merriam. Kansas Geological Survey, Bulletin 169.

Smith, D. C. 2000. *Guide to Selected Industrial Mineral Producers, Preliminary Reconnaissance Bedrock Geology and Pennsylvanian Stratigraphy of the St. Joseph, Missouri Area, Guidebook.* 47th Annual Meeting, Missouri Association of Geologists, September 29–30, 2000, St. Joseph.

Smith, D. C., and R. C. Beste. 2001. *Selected Industrial Mineral Producers along Interstate 70 and Missouri Highway 94, St. Charles County, Missouri, Guidebook.* 48th Annual Meeting, Missouri Association of Geologists, September 28–29, 2001, St. Charles.

Snyder, F. G. (ed.) 1964. *Guidebook: Cryptovolcanic Structures of South Central Missouri.* 11th Annual Meeting, Association of Missouri Geologists, September 25–26, 1964, Lebanon.

Spooner, J. 2001. *The Evolution of the Lower Missouri River: Preliminary Results of NMD Research at Lisbon Bottom.* U.S. Geological Survey Open File Report 01-368.

Spreng, A. C., and R. C. Laudon. 1990. *Part I: Stratigraphy of the Rolla Area, Field Trip Guidebook.* 37th Annual Meeting, Association of Missouri Geologists, September 28–29, 1990, Rolla.

Stack, C. E., and J. F. Westcott. 1990. *Part II: Geology of the East-Central Missouri Fireclay District, Field Trip Guidebook.* 37th Annual Meeting, Association of Missouri Geologists, September 28–29, 1990, Rolla.

Stewart, D. A., and R. Knox. 1993. *The Earthquake That Never Went Away.* Marble Hill, Missouri: Gutenberg-Richter Publications.

Thacker, J. L., and I. R. Satterfield. 1977. *Guidebook to the Geology along Interstate-55 in Missouri.* Missouri Geological Survey, Report of Investigations No. 62.

Thompson, T. L. 1995. *The Stratigraphic Succession in Missouri, Volume 40, Revised.* Missouri Department of Natural Resources, Division of Geology and Land Survey.

Thompson, T. L. 1993. *Paleozoic Succession in Missouri, Part 3: Silurian and Devonian Systems.* Missouri Department of Natural Resources, Division of Geology and Land Survey, Report of Investigations No. 70.

Thompson, T. L. 1991. *Paleozoic Succession in Missouri, Part 2: Ordovician System.* Missouri Department of Natural Resources, Division of Geology and Land Survey, Report of Investigation No. 70.

Thompson, T. L. 1986. *Paleozoic Succession in Missouri, Part 4: Mississippian System.* Missouri Department of Natural Resources, Division of Geology and Land Survey, Report of Investigations No. 70.

Thompson, T. L., and C. E. Robertson. 1993. *Guidebook to the Geology along Interstate Highway 44 (I-44) in Missouri.* Missouri Department of Natural Resources, Missouri Division of Geology and Land Survey, Report of Investigations No. 71 (Guidebook No. 23).

Thomson, K. C. (ed.). 1984. *Geology of the Bolivar-Mansfield Fault Zone, Guidebook.* 31st Annual Meeting, Association of Missouri Geologists, September 28–29, 1984, Springfield.

Unfer, L., Jr. (ed.). 1981. *Paleozoic Stratigraphy and Tertiary Clay Deposits of the Cape Girardeau Area; Geomorphology of Thebes Gap, Guidebook.* 28th Annual Meeting, Association of Missouri Geologists, October 3, 1981, Cape Girardeau.

Unklesbay, A. G. 1973. *The Common Fossils of Missouri.* Columbia: University of Missouri Press.

Unklesbay, A. G., and J. D. Vineyard. 1992. *Missouri Geology.* Columbia: University of Missouri Press.

U.S. Army Corps of Engineers. 2004. *The Mississippi River and Tributaries Project, New Orleans District.* www.mvn.usace.army.mil/pao/bro/misstrib.htm.

U.S. Geological Survey. 2008. *The Great Flood of 1993.* Missouri Water Science Center. http://mo.water.usgs.gov/Reports/1993-Flood/index.htm.

Van Arsdale, R., and M. Ellis. 2004. *Characterization of Active Faults in the New Madrid Seismic Zone, Final Report for SG-4.* University of Memphis, Center for Earthquake Research and Information.

Vineyard, J. D. (ed.). 1985. *Geology of the Springs in the Ozarks of South-Central Missouri, Guidebook.* 32nd Annual Meeting, Association of Missouri Geologists, September 27–28, 1985, Salem.

Vineyard, J. D. 1980. *Geology of the Devil's Icebox Karst, Boone County, Missouri, Guidebook.* 27th Annual Meeting, Association of Missouri Geologists, September 28, 1980, Columbia.

Vineyard, J. D., and G. L. Feder. 1982. *Springs of Missouri.* Missouri Department of Natural Resources, Division of Geology and Land Survey.

Vineyard, J. D., and L. D. Fellows. 1967. *Guidebook to the Geology between Springfield and Branson Emphasizing Stratigraphy and Cavern Development.* Missouri Geological Survey and Water Resources, Report of Investigations No. 37.

Vita-Finzi, C. 2004. Buckle-controlled seismogenic faulting in peninsular India. *Quaternary Science Reviews* 23(23-24):2405–12.

Wagner, R. G. (ed.). 1970. *Highway Geology of Route 79TR, Hannibal to Clarksville, Guidebook.* 17th Annual Meeting, Association of Missouri Geologists, September 25–26, 1970, Hannibal.

Whitfield, J. W. 1981. *Underground Space Resources in Missouri.* Missouri Division of Geology and Land Survey, Report of Investigations No. 65.

Wicander, R., and J. S. Monroe. 2000. *Historical Geology.* Pacific Grove, California: Brooks-Cole.

Williams, S. K. 2005. *Underground Coal and Clay Mines in the City of St. Louis.* www.usgennet.org/usa/mo/county/stlouis/underground_stl.htm.

Williams, S. K. 2005. *Before Man: Prehistoric Life and Geology of St. Louis City/County, Mo.* www.usgennet.org/usa/mo/county/stlouis/prehistory.htm.

Wilson, P. B. Undated web site. *Geological History of the Central Highlands.* www.esu.edu/~pwilson/rsch/merhis.htm.

Ziegler, P. A., S. Cloetingh, and J. D. van Wees. 1995. Dynamics of intra-plate compressional deformation: The Alpine foreland and other examples. *Tectonophysics* 252:7–59.

Informational Web Sites

Arabia Steamboat Museum
www.1856.com/
  Information about the wreck and rediscovery of the paddle-wheel steamer
  that sank in the Missouri River near Parkville, Missouri.

Association of Missouri Geologists
www.missourigeologists.org/
  Field trip guidebooks from nearly all of the group's annual meetings since
  the mid-1950s; many of these were used in preparation of the road logs in
  this book.

Bollinger County Museum of Natural History
www.bcmnh.org/
  Missouri's dinosaur fossils are housed here.

Earth Impact Database
www.unb.ca/passc/ImpactDatabase/index.html
  Compilation of information about all known impact structures on the planet.

Jo Schaper's Missouri World
http://members.socket.net/~joschaper/index.html
  General information about Missouri geology.

Lewis and Clark Bicentennial Space-Age Atlas,
J. Aber and M. Nowak, eds., 2005
www.geospectra.net/lewis_cl/intro.htm
  In addition to historical information, this site has geologic information
  about areas along the Missouri River.

Missouri Caves Association
www.missouricaves.com/
  Information about Missouri caves and spelunking.

Missouri Department of Natural Resources Geology Store
www.missourigeologystore.com/
  Online shop for geology publications available from Missouri Department
  of Natural Resources.

Missouri Division of Geology and Land Survey
www.dnr.mo.gov/geology/index.html
  Publications, including free Fact Sheets online.

Missouri State Parks and Historic Sites
www.mostateparks.com/
    Information about all parks and historic sites, including descriptions of points of geologic interest.

National Park Service geology website
www.nature.nps.gov/geology/

National Park Service National Natural Landmarks Program website
www.nature.nps.gov/nnl/

New Madrid Historical Museum
www.newmadridmuseum.com/
    This museum is located on the banks of the Mississippi River, not far from the former town site that was submerged by a shift in the channel during the 1811–1812 earthquakes. It has much information about the event.

Ozark Caving
www.ozarkcaving.com/
    Information on Missouri caves.

University of Missouri, Center for Applied Research and Environmental Systems (CARES)
www.cares.missouri.edu/
    The web site includes a map room in which geologic, hydrologic, and soils maps for the entire state are available at no charge.

U.S. Fish and Wildlife Service, Mingo National Wildlife Refuge
www.fws.gov/midwest/Mingo

U.S. Geological Survey
www.usgs.gov
    Information and imagery about all things geological.

U.S. Geological Survey, National Earthquake Information Center Webpage
earthquake.usgs.gov/regional/neic/
    Information including real-time seismic monitoring data.

INDEX

Page numbers in italics refer to photographs.

Weston, 67
Weston Bend State Park, 67
Westphalia, 189
Westport Landing, 49
wetlands, 66, 238. *See also* swamps
Wheatland, 121
White River, 125, 133
Wilcox Group, 39, 224, 236
wind, 6
Winfield, 80
Winona, 187

Wisconsinan glaciation, 40. *See also*
  glaciation
Woodland Culture, 151
Worthenia, 100
Wright County, 7
Wyaconda River, 76, 77
Wyandotte Formation, 18, 99

zinc, 29, 34, 36, 108, 205
Zuni sequence, 38

About the Author

Charles G. Spencer grew up in Lee's Summit, Missouri, and became interested in geology while walking along the railroad tracks near his home, collecting interesting rocks from the gravel ballast. He earned his geology degrees at the University of Missouri–Kansas City, the last being a Ph.D. in interdisciplinary studies (geosciences and physics) in 1995. He currently works as a consultant, advising residential and commercial clients on environmental and engineering geology issues. He is also an adjunct professor of geosciences at the University of Missouri–Kansas City. Charlie still lives in Lee's Summit, along with his wife, Shirley, and daughter, Sarah, their dogs, cats, horse, and various domesticated rodents, and a basement full of rocks.